ROADSIDE GEOLOGY
OF NEW JERSEY

David P. Harper

2013
Mountain Press Publishing Company
Missoula, Montana

Cover image constructed from 2006 GIS
data from the U.S. Geological Survey

ACKNOWLEDGMENTS

I'd like to thank the following people for their help on this book: Neitzke Adamo, Zehdreh Allen-Lafayette, Jennifer Carey, William Crepet, Richard Dalton, John Dooley, Chelsea Feeney, Michael Flite, Sondra Flite, Patti Gaspari-Bridges, Bill Graff, David Grimaldi, William Harper, Richard Hauck, Gregory Herman, Gregory Lattanzi, Lee Lowell, Walt Marzulli, Carl Mehling, Charles Merguerian, Robert Metz, Ken Miller, Don Monteverde, Karl Muessig, Lloyd Mullikin, Richard Olssen, Ted Pallis, David Parris, Ron Pristas, Terry Schmidt, Sue Schutte, Scott Stanford, Steve Urbanik, Richard Volkert, Jim Walters, and Ron Witte.

Library of Congress Cataloging-in-Publication Data

Harper, David (David Paul)
Roadside geology of New Jersey / David P. Harper. — 1st ed.
   p. cm. — (Roadside geology series)
Includes bibliographical references and index.
ISBN 978-0-87842-600-3 (pbk. : alk. paper)
1. Geology—New Jersey—Guidebooks. 2. New Jersey—Guidebooks. I. Title.
II. Series: Roadside geology series.
QE141.H37 2013
557.49—dc23

2012048777

PRINTED IN HONG KONG BY MANTEC PRODUCTION COMPANY

MP Mountain Press
PUBLISHING COMPANY
P.O. Box 2399 • Missoula, MT 59806 • 406-728-1900
800-234-5308 • info@mtnpress.com
www.mountain-press.com

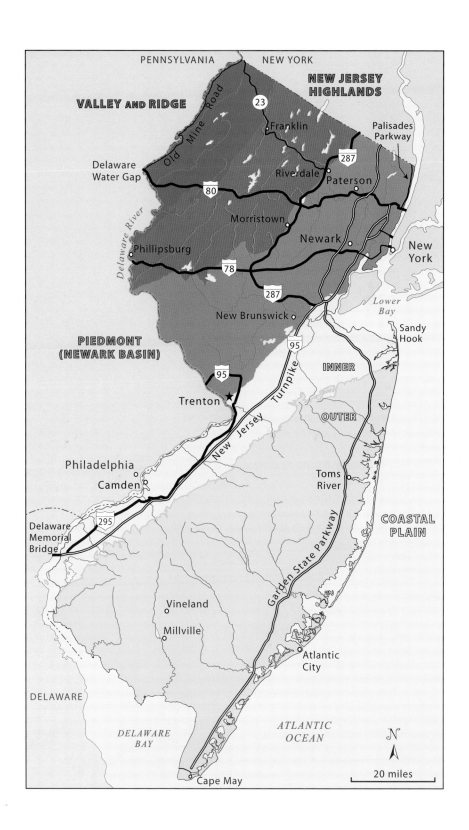

PENNSYLVANIA   NEW YORK

VALLEY and RIDGE   NEW JERSEY
                                    HIGHLANDS

23

Franklin   Palisades
                            Parkway

Delaware
Water Gap   Riverdale   287

                            Paterson
80
                    Morristown

                            Newark   New
Phillipsburg   York

78   Lower
                                      Bay
287
                                          Sandy
New Brunswick   Hook

PIEDMONT
(NEWARK BASIN)   95   INNER

                                        OUTER
95
Trenton

Philadelphia   Toms
Camden   River   COASTAL
                                          PLAIN
Delaware
Memorial
Bridge   295

                    Vineland

                    Millville

DELAWARE   Atlantic
                                          City

                DELAWARE
                BAY   ATLANTIC
                                OCEAN   N

                                          20 miles

                Cape May

Delaware River · *New Jersey Turnpike* · *Garden State Parkway* · *Old Mine Road*

CONTENTS

GEOLOGIC TIME SCALE

EON	ERA	PERIOD / EPOCH	AGE (millions of years)	GEOLOGIC EVENTS IN NEW JERSEY
PHANEROZOIC	CENOZOIC	QUATERNARY — HOLOCENE	0.01	Humans become agents of geologic change
		QUATERNARY — PLEISTOCENE	3	Humans arrive Sea level rises as Wisconsinan glaciers recede Today's beaches, tidal marshes, and estuaries take shape Glaciers reach New Jersey in three different ice ages Sea level falls during ice advance and rises during retreat
		TERTIARY — NEOGENE — PLIOCENE	5	Relief increases in northern New Jersey due to deepening valleys
		TERTIARY — NEOGENE — MIOCENE	23	Erosion lowers land surface throughout New Jersey Cohansey Formation deposited as sea level drops
		TERTIARY — PALEOGENE — OLIGOCENE	34	Erosion of northern New Jersey bedrock to subdued Schooley surface
		TERTIARY — PALEOGENE — EOCENE	55	Seven cycles of marine advance and retreat
		TERTIARY — PALEOGENE — PALEOCENE	65	Continued deposition of Coastal Plain sediments
	MESOZOIC	CRETACEOUS	145	Atlantic Ocean sedimentation begins on Coastal Plain
		JURASSIC	201	Atlantic basin opens and begins widening Marine sediment deposited in the Baltimore Canyon Trough Widespread basaltic magmatism toward end of rifting
		TRIASSIC	251	Newark rift basin begins downdropping
	PALEOZOIC	PERMIAN	299	Alleghanian Orogeny
		PENNSYLVANIAN	318	
		MISSISSIPPIAN	359	No rock record in New Jersey
		DEVONIAN	416	Sediment shed across northwestern New Jersey includes Skunnemunk Conglomerate Acadian Orogeny Highlands rise to east
		SILURIAN	444	Thin limestone, sandstone, and shale formations deposited in shallow sea Sediment erodes from Taconic Highlands, including Shawangunk Formation and Green Pond Conglomerate
		ORDOVICIAN	488	Taconic Orogeny builds highlands to east (470–430 million years ago) Jacksonburg and Martinsburg Formations deposited as Taconic island arc approaches Carbonate bank forms Kittatinny limestones
		CAMBRIAN	542	Iapetus Ocean encroaches onto New Jersey Hardyston Formation deposited
PROTEROZOIC			2,500	Rodinia rifts apart; Iapetus Ocean opens at end of Proterozoic Ottawan Orogeny (1,045 million years ago) forms Rodinia Byram and Lake Hopatcong Intrusive Suites (1,185 million years ago) Losee magmatic arc forms above subduction zone on margin of Laurentia (1,282–1,254 million years ago)
				Origin of Earth about 4,500 million years ago

OVERVIEW OF
NEW JERSEY GEOLOGY

New Jersey lies on the eastern seaboard and has been at the eastern edge of the section of continental crust that became North America for over 1 billion years. Today there are no high mountains, volcanoes, or glaciers, and there have been no strong earthquakes in recorded history. All of these were important, however, in New Jersey's past when North America moved here and there across the Earth's surface. Sometimes it collided with other continents in mountain building events known as orogenies (from the Greek *oros* for "mountain" and *genesis* for "birth" or "origin"). The Himalayas are similarly forming today where India is colliding northward into Asia. Sometimes, when high mountains had been subject to millions of years of erosion, New Jersey lay at the middle of a continent and was crossed by the eroded roots of mountains that had formed much earlier. Sometimes New Jersey lay where continents were being torn apart along breaks in the Earth's crust. The tearing created long, straight rift valleys and allowed rock within the Earth to melt, rise upward, and erupt to the surface through volcanoes. Rift valleys crossing East Africa today have much in common with rift valleys that crossed New Jersey between 225 and 195 million years ago. The Atlantic Ocean started as a narrow sea between North and South American continental crust to the west and European and African crust to the east, much like the Red Sea is now forming between African and Arabian crust in the growing rift there.

The movement and collisions of continents are best understood as the result of plate tectonics. The plates in plate tectonics are thick slabs of solid crust floating on a hot, semimolten mantle, which makes up the bulk of the Earth's volume. *Tectonics* is from a Greek word meaning "to build," and refers to mountain building, continental rifting, ocean widening, and other large-scale effects of plate movement. The plates are moved by convection currents rising and sinking within the mantle. Where plates are being moved apart, there is rifting of continents or widening of oceans. The pulling apart decreases pressure in the mantle and generates molten rock, or magma, by decompression melting. The magma rises to the surface, fills the space left where the crust is splitting, and cools to become new oceanic crust. Where two plates of oceanic crust are being forced together, the crust of the older plate is usually colder and heavier and sinks beneath the newer, lighter crust along a linear subduction zone. The newer, lighter oceanic crust is lifted upward into an island arc, like Alaska's Aleutian Islands, paired with a deepwater oceanic trench, like the Aleutian Trench, where the sinking plate is bent downward.

Continental crust is made of lighter rock than oceanic crust, too light to sink into the mantle. Where continental crust is forced against oceanic crust, the oceanic crust tends to sink downward, and the continental crust tends to buckle upward into mountains like the Andes, which are rising where Pacific

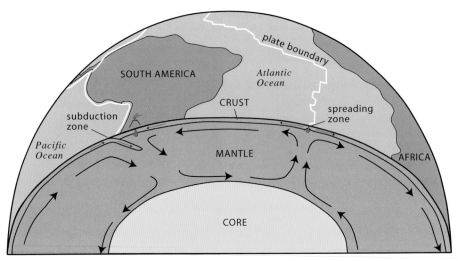

Convection currents in the Earth's mantle cause crustal plates to move.
—From Kious and Tilling, 1996

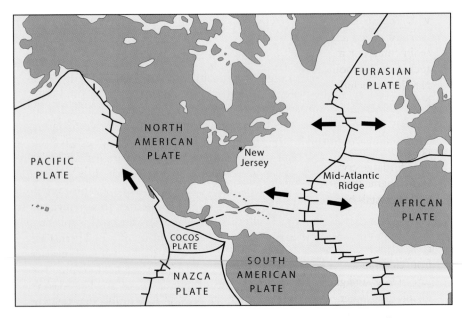

North American crustal plate and surrounding plates. Arrows indicate direction of plate movement. Today, New Jersey is far from a plate boundary.
—Modified from the U.S. Geological Survey

Ocean crust is sinking beneath South American continental crust. Where two plates of continental crust are being pushed together, neither plate can sink into the mantle and still higher mountains, like the Himalayas, rise as the crust compresses and thickens.

Today, and for the past 195 million years, New Jersey has been on a passive continental margin. Mid-Atlantic North America is recognized worldwide as an outstanding example of a passive margin between an ocean and a continent at the middle of a crustal plate. The plate is called the North American crustal plate but is much larger than the continent of North America. It extends from the Mid-Atlantic Ridge, along the centerline of the Atlantic Ocean, westward to the Pacific Coast. The Mid-Atlantic Ridge, 2,000 miles east of New Jersey, runs along the boundary between the North American Plate, which is moving west, and the Eurasian and African Plates, which are moving east. New oceanic crust is being created along the Mid-Atlantic Ridge by lava upwelling into the space left where the plates move apart. At the passive continental margin, New Jersey sits passively between oceanic crust of the Atlantic Ocean and continental crust of North America as both parts of the North American crustal plate drift westward at just over one-half inch per year.

ROCKS AND SEDIMENTS

Geology is commonly thought of as the study of rocks. It is also, of particular importance in New Jersey, the study of sediments. The southern two-thirds of the state, the Coastal Plain, is covered with unconsolidated layers of sand, silt, and clay that were deposited, and are still being deposited, along the edge of the widening Atlantic. The accumulation is over a mile thick at Cape May.

Hard rocks, commonly thought of as the stuff of geology, can be igneous, sedimentary, or metamorphic. All three are common in New Jersey. Igneous rocks form by cooling and crystallizing of molten magma. The igneous rocks of New Jersey include relatively coarse-grained varieties such as the granites of the New Jersey Highlands and the diabase of the Palisades and finer-grained varieties, such as basalt of the Watchung Mountains, in which the individual crystals can be so small as to be invisible without magnification. The coarse-grained igneous rocks cooled slowly beneath the Earth's surface, and there was a long time for large crystals to grow. The finer-grained igneous rocks mostly cooled from magma that erupted to the surface and cooled so quickly that large, easily visible crystals had no time to form.

Sedimentary rocks form most commonly from bits of rock, known as clasts, worn or weathered from older rock. These are known as clastic sedimentary rock. The most common of New Jersey's clastic rocks are shale, which forms from clay; sandstone, which forms from sand; and conglomerate, usually a mixture of sand and gravel. Chemical sediments, by contrast, form from chemicals dissolved in water instead of from particles worn or broken from older rocks. The most common of New Jersey's sedimentary rocks formed from chemicals dissolved in seawater are limestone (calcium carbonate) and dolomite (calcium magnesium carbonate).

Diabase from the Palisades of the Hudson (above) and basalt from the First Watchung Mountain (below). These igneous rocks cooled from nearly identical magmas. The diabase cooled several thousand feet below the surface over thousands of years and had time to develop easily visible crystals. The lighter colored crystals are mostly feldspar. The darker crystals are mostly pyroxene. The basalt cooled quickly at the land surface from a lava flow. It solidified before easily visible crystals could grow. —Photos by D. Harper

The Allentown Dolomite, a sedimentary rock near Hamburg. Layering from deposition of beds of slightly different sediment one on top of another is conspicuous in many sedimentary rocks. —Photo by Michael Flite

Metamorphic rocks form from older rocks subjected to enough heat or pressure to change them into new kinds of rock. In lower-grade (less severely transformed) metamorphic rocks, such as the quartzite of the Delaware Water Gap and the black slates just east of the gap, it is easy to judge the parent rock. The quartzite formed from quartz sandstone; the slate formed from shale. In higher-grade (more severely transformed) metamorphic rocks of the New Jersey Highlands, detailed chemical analyses are often necessary to identify the parent rock. A dark-colored variety of gneiss known as amphibolite, for example, usually forms from igneous rocks, such as basalt or gabbro, which are rich in iron, magnesium, and aluminum. It can also form from limy shale. Both kinds of amphibolite outcrop in the New Jersey Highlands, and it is sometimes difficult to tell the parent rock simply by looking.

In New Jersey, as anywhere else in the world, sediment deposition, lithification (the changing of sediment into rock), metamorphism, igneous activity, and erosion have not been continuous and uninterrupted. The processes have been continuous through Earth history but at constantly shifting locations. The rock cycle traces earth materials as they cycle between sediment and rock. Rocks are weathered to sand, silt, and clay, which are then transported and deposited, often in an ocean, by water, wind, or ice. After sediment is deposited, it is sometimes changed to rock; the rock is sometimes metamorphosed and sometimes melted to become igneous rock. Eventually the rock may be raised above sea level once again to be eroded, transported, and deposited.

The Shawangunk Formation of Kittatinny Mountain is quartzite, a common metamorphic rock in New Jersey. Channel crossbedding from deposition in a river or shoreline environment is still visible to the center left of the photo. —Photo by Don Monteverde, N.J. Geological Survey

This gneiss has been severely metamorphosed. Some layering in gneiss is inherited from the parent rock. Some is from pressure and shearing during metamorphism. —Photo by D. Harper

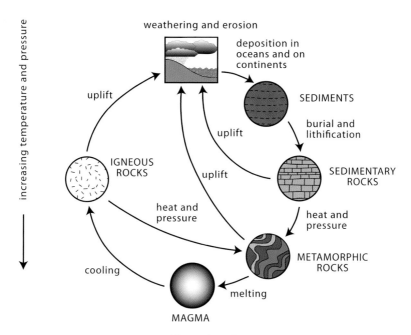

The rock cycle.

Much of the research by geologists has involved determining when rocks formed and when sediments were deposited. One of the key achievements of nineteenth-century geology was the establishment of a geologic time scale based on relative ages of rocks and their fossils. Geologic time was subdivided into four major eras and numerous shorter periods based primarily on fossils. These are shown on the geologic time scale near the beginning of this book. One of the key achievements of twentieth-century geology was the determination of the ages, in years, of the eras and periods. The relative ages of geologic formations can often be judged by position (for example, younger sedimentary rocks usually lie on top of older sedimentary rocks), crosscutting relationships (for example, an igneous rock intruding a sedimentary rock is younger than the sedimentary rock), or fossils (for example, a formation with trilobites is older than a formation with dinosaur bones). The relationships tell which rocks are older and younger but do not tell whether a rock is 1 million years old, 10 million years old, or 100 million years old. The key to determining the ages of rocks in years, the absolute ages as opposed to relative ages, came with the discovery of radioactivity by Henri Becquerel in 1896. Radioactivity is the breakdown of unstable elements to daughter products. Uranium, for example, decays eventually to lead. Carbon 14, a radioactive isotope of carbon, decays to nitrogen. Radiometric dating using uranium is done by measuring the amounts of the radioactive element and daughter product in a rock or, more usually, in a single crystal grain. Because radioactive elements decay to daughter products with a constant half-life, the age at which a crystal formed and locked in the radioactive elements and daughter products can be calculated from the amounts of the radioactive element that remains and daughter product that has been created. Radioactive dating using carbon 14 is done by measuring the ratio of undecayed carbon 14 to nonradioactive carbon in a sample of organic material. Carbon 14 is constantly being created by cosmic ray bombardment of nitrogen in the atmosphere. Once carbon dioxide has been removed from the atmosphere and become fixed in wood or some other organic material, the amount of carbon 14 relative to nonradioactive carbon decreases at a predictable rate.

New Jersey's Geologic Provinces

The rocks in New Jersey today date from sedimentation and igneous and metamorphic activity of four distinct intervals of geologic time and are exposed predominantly in four different geologic provinces: the New Jersey Highlands, the Valley and Ridge, the Piedmont, and the Atlantic Coastal Plain. These four distinct geologic areas have been recognized since the infancy of North American geology and are clear in geologic maps published as long ago as 1816. Working out the events that produced these rocks has been ongoing through the ensuing two centuries, and much still remains to be learned.

The oldest of New Jersey's rocks, the granite and gneiss of the rugged Highlands Province, date from the Proterozoic Eon and are between 1,363 and 980 million years old. Second oldest and exposed mostly in the Valley and Ridge Province in the northwestern part of the state are Early and Middle Paleozoic sedimentary and metamorphic rocks, mostly dolomite, slate, and quartzite. These are between 540 and 400 million years old. Third oldest and exposed in the Piedmont are Triassic and Jurassic rocks: sedimentary sandstone, shale, and mudstone and igneous basalt and diabase between 225 and 195 million years old. The New Jersey Piedmont rocks, except for a few square miles around Trenton and a few square miles between Hoboken and Bayonne, are entirely in the Newark Basin, a sediment-filled rift valley that was active when North America first began to split westward from Africa. For simplicity the Piedmont Province in New Jersey is commonly referred to as the Newark Basin.

The youngest geologic formations, in the Coastal Plain of southern New Jersey, are sand, gravel, clay, and greensand formations deposited along the margin of the Atlantic Ocean, some on land, some at the water's edge, and some offshore. Coastal Plain deposition began onshore in New Jersey in the Cretaceous Period, about 120 million years ago, and ended with a worldwide drop in sea level in the Miocene Epoch between 15 and 10 million years ago. The Coastal Plain is commonly subdivided into the Inner Coastal Plain, featuring a succession of sandy and clayey formations, and the Outer Coastal Plain, veneered by sandy soil that gives rise to New Jersey's Pinelands, a vast expanse of pine barrens supporting many rare plant species. Offshore on the continental shelf, sedimentation began earlier, about 195 million years ago in the Jurassic Period when North America finally broke apart from Africa following tens of millions of years of rift valley widening.

The rocks are all that remain from some of the state's large but long-gone or long-dormant features, including oceans that narrowed and closed when seafloor crust subducted, mountains that eroded to their roots, and rift basins that ceased rifting when continental crust finally broke apart. For the more recent geologic past, however, generally the last 10 million years from the Miocene Epoch on, landforms and sediment can be as important as the rock record when interpreting the geologic history. The Miocene rivers of 10 million years ago, for example, were cutting downward in the Highlands, Valley and Ridge, and Newark Basin, but depositing sediment in the Coastal Plain.

New Jersey geology from an 1816 geologic map of eastern North America. On the original map, New Jersey is the size of a large postage stamp. Still, the map shows that the major geologic subdivisions of New Jersey were already well-known. —Cleveland, 1816

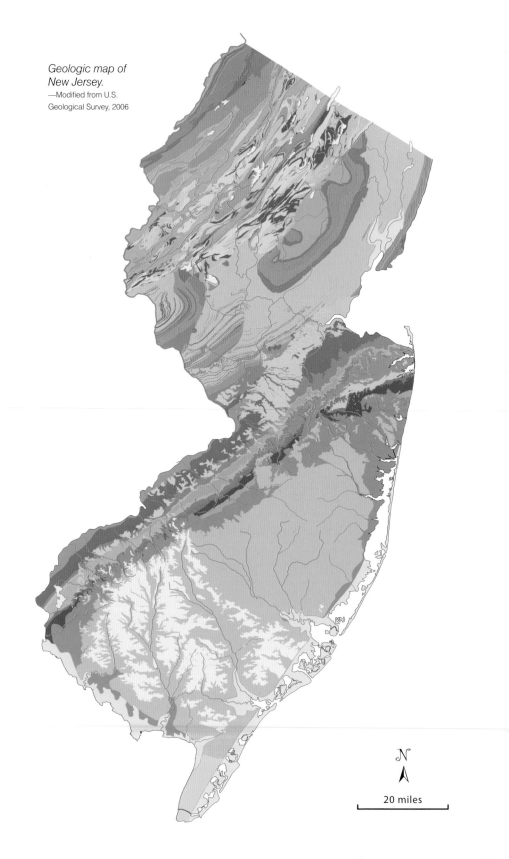

*Geologic map of
New Jersey.*
—Modified from U.S.
Geological Survey, 2006

N

20 miles

QUATERNARY
- Holocene beach and estuarine deposits

TERTIARY
- Pensauken Formation
- Bridgeton Formation

OUTER COASTAL PLAIN
- unnamed unit at Cape May
- Cohansey Formation
- Kirkwood Formation
- Shark River Formation
- Manasquan Formation
- Vincentown Formation
- Hornerstown Formation

CRETACEOUS
INNER COASTAL PLAIN
- Tinton Formation
- Red Bank Formation
- Navesink Formation
- Mount Laurel Formation
- Wenonah Formation
- Marshalltown Formation
- Englishtown Formation
- Woodbury Formation
- Merchantville Formation
- Cheesequake Formation
- Magothy Formation
- Raritan Formation
- Potomac Formation

PIEDMONT / NEWARK BASIN
JURASSIC
- diabase sill

NEWARK SUPERGROUP
- Boonton Formation
- Hook Mountain Basalt
- Towaco Formation
- Preakness Basalt
- Feltville Formation
- Orange Mountain Basalt
- Jurassic-Triassic Passaic Formation (cyclic bedding)

TRIASSIC
- Lockatong Formation
- Stockton Formation

VALLEY AND RIDGE
DEVONIAN
- Marcellus Shale
- Buttermilk Falls and Onondaga Limestone
- Schoharie Formation
- Esopus Formation
- Oriskany Group

DEVONIAN-SILURIAN
Helderberg Group
- Port Ewen Shale
- Minisink Limestone and New Scotland Formation
- Kalkberg Limestone, Manlieus Limestone, and Coeymans Formation
- Rondout and Decker Formations
- Bossardville Formation
- Poxono Island Formation
- Bloomsburg Red Beds
- Shawangunk Formation

~~~ unconformity ~~~

GREEN POND OUTLIER
DEVONIAN
- Skunnemunk Conglomerate
- Bellvale Sandstone
- Cornwall Shale
- Kanouse Sandstone, Esopus Formation, and Connelly Conglomerate

SILURIAN
- limestone, sandstone, and shale
- Green Pond Conglomerate

SILURIAN
- Beemerville Intrusive Suite

ORDOVICIAN
- Martinsburg Formation
- Jacksonburg Formation

~~~ Beekmantown Unconformity ~~~

ORDOVICIAN-CAMBRIAN
- Kittatinny Supergroup

JUTLAND KLIPPE AND PEAPACK KLIPPE
- metasedimentary rocks

CAMBRIAN-PROTEROZOIC
TRENTON PRONG
- igneous and metamorphic rocks

PROTEROZOIC
NEW JERSEY HIGHLANDS
- Chestnut Hill Formation
- Mount Eve Granite
- Byram Intrusive Suite
- Lake Hopatcong Intrusive Suite
- Losee Metamorphic Suite
- metasedimentary rocks
- marble

Rocks of uncertain origin
- gneiss, diorite, amphibolite, migmatite, and alaskite

MANHATTAN PRONG
- Manhattan Schist
- serpentine

PROTEROZOIC EON
2.5 billion to 542 million years ago

When the oldest rocks in New Jersey, 1,360-million-year-old gneiss from the New Jersey Highlands, were forming, Earth had already come to resemble the planet we live on today. Much of the continental crust now in existence had formed, and plate tectonics was operating much as it does at present. New Jersey's oldest rocks were forming on the eastern margin of a continent known as Laurentia, named from rocks in the St. Lawrence area of Canada.

The atmosphere of early Earth had no oxygen. By about 3,500 million years ago, however, photosynthetic bacteria had evolved and were combining water and carbon dioxide to produce organic compounds and oxygen. By 2,000 million years ago, enough carbon had been sequestered in organic compounds and carbonate rock to allow oxygen to begin building up in the atmosphere. Fossils of the individual bacteria that were transforming the atmosphere can be difficult to find and identify, but they commonly grew by the billions in blankets and mounds in shallow water and intertidal limestone environments. They left layered, mound-shaped fossil masses known as stromatolites, which are the most common fossils from 2,000 million years ago to the end of the Proterozoic Eon, 542 million years ago. They are so common, in fact, that that the time has informally been called the Age of Stromatolites. New Jersey has Proterozoic marble formed from limestone, but the rock has been so thoroughly metamorphosed that fossils were completely unexpected until 2004, when Richard Volkert of the New Jersey Geological Survey reported well-preserved stromatolites in marble that had somehow escaped complete recrystallization.

Modern stromatolite mounds in Shark Bay on the west coast of Australia.
—Photo by Richard W. Ojakangas

1,360-million-year-old stromatolite from the Franklin Marble. —Photo by Richard Volkert, N.J. Geological Survey

While in some ways the Earth had come a long way toward its present condition by 1,360 million years ago, in other ways it had far to go. The land was barren, more closely resembling the surface of Mars than the Earth of today. Even in moist climates there was nothing to stabilize soil. Sand dunes and dust storms were not restricted to deserts.

GRENVILLE PROVINCE AND OTTAWAN OROGENY

The Proterozoic rocks of the New Jersey Highlands are predominantly erosion-resistant granite and gneiss, and the resistance gives the Highlands their rugged topography. The rocks are part of a long, wide belt of Proterozoic igneous and metamorphic rocks commonly grouped as the Grenville Province. Grenville rocks, now buried below younger rocks in many places, extend far beyond New Jersey along a wide belt from eastern Canada along eastern North America through Alabama and Texas and into Mexico. Grenville rocks are widespread on all continents. The Grenville Province is arguably the oldest assemblage of rocks for which a reasonably complete history is known. Much of that history has been deciphered for the New Jersey's Grenville rocks only since the early 2000s when radiometric dates were determined for numerous previously undated bodies of rock.

Formation of the Grenville rocks began with the narrowing and closing of an ocean basin separating Laurentia to the west from another continent, known as Amazonia, to the east and culminated, over 1,000 million years ago, in a collision between the continents. The collision raised a lofty mountain chain thousands of miles long and united the Earth's landmasses into the supercontinent Rodinia. The closing of the ocean and subsequent mountain building took place in several phases that together lasted about 350 million years. Many of the Grenville rocks formed long before the final collision between continents, and some formed after the ensuing mountain building. While the entire belt of rocks continues to be referred to as the Grenville Province, an older term, Grenville Orogeny, referring to the formation of the rocks, has been recognized as too broad, grouping rocks formed through numerous events beyond a single

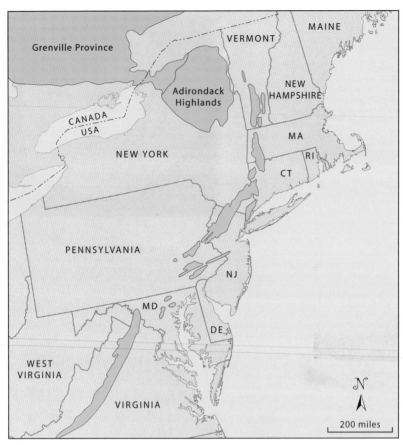

Surface outcrops of Grenville rocks of northeastern North America. Additional large areas of Grenville rocks undoubtedly lie buried beneath younger rocks to the east and west of outcrops in the Appalachians. —Modified from Volkert, Aleinikoff, and Fanning, 2010

collision between continents. The final collision and mountain building are now more appropriately referred to by the less inclusive name Ottawan Orogeny.

New Jersey's oldest rocks date from the narrowing of the ocean. Most of these rocks, the Losee Metamorphic Suite, are between 1,282 and 1,254 million years old. Dates averaging 1,363 million years for a still older suite of rocks, the Wanaque tonalite gneiss, suggest that the narrowing of the ocean began well before the emplacement of the Losee rocks. Large volumes of molten rock were produced as the subducting plate passed downward into the hot mantle. Some of it came to the surface as volcanic rock. Some cooled below the surface to become intrusive igneous rock. There are several lines of evidence confirming that the subduction occurred along a continental margin arc, like the Andes, where oceanic crust was sinking beneath continental crust, rather than along an oceanic island arc, like the Aleutians, where two plates of oceanic crust meet and one overrides the other. For New Jersey's Grenville rocks, the most

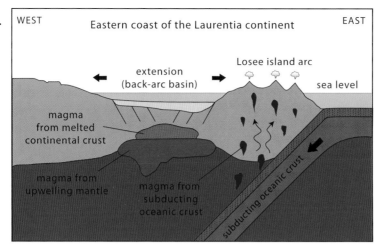

A. About 1,250 million years ago, oceanic crust was subducting beneath the east coast of Laurentia, the predecessor to North America. Magma produced by the subduction created the Losee magmatic arc. The crust stretched and thinned above the descending slab, creating a back-arc basin.

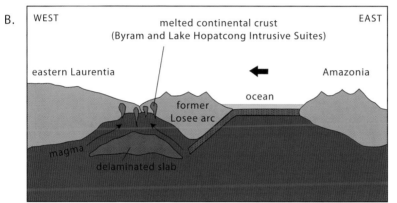

B. The closing of the back-arc basin was followed by delamination of a slab from the base of the crust. Hot magma welling upward into the space left by the delaminated slab melted almost half of the New Jersey Highlands rocks exposed today.

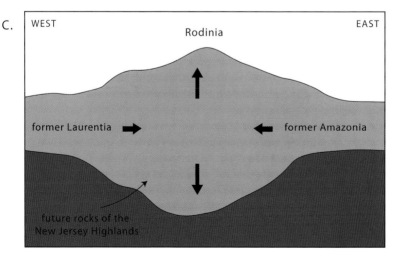

C. The final closing of the ocean with the collision between Laurentia and Amazonia in the Ottawan Orogeny created the supercontinent Rodinia. The collision compressed and thickened the continental crust. Some rock rose up and became the peaks of mountains. Other rock was pushed miles down into the Earth. Erosion has stripped away the uplifted rock and exposed rock metamorphosed deep below the surface. —A and B modified from Volkert, Aleinikoff, and Fanning, 2010

compelling evidence suggesting a continental margin arc is the wide variety of volcanic and intrusive igneous rocks. The rocks have compositions indicating that they melted from a variety of parent rocks: the subducting slab of oceanic crust, deeply buried juvenile continental crust that had never been exposed at the surface, and recycled continental crust that had gone through at least one cycle of erosion and redeposition. If the overriding crust had been made of oceanic crust, fewer kinds of rock would have been melted and a more limited variety of igneous rocks would have been generated, mostly basalt and basalt-related rocks. Basaltic rocks are present but not dominant in the igneous rocks of the Losee Metamorphic Suite.

In the New Jersey Highlands, unlike in the Andes, extension above the subsiding oceanic crust landward from the mountains caused the overlying continental crust to become so thin that the land surface dropped below sea level. This formed a back-arc basin between the mountainous offshore island arc and the interior of North America.

Sediment was deposited across the width of the back-arc basin but differed from east to west. In the western part of the Highlands, sediment rich in quartz, calcium silicates, and carbonate became quartzite, gneiss, and the Franklin Marble. The abundance of quartz suggests that the sediments were eroded from quartz-rich continental rocks and that erosion was slow enough that more easily weathered minerals, like mica and feldspar, were exposed long enough or traveled far enough to be reduced to clay. The abundance of calcium silicates suggests that sedimentation was slow enough to allow precipitation of calcium carbonate dissolved in seawater to make up a substantial proportion of the rock. The obvious source was Laurentia to the west. Sedimentation was slow enough sometimes that limestone, now the pure white Franklin Marble, accumulated undiluted by silicate minerals.

Sediment in the eastern portion of the basin was from highlands of the offshore island arc to the east. Because of the mountainous terrain, the rocks eroded quickly and were washed to the sea with less time to weather or be broken apart. New Jersey's eastern metasedimentary gneisses appear to have formed mostly from graywacke, an impure sandstone that includes substantial amounts of mica, feldspar, and rock fragments. Most of these would have been broken down if they had been transported long distances by rivers or exposed to prolonged weathering by the atmosphere.

As might be expected where the Earth's crust is stretching and thinning, magma from the mantle rose and melted the base of the overlying crust. Melted continental crust is lighter than magma from the mantle, and the crust-derived magma floated above the mantle-derived magma with little mixing. Magma from both the mantle rock and the overlying melted crust intruded the overlying, still solid crust and erupted through volcanoes, some spewing mantle-derived magma and some spewing magma from melted crust. Superheated water above the magma is believed to have carried the zinc mined at the Franklin and Sterling Hill Mines of Sussex County and the iron mined at a few of New Jersey's many magnetite mines.

At about 1,200 million years ago, tectonic forces west of the continental margin arc shifted from extensional to compressional, and the back-arc basin

Franklin Marble at the abandoned Limecrest Quarry near Newton in Sussex County. The rock was deposited as limestone and metamorphosed to marble in the Ottawan Orogeny. —Photo by Richard Volkert, N.J. Geological Survey

closed. The next development to affect the New Jersey's Grenville rocks, about 1,185 years ago, was an immense input of heat that melted much of the Highlands rock to produce granitic rocks grouped as the Byram Intrusive Suite and Lake Hopatcong Intrusive Suite. The likely cause was delamination: the breaking loose of a slab from the bottom of crust that had been overthickened by compression when the back-arc basin closed. Hotter mantle material rose up and around the delaminated slab, heating and melting the overlying crust. As roughly half of the rock in the Highlands is granite melted from this pulse of heat, the size of the delaminated slab must have been substantial.

Eventually the ocean to the east of New Jersey closed and, in the Ottawan Orogeny, the continents of Laurentia (now mostly part of North America) and Amazonia (now mostly part of South America) collided. The collision welded Laurentia to the growing supercontinent Rodinia, named from a Russian word for "motherland." The mountain building had begun by 1,045 million years ago and was over by 1,024 million years ago. The Grenville rocks of New Jersey were among those shoved downward as the crust compressed and thickened. The rocks were subjected to temperatures of 1,240 to 1,260 degrees Fahrenheit and pressures of 4,200 to 6,300 atmospheres. This completed the transformation of the continental arc and back-arc rocks to gneisses, quartzite, and marble and added a metamorphic overprint to the granitic rocks of the Byram and Lake Hopatcong Igneous Suites.

The final chapter in the development of the Grenville rocks came with the relaxation of the compressional stresses of the collision. Between 1,020 and 980 million years ago, decompression melting of small volumes of rock produced the Mount Eve Granite of Pochuck Mountain near Glenwood, the Pompton Pink Granite of Pompton Plains, and widespread small dikes and veins of granitic pegmatite. Hydrothermal mineralization from about the same time left magnetite deposits enriched in uranium and rare earths. For many years, the Pompton Pink Granite was one of New Jersey's premier building stones. It was shipped as far as Washington, DC, where it was used at the entrance to the Smithsonian Institution. Closer by it was used, both polished and rough-hewn, in St. Paul's Episcopal Church in Paterson.

Granite gneiss in the Ramapo Mountains. Magma generated by the delaminated slab from the bottom of the crust cooled to form granite. It was then metamorphosed to gneiss during the Ottawan Orogeny. —Photo by Richard Volkert, N.J. Geological Survey

Some Pompton Pink Granite is specifically granite pegmatite—granite because of its composition chiefly of quartz and feldspar with lesser amounts of iron and magnesium silicates, and pegmatite because the crystals are unusually large. —Photo by Richard Volkert, N.J. Geological Survey

Pompton Pink Granite at St. Paul's Episcopal Church in Paterson.
—Photo by Richard Volkert, N.J. Geological Survey

RIFTING OF RODINIA AND THE IAPETUS OCEAN

Assembly of continents by collision and disassembly by rifting are common occurrences in Earth history, and the rifting of the supercontinent Rodinia is no exception. Toward the end of the Proterozoic Eon, Rodinia, assembled in the Ottawan Orogeny, began rifting into smaller continents as seaways began to open and widen. Often when a continent breaks apart, the break more or less follows the weak suture where two pieces of continental crust previously collided. Thus, when the North American crust rifted from the supercontinent Rodinia, the break followed the suture formed between Laurentia and Amazonia a few hundred million years before. The rifting opened a new ocean, Iapetus, named for the father of Atlas in Greek mythology.

There are two phases to the splitting of a continent, rifting and drifting. In the rifting phase, the plates have not yet fully separated. The crust is pulling apart, thinning, and downdropping along faults bordering rift valleys. In the drifting phase, the plates have fully separated, faulting diminishes, a passive margin develops, and the two pieces drift apart, leaving a widening ocean between. Rocks from the rifting phase of the breakup of Rodinia, referred to as Iapetan rift deposits after the ensuing ocean, are well-known to the north and south of New Jersey, but few exposures were expected here because the New Jersey section of the rift is east of the New Jersey Highlands and covered by younger rocks.

A few iron mines in the Highlands, the Andover Mine and a number of much smaller mines, produced hematite ore rather than the usual magnetite, but there was no reason to associate it with the rifting of Rodinia. The smaller mines were historically little studied. The Andover Mine was the subject of numerous investigations but was for many years an enigma. In geology, as in most other endeavors, however, context is as important as isolated facts, and beginning in the late 1960s the hematite mines began to acquire a context that eventually led to their recognition as isolated remnants of rift basins from the splitting apart of Rodinia. The context began forming when it was recognized that a number of conglomerates and sandstones previously thought to be part of the Hardyston Formation, a quartzite from the Cambrian Period, were deposited several million years before deposition of the Hardyston began. The Hardyston Formation is a passive margin deposit postdating the rifting of

ANDOVER IRON MINE, SUSSEX CO

The Andover Mine in 1854. Even by this time the ore at the Andover Mine was recognized as unique and enigmatic. —Lithograph from Kitchell, 1855

Rodinia. The older conglomerates and sandstones, given the name Chestnut Hill Formation after a Pennsylvania occurrence, had been lithified and tilted before the Hardyston was deposited. They resembled well-known Iapetan rift basin deposits in being interbedded with volcanic materials not found with the Hardyston; having features suggesting deposition in alluvial fans, rivers, and lakes, rather than in marine environments like the Hardyston; and being closely associated with faults that appear to have been active while the sediments were being deposited. Some fragments of Chestnut Hill rock had even become embedded in the faults while they were moving. Clearly the rocks were older than the Hardyston Formation, but they were only slightly metamorphosed and therefore younger than the Grenville rocks. Their age, depositional setting, close association with faults, and close resemblance to known Iapetan rift sediments together show that the rocks were deposited in outlying rift basins during the splitting of Rodinia. Additional evidence for rift activity in northwestern New Jersey comes from numerous diabase dikes cutting across older Proterozoic rocks. For many years the dikes were believed to be related to the rifting of North America from Africa during the Mesozoic Era, but radiometric dating of the dike rocks shows that they are much older, related to the Iapetan rifting. Sedimentation in rift basins further explains the hematite ore. Each of the hematite mines was found to be in the Iapetan rift deposits rather than the Grenville rocks. The rocks had never been subjected to the heat and pressures that formed the magnetite ore of most of the Highlands mines, and the hematite ore is no longer an enigma.

PALEOZOIC ERA
542 to 251 million years ago

By the beginning of the Cambrian Period, about 542 million years ago, Rodinia had rifted apart and New Jersey was once again bordered to the east by an ocean. As in the Proterozoic, the land was barren and lifeless. In the seas, by contrast, most of the major groups of animals now living had appeared at the beginning of the Cambrian Period in a sudden burst of evolution, the Cambrian explosion. Trilobites are emblematic, but worms, snails, brachiopods, sponges, and coelenterates also filled the seas. Chordates, ancestral to the vertebrates, are first known from the Cambrian, but true fish did not become abundant until the Ordovician Period.

Unlike the active margin that characterized New Jersey through the events leading to the Ottawan Orogeny, the edge of the continent in Cambrian time was a passive margin, similar to the continental margin New Jersey sits on today. Passive margins form along the rifted edges of continents where the crust has been thinned by extension during the pulling apart of crustal plates and heated by magma rising beneath the thinned crust. After the rifting, crustal thinning and magmatic activity usually cease, and over the next 50 to 100 million years the crust and magma cool, sink downward because of their increasing density, and commonly become covered by enormous wedges of sediment.

CARBONATE BANK OF
CAMBRIAN-ORDOVICIAN TIME

The Early Paleozoic passive margin along Iapetus and the modern passive margin along the Atlantic are similar in their large, seaward-thickening sediment wedges but differ sharply in the kind of sediment that was deposited. The Mid-Atlantic today is in an area of temperate to glacial climate along a coastline where rivers are carrying substantial amounts of sediment to the ocean. The sediment wedge consists mostly of sand, silt, and clay. The North American passive margin bordering Iapetus, by contrast, was in the tropics and formed at a time when shallow seas covered much of inland North America, erosion was minimal on the low-lying lands that were exposed, and little sediment was carried eastward to the sea. Other than the thin, discontinuous sandstone of the Hardyston Formation, which was deposited when the sea first began encroaching onto the land, the sediment wedge was built predominantly from calcium and magnesium carbonate dissolved in seawater. The accumulation is usually referred to as a carbonate bank rather than a reef because it lacked skeletal organisms, such as corals, that give reefs their resistance to waves. Most of the carbonate was extracted from the seawater instead by algae and photosynthetic bacteria. The bank was larger and thicker than the Great Barrier Reef of Australia. It stretched from eastern Canada at least to Georgia. In New Jersey several carbonate formations (formally known as the Kittatinny Supergroup and informally called the Kittatinny limestones) total over 2,500 feet thick. In actuality, the limestone is almost entirely dolomite (calcium magnesium carbonate) rather than limestone (calcium carbonate) in the strict sense.

How could so much carbonate accumulate? The solubility of calcium carbonate depends on the amount of carbon dioxide dissolved in the water. With more dissolved carbon dioxide gas, the water can dissolve more calcium carbonate. The amount of carbon dioxide dissolved in seawater depends in good part on the water temperature and on the amount of photosynthesis going on. As anyone who has opened a warm soda and experienced the sudden release of carbon dioxide can attest, warm solutions hold less dissolved gas than cold solutions. In the oceans, warm tropical waters hold less carbon dioxide than colder waters to the north and south, and the dissolved calcium carbonate is more easily precipitated. Photosynthesis further accelerates the precipitation of carbonate minerals by removing additional carbon dioxide from the water and using it to manufacture carbohydrates.

Even though the carbonate rock was 2,500 feet thick, almost all of the carbonate was precipitated within a few tens of feet of sea level, where the sun warmed the water and encouraged photosynthesis. Through their entire thickness, New Jersey's Paleozoic carbonate bank deposits have sedimentary features that show they were deposited in shallow water. As the edge of the continent subsided, the carbonate rock accumulated fast enough to keep the top of the bank in shallow water. Among the most common shallow-water features are ooliths, small circular grains formed by precipitation of calcium carbonate around a central grain as it rolls in the waves, and stromatolites, fossilized

These desiccation cracks, on a bedding surface of dolomite of the Kittatinny limestones, indicate the carbonate bank was above water for a while. —Photo by Don Monteverde, N.J. Geological Survey

mounds of algae. Desiccation cracks are common and show that, as in today's reefs, it was not unusual for parts of the bank to be above water.

TACONIC OROGENY AND THE ASSEMBLY OF PANGEA

Even while the eastern edge of North America remained a passive margin and the carbonate bank continued to thicken, the African and Eurasian landmasses were moving toward North America and would eventually collide during the assembly of the supercontinent Pangea. The assembly of Pangea was not the simple closing of an ocean followed by a collision between continents. There were three distinct mountain building events in eastern North America alone. The first was the Taconic Orogeny of Ordovician and Silurian time, which began about 470 million years ago and lasted until about 430 million years ago. In the Iapetus Ocean, oceanic crust was moving east and subducting, or sinking, beneath the Taconic island arc. Although the width of ocean between North America and the subduction zone was shrinking, the uplift, igneous activity, faulting, and earthquakes associated with the subduction zone remained well removed from the carbonate bank.

Eventually the distance to the subduction zone had shortened enough that effects began to be noticeable. As crust at the subduction zone bent downward, crust farther back bent upward in a peripheral bulge some hundreds of miles west of the subduction zone. The Kittatinny carbonates were lifted above sea level. The rocks began to erode, and caves formed in the water-soluble dolomite. The eroded surface is the Beekmantown Unconformity, an unconformity because the bedding of the underlying rock does not conform to that in rocks deposited later.

The Ordovician caves have long since collapsed or filled in with sediment, but collapse breccias and passageway fillings can still be found in outcrops.

As oceanic crust continued to sink beneath the Taconic island arc, the subduction zone came closer to North America. The peripheral bulge moved westward toward the midcontinent, and the continental margin beneath New Jersey began to bend downward toward the subduction zone. The continental

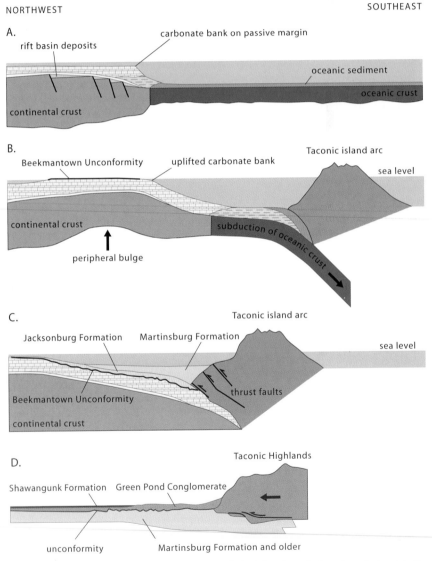

Events leading up to the Taconic Orogeny in Ordovician time. A. A carbonate bank built up in shallow water along the coast. B. The Taconic island arc approached from the east and oceanic crust was subducted beneath it. The edge of the continent bulged up, exposing the carbonate bank to erosion. C. As the island arc approached land, sedimentation resumed above the carbonate bank. D. Sediments shed westward off the Taconic Highlands form rocks in New Jersey today. —Modified from Monteverde, 2004

Breccia from the collapse of a cave in the Kittatinny limestones at the time of the Beek-mantown Unconformity. The broken rock (breccia) is from collapse. The light brown material is sand and silt washed in by water. —Photos by Frank Markewicz, N.J. Geological Survey

margin sank beneath sea level and oceanic sediments again began to be deposited. The first sediment deposited above the Beekmantown Unconformity was the Jacksonburg Formation, a relatively thin limestone. As the water continued to deepen, sediment changed from limestone to deepwater mud that became the Martinsburg Formation, a 6,000-foot-thick sequence of slate. Finally, as the last remaining oceanic crust between North America and the island arc passed downward into the subduction zone, the island arc began to push upward and over the downwarped North American continental crust, raising mountains from eastern Canada to Virginia. The mountain building was centered along an axis through present-day Philadelphia, New York City, and northward through New England. Most of New Jersey was west of the collision. Rocks roughly equivalent to the dolomitic limestone of the carbonate bank in northwestern New Jersey were completely recrystallized to the Inwood Marble in New York. Slate similar to the Martinsburg Formation was metamorphosed to the Manhattan Schist. In northwestern New Jersey, the flank of the uplifted crust was buried beneath an apron of sand and gravel that became the Shawangunk Formation, Green Pond Conglomerate, and Bloomsburg Red Beds.

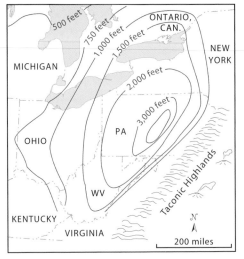

Sediment was shed off the Taconic Highlands in Silurian time.
—Modified from Van Diver, 1990

With no more oceanic crust left to subduct, subduction stopped and eventually its lingering effects ceased. The highlands eroded to low hills, and shallow seas then covering the interior of North America to the west encroached eastward. Thin limestone, sandstone, and shale formations were deposited above the much thicker formations related to crustal plate movement.

ACADIAN AND ALLEGHANIAN OROGENIES

In the Taconic Orogeny an island arc was welded onto North America, but North America did not yet become part of Pangea. North America was still at the western shore of an ocean. Other pieces of continental crust that would eventually collide to form the supercontinent Pangea were on the eastern shore of the ocean, encroaching toward North America. The welding of North America onto the growing supercontinent was the result of two additional mountain building events: the Acadian Orogeny in the Devonian Period and the Alleghanian Orogeny in the Pennsylvanian and Permian Periods.

During the Acadian Orogeny, both an island arc and a piece of continental crust welded onto North America. The strongest effects of the mountain building were felt to the north of New Jersey, in New England and Canada's Maritime Provinces. Nevertheless, highlands were raised to the east and New Jersey was again on the flank of the upraised crust and likely was covered by an apron of sediment shed westward from the Acadian Mountains. Most of the sediment was deposited to the west of New Jersey in a thick accumulation known as the Catskill Wedge.

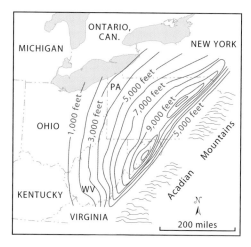

The Catskill Wedge is a thick accumulation of sediment deposited to the west of the Acadian Mountains. The sediment came from New Jersey and other mountainous states along the line of impact between North America and the colliding landmasses.
—Modified from Van Diver, 1990

Whatever once existed of the Catskill Wedge in New Jersey has been eroded except in the Green Pond Outlier, a belt of Paleozoic rock faulted downward into the New Jersey Highlands. Within the outlier, the Bellvale Sandstone and Skunnemunk Conglomerate remaining from the Acadian Orogeny somewhat resemble the Green Pond Conglomerate, shed westward from the highlands raised in the Taconic Orogeny.

The Alleghanian Orogeny in Pennsylvanian and Permian time was caused by a collision between continents in which North America was finally welded onto the growing supercontinent Pangea. New Jersey was, for the third time in the Paleozoic Era, on the west flank of mountains, which this time stretched from east of Greenland to the tip of South America. Rocks of the Valley and Ridge and Highlands Provinces in New Jersey were folded and faulted but were too far west to be subject to intense metamorphism. However, beneath the more recent Coastal Plain sediments, a sample of gneiss was recovered in 1962 from a well drilled at Island Beach to 3,891 feet below sea level. The rock was metamorphosed 244 million years ago, at the end of the Alleghanian Orogeny.

In New Jersey, rocks were uplifted and thrust westward across a wide belt extending across all of New Jersey and almost to the middle of Pennsylvania.

New Jersey was most likely in an erosional setting. The bulk, if not all, of the sediment bypassed New Jersey and was deposited across much of the interior of eastern North America. Coal swamps and floodplains covered with sand and clay from the highlands to the east extended from the anthracite fields of eastern Pennsylvania to the bituminous coalfields of Illinois and southward to Mississippi and Alabama.

MESOZOIC ERA
251 to 65 million years ago

NEWARK RIFT BASIN

Pangea stayed intact for millions of years, with New Jersey near the center of this very large continent, before it began to rift apart 225 million years ago. The rifting that affected New Jersey began to the south, toward the southern United States and worked its way zipperlike northward toward Greenland and southward between South America and Africa. Rift valleys similar to those now crossing east Africa widened over about 30 million years until finally the continental crust on the opposite sides came apart. Magma welled upward between the separating crustal plates to form new oceanic crust, and the Atlantic was born.

Unlike the rifting of Rodinia, which left only a scant record in New Jersey, the rifting of Pangea left an assemblage of sedimentary and igneous rocks over

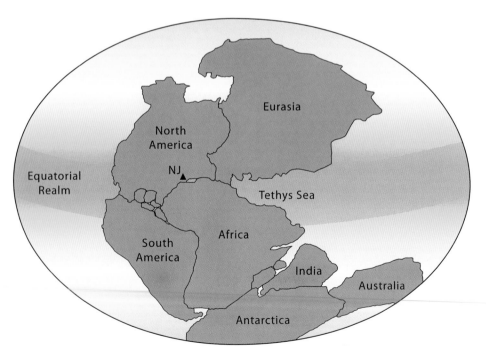

New Jersey was far inland within the supercontinent Pangea.
—Modified from U.S. Geological Survey's New York City Regional Geology website

15,000 feet thick in the Newark Basin. Rift basins are known from up and down the East Coast, some exposed, some buried beneath Coastal Plain deposits, and some offshore. The Newark Basin is the largest of the exposed basins, has the best exposures of the igneous and sedimentary rocks, and is a commonly used as an example in illustrating the sequence of events early in the breaking apart of continents.

As Pangea began to rift, the crust began to stretch and, much like a stretched piece of chewing gum, it got thinner. The thinning affected both the lower part of the crust, which was hot and plastic and stretched without breaking, and the upper part, which was cold and brittle and in good part broke apart by reactivating faults still weak from the Alleghanian Orogeny and before. Rather than

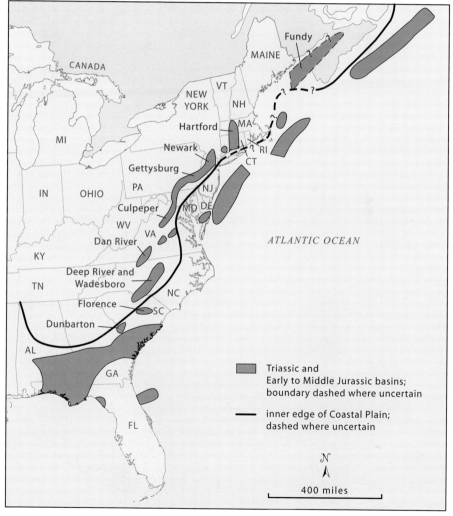

When the Atlantic Ocean rifted open in Triassic and Jurassic time, rift basins formed along the east coast of the new continent. —From Owens and others, 1998

being thrust upward and westward, however, blocks of crust slid downward and eastward as the crust thinned. The best known of the New Jersey faults active during the rifting is the Ramapo Fault, along the northwestern part of the Newark Basin. Downdropping in the thousands of feet occurred as well at other faults through the eastern half of the Highlands and along rift basins now buried beneath Coastal Plain and continental shelf deposits. When the faults were active, the land was crossed by a series of northeast-southwest-trending basins and ranges topographically similar to today's Basin and Range Province of the American Southwest, though along a narrower belt and the result of dissimilar geologic processes.

A. EARLY TRIASSIC (240 million years ago)

supercontinent Pangea

B. LATE TRIASSIC   (200 million years ago)

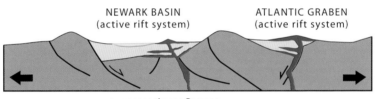

supercontinent Pangea

C. LATE JURASSIC   (160 million years ago)

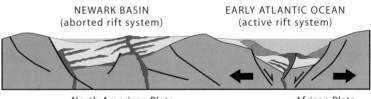

Breakup of Pangea in Triassic and Jurassic time. A. In Early Triassic time, the supercontinent Pangea was under tension and uplifted. Faults active in the Alleghanian, Taconic, and probably Ottawan Orogenies were reactivated. B. As the crust thinned in Late Triassic time, blocks dropped down along faults, sediment was deposited in rift basins, and magma rose to the surface. C. In Late Jurassic time, the North American and African plates separated, and sediment deposition began along the passive continental margin. —Modified from the U.S. Geological Survey's New York City Regional Geology website

The border faults bounding the downdropped basins are steep toward the surface and flatten out deeper underground. Each of the basins dropped downward primarily along a single fault zone, to the east or west of the basin, and tilted toward the fault as it as it moved downward on the curved surface. The basins are thus half grabens. (A graben, from the German for "ditch," is an elongate basin bounded by faults on both sides.)

ATLANTIC COASTAL PLAIN

After 30 million years of rifting, North America broke apart from North Africa about 195 million years ago in the Jurassic Period. Rifting ceased, and ocean widening and sedimentation began. The Atlantic margin subsided for tens of millions of years and accumulated thousands of feet of sediment. To some extent, the subsidence can be seen as the aftermath of rifting. Before rifting took place, the crust stretched and thinned. Magma welling up from below heated the rock and caused it to expand and rise upward even though the crust was thinning. After rifting, the heated crust and underlying magma cooled and contracted through tens of millions of years and subsided as the rocks became progressively denser and thinner.

Along many passive continental margins, including the mid-Atlantic, sediment deposited on the subsiding crust weighed down the crust, causing it to sink farther than it would have by cooling alone. In New Jersey, Coastal Plain sediments thicken from a feather edge along the fall line, the boundary between the Piedmont and the Coastal Plain, to over a mile thick beneath Cape May, 60 miles to the southeast. Seaward of a hinge line near the present Jersey Shore,

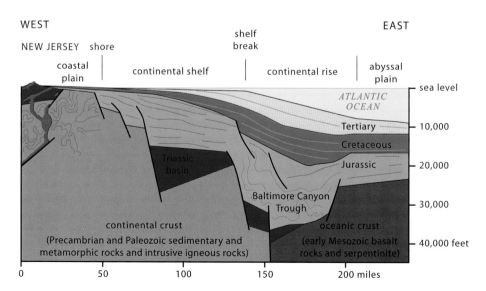

Cross section through the modern Coastal Plain and continental shelf. Note the deep accumulation of sediment in the Baltimore Canyon Trough. —U.S. Geological Survey's New York City Regional Geology website

the crust subsided still more rapidly. About 60 miles east of New Jersey, in a sediment accumulation known as the Baltimore Canyon Trough, the sediment is around 10 miles thick. The sedimentation on the continental shelf that began in Late Jurassic time continues today.

CENOZOIC ERA
65 million years ago to the present

While the rocks of New Jersey record a complex and eventful history, the state is now in a relatively stable part of North America. Over the past several million years, erosion has been the predominant geologic process. Topographic features are not the result of upwellings of lava, like the Hawaiian Islands. They are not the result of uplifting of large areas of continental crust, like the Rockies or the Colorado Plateau. They are not the result of massive deposition, like the Mississippi Delta. They are instead the result of differential erosion and local, temporary deposition. Belts of softer rock eroded to form valleys, while belts of more resistant rock stand as ridges. The Watchung Mountains, for example, are ridges of volcanic rock, but they are not mountains because they are volcanoes; they are mountains because they are made of harder rock than the sandstone and shale to the east and west and were left high when the softer rock eroded.

For an in-depth discussion of the erosion in the uplands during the Cenozoic Era, see the chapter on the Highlands and Valley and Ridge. See the chapter on the Coastal Plain for an in-depth discussion of the sedimentation and erosion there.

PLEISTOCENE ICE AGES

About 2.5 million years ago, long after the continental ice cap became permanent in Antarctica, large ice caps grew in the northern hemisphere. Unlike the Antarctic glaciers, the northern hemisphere ice caps came and went at intervals of about 80,000 years, with ice sometimes extending far into the midlatitudes during ice ages and receding to Greenland and a few northern islands between ice ages.

Glaciers made it to northern New Jersey in three of the ice ages but never covered the entire state. The oldest glacial deposits in New Jersey date, probably, from about 2 million years ago, but they are difficult to correlate with glacial deposits elsewhere. The usual evidence for dating—fossils, radioactive minerals, position above and below well-dated beds, changes in the Earth's magnetic polarity, and the like—are ambiguous or nonexistent. Instead, the age of the deposits has been estimated mostly based on how thoroughly the deposits have weathered and decomposed. The degree of weathering is an inexact measure at best. Clearly the deposits are older than midcontinent glacial deposits of the Illinoian advance of about 150,000 years ago. In the absence of well-documented correlations with deposits elsewhere, these oldest New Jersey glacial deposits are generally referred to simply as pre-Illinoian. The pre-Illinoian glacial deposits are found as far south as Somerville but have been mostly obliterated by weathering and erosion.

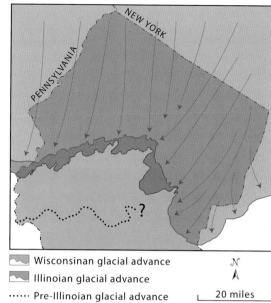

*Southern-
most limits of
Wisconsinan,
Illinoian, and
pre-Illinoian
glacial
advances.*
—Modified from
Stone and others,
2002

Wisconsinan glacial advance
Illinoian glacial advance
Pre-Illinoian glacial advance

20 miles

*Deeply weath-
ered pebbles
of Proterozoic
rock from pre-
Illinoian glacial
deposits.* —Photo
by Scott Stanford, N.J.
Geological Survey

The second advance, the Illinoian, reached its maximum about 150,000 years ago and made it as far as Warren and Morris Counties.

The most recent glaciation, the Wisconsinan, reached New Jersey about 25,000 years ago. While the broad outlines of New Jersey came into view over tens of millions of years, many of the features we see today, north and south of the limit of glaciation and even far offshore on the continental shelf, came into existence only within the last 25,000 years, when the continental ice caps of the Wisconsinan ice age were at their maximum, melting back, or gone from New Jersey.

The southernmost advance of the Wisconsinan ice is marked by the hummocky terminal moraine, which crosses New Jersey from Perth Amboy through Metuchen, Short Hills, Madison, Morristown, and westward to the Delaware

River. Here, at the southern limit of the continental ice cap, was a complex, constantly changing environment. Torrential summertime meltwater streams moving boulders weighing hundreds of pounds could suddenly change course. Several feet of sediment could be deposited in a matter of hours and swept away just as quickly.

Much of the glacial meltwater flowed to glacial lakes that formed where ice or sediment blocked river flow. The largest of these glacial lakes, Glacial Lake Passaic, was centered in what is now the Great Swamp National Wildlife Refuge in Morris County and was larger than some of the state's counties. Elsewhere,

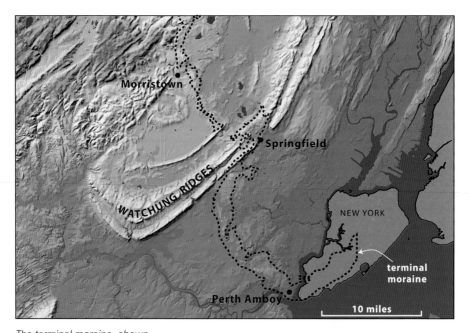

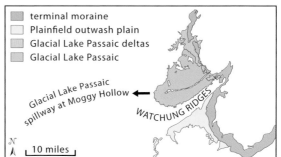

The terminal moraine, shown with dotted lines, is visible as low hills on the relief map of eastern New Jersey. Between Morristown and Springfield the moraine crosses the basin of Glacial Lake Passaic. Between Springfield and Perth Amboy it arcs across relatively flat areas east of the Watchung ridges. Northwest of Morristown the moraine passes across more rugged areas of the New Jersey Highlands and Valley and Ridge Provinces and does not stand out as clearly. The Plainfield outwash plain, deposited by water flowing from the ice, is a large flat area west of the moraine.
—Shaded-relief image from EROS Data Center, U.S Geological Survey

meltwater streams deposited floodplains of sand and gravel south of the glaciers. A wide, prominent outwash plain north of Bound Brook gives Scotch Plains and the Plainfields their names. In contrast, only a narrow plain could be deposited in the constricted upper Delaware Valley north of Trenton. Much of the sand and gravel instead was channeled to where the valley widens north of Trenton and was deposited as an outwash plain on which much of Trenton

Sand and gravel beds from a glacial lake delta deposited under suddenly shifting depositional conditions. —Photo by D. Harper

Dropstone in a glacial lake delta. The boulder was likely frozen in glacial ice floating in the water and dropped in the fine sand when the ice melted or turned over. Eddies around the boulder caused the contorted bedding. —Photo by D. Harper

was built. Some was channeled past Philadelphia and the present Delaware Bay toward the Atlantic Ocean. At that time of lowered sea level, Delaware Bay did not exist. The shoreline was about 100 miles to the east, and the Delaware River had cut its channel to 150 feet below present sea level near Cape May.

Like all glaciers, the ice sheet flowing across northern New Jersey continued to move across the land, even if it was melting so fast at its southern edge that it didn't advance farther. This continual movement scoured the soil from the bedrock, and rocks embedded in the ice carved grooves into the exposed bedrock. You can see these grooves on the diabase of the Palisades and the gneiss of the Highlands. The moving ice also shaped unconsolidated sediment into elongated hills, called drumlins, many of which are clustered in the northern portion of the Newark Basin.

The ice age first calls to mind the glaciated northern part of the state, but severe climate and permafrost (year-round freezing of the ground) left a record of ice wedge polygons, patterned ground, and solifluction (soil flow) across nonglaciated New Jersey and as far south as Virginia. Even the hard rocks of the mountains were affected by the severe climate. The expansion of water, as it froze in fractures and crevices, broke and heaved quartzite and gneiss, leaving boulder fields on the slopes of the mountains.

Ice began to retreat from New Jersey about 20,000 years ago. Through the 2,000 or so years it took for ice to recede to the New York border, the glaciers remained active, continuing to flow southward. Under an increasingly negative balance between melting and ice flow, however, they did not flow as far.

Ice wedge on the Rutgers University campus in Piscataway. The wedge is now filled with soil but was filled with ice at one time. The ice built up and bent the shale bedrock layers upward as the frozen rock repeatedly expanded and contracted when it warmed and cooled. —Photo by Jim Walters

Ice wedge polygons, Hillsborough Township. The photo was taken in dry weather. Crops on the deep soil filling the ice wedges were still growing. Those on the thin, dry soil between the wedges had browned. —Photo by Jim Walters

Contorted bedding from soil flow during ice age permafrost. In today's climate, rain soaks into the ground, percolates downward to the water table, then flows underground to streams or lakes. Under permafrost conditions, water freezing in the cold soil filled the pore spaces between grains with ice and created an impermeable barrier. In the ice age, sediment in this photo was above impermeable permafrost and could not drain. Summertime melting of the top few feet turned the soil into saturated, unstable mud that flowed. —Photo by D. Harper

Boulder field from the ice age. —Photo by Ron Witte, N.J. Geological Survey

Retreat of the Wisconsinan ice sheet from New Jersey. Box A shows the maximum extent of the ice. Glacial lakes formed at the southern edge of the ice as it receded to the north. —Modified from Stone and others, 2002

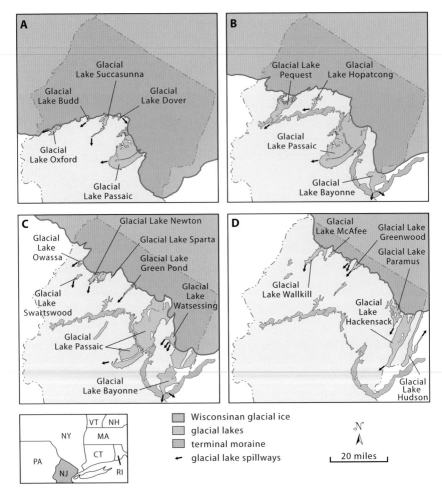

A

Glacial Lake Succasunna

Glacial Lake Budd

Glacial Lake Dover

Glacial Lake Oxford

Glacial Lake Passaic

B

Glacial Lake Pequest   Glacial Lake Hopatcong

Glacial Lake Passaic

Glacial Lake Bayonne

C

Glacial Lake Newton

Glacial Lake Owassa

Glacial Lake Sparta

Glacial Lake Green Pond

Glacial Lake Swartswood

Glacial Lake Watsessing

Glacial Lake Passaic

Glacial Lake Bayonne

D

Glacial Lake McAfee   Glacial Lake Greenwood

Glacial Lake Paramus

Glacial Lake Wallkill

Glacial Lake Hackensack

Glacial Lake Hudson

VT / NH

NY   MA

CT

PA

NJ   RI

☐ Wisconsinan glacial ice
☐ glacial lakes
☐ terminal moraine
← glacial lake spillways

N

20 miles

Some of the glacial lakes that existed when the ice was at its maximum drained when the ice retreated, but many new lakes formed. The southern edge of the ice was essentially a large dam, blocking drainage to the north. Meltwater flowing from the ice ponded at the edge, forming lakes. As the ice receded northward, lower drainages were sometimes exposed, allowing the lake water to drain until a new stable level was reached. We know of more than one hundred large glacial lakes from deltas, bottom sediments, shoreline features, and outlet channels that still can be seen today. At least fifteen of the glacial lakes were larger than Lake Hopatcong, now New Jersey's largest lake. More than two hundred present-day lakes and many thousands of acres of wetlands owe their existence in large part to disruption of preglacial drainage by ice age erosion and sedimentation.

At the height of the ice age, sea level was much lower, and beaches in southern New Jersey receded 100 or so miles, to the edge of the continental shelf, causing rivers to cut downward and widen their valleys. Submerged offshore today are abandoned shorelines, deltas, sand shoals, channels, and even long gouges made by the keels of icebergs from this time of lowered sea level. The shoals and channels are like those formed today by waves and currents at the mouths of estuaries. As sea level rose they progressively drowned and became inactive. Their distribution across the continental shelf marks the westward retreat of estuaries before the encroaching ocean. When the ice melted, the rising oceans created today's beaches, barrier islands, and drowned valley estuaries, including the Hackensack Meadowlands and Delaware Bay.

Another interesting ice age feature hidden below the Atlantic Ocean is the Hudson Channel, which crosses the continental shelf from New York Bay to the head of the Hudson Canyon. A channel crossing the continental shelf would seem easily explained by erosion during the lowered sea level of the ice age, but on a closer look further explanation is needed. The channel is continuous from near the apex of the New York Bight to the edge of the continental shelf. Early on in the ice retreat there would have been little or no water flowing where the Hudson Channel crosses the continental shelf. The Verrazano Narrows was blocked by the terminal moraine, and drainage was ponded north of the moraine to form Glacial Lake Hudson, which drained eastward through a lake in Long Island Sound rather than southward through Verrazano Narrows.

Large floods from the draining of Glacial Lakes Passaic and Hackensack crossed New Jersey during the retreat of the glaciers, but these probably had little to do with the Hudson Channel. Both floods emptied into Glacial Lake Hudson, then passed eastward around Long Island rather than southward down the Hudson Channel. Likely the moraine dam at Verrazano Narrows was breached by the release of a still larger lake, Glacial Lake Wallkill, in the Wallkill valley mostly in New York. At this time sea level was still low enough that the flood and the Hudson River after the flood would have crossed the entire continental shelf to the head of the Hudson Canyon.

Numerous other lakes north of New Jersey were released by the retreating ice and sent floods down the Hudson Valley. The largest was from a 120-foot-drop in the level of Glacial Lake Iroquois, a predecessor to the modern Great Lakes. The Glacial Lake Iroquois flood has been offered as an alternative explanation

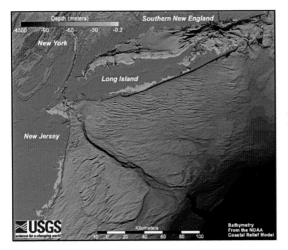

Hudson Channel.
—Image from U. S.
Geological Survey

for the incision of the Hudson Channel. Ice age drainage of the Great Lakes area was primarily down the Mississippi at the glacial maximum. After deglaciation of the Niagara and Mohawk Valleys, it shifted eastward to the Hudson Valley. Finally, after deglaciation of the St. Lawrence Valley, it abandoned the Hudson watershed for a more northerly route marked by the present-day St. Lawrence River. The Glacial Lake Iroquois flood passed down the Hudson Valley about 11,000 years ago. It sent over 2,500,000 cubic meters of water per second, about ten times the average flow of the Mississippi, down the Hudson. Onshore the potential for erosion by such a flood is obvious. By this time sea level was rising and offshore erosion from the shoreline to the head of the Hudson Canyon requires explanation. Clean, clear freshwater is lighter than salt water and will float across the sea surface from a river mouth. Glacial lake floodwaters, on the other hand, are heavy with tons of sediment. The added weight pulls them to the steepest path across the sea bottom and gives them the power to continue erosion even underwater across the seafloor. Seaward of the New York Bight, this could account for the scouring of the Hudson Channel.

GEOLOGY AND HUMANS IN NEW JERSEY

Geology has had a profound influence on the people of New Jersey since the arrival of its earliest residents near the close of the ice ages. How they first got here is open to some question. For many years, virtually all anthropologists believed that people first came to the Americas across a land bridge that connected Siberia to Alaska during the lowered sea levels of the ice ages. In 1998, however, Dennis Stanford of the Smithsonian Institution and Bruce Bradley of the University of Exeter, England, proposed the Solutrean hypothesis. According to their theory, some people traveled across the Atlantic sea ice rather than across the Bering land bridge. Through the proposed journey they would have lived by fishing, hunting seals, and melting icebergs for freshwater. Eventually they landed at the edge of the ice pack in the mid-Atlantic area. The hypothesis is based in good part on stone-flaking techniques common to the Solutrean people of Europe and the Clovis people of North America, but not known to the people of Siberia or the Bering Sea area of Alaska. The stone tools are fairly common through the mid-Atlantic, and dozens have been found in New Jersey, but the similar technologies in no way prove that the Clovis people landed here in small sealskin boats. There are many objections to the idea, and most serious anthropologists believe that the stone-working techniques were worked out independently. Still, the hypothesis has not been disproven and remains attractive.

New Jersey spear point showing the distinctive flaking style common to the Clovis people of North America and the Solutrean people of Europe. In the Clovis points, the last two flakes removed, one large flake on each side, created the groove into which the spear shaft was fitted. —N.J. State Museum specimen; photo by D. Harper

However the Clovis people got here, they are widely believed to have subsisted in large part on big game animals living south of the glaciers. Among the large mammals of the ice age, mastodons, mammoths, giant ground sloths, and giant beavers are all known from New Jersey.

Eventually the Clovis culture, with its distinctive stoneworking techniques, gave way to woodland cultures that developed or adopted the bow and arrow, domestic animals, agriculture, and pottery through the millennia. At the time of European colonization, the Indians were taking full advantage of the varied resources and habitats of New Jersey, moving and trading to utilize the best soils for agriculture; mining the best chert of northwestern New Jersey for arrowheads, scrapers, and knives; harvesting seasonally migrating fish from the estuaries and rivers; and gathering and preserving the wild plants abundant in different areas of the state.

From the earliest colonial times, European settlements were first established and largest where geologic conditions created deepwater ports and allowed easy access to inland resources. The most favorably located became New York and Philadelphia. Even though New Jersey is surrounded by water on three sides, from the Hudson around the shore and up the Delaware River, long stretches would have been unattractive to the colonials for establishing ports. The northeastern few miles are isolated east of the Palisades cliffs, and much of the remaining coastline was either marshland or, along the sandy Coastal Plain, bordering on land poorly suited for agriculture. Small ports and fishing villages were established at most of the rivers and at the head of tide on the Raritan in New Brunswick and the Delaware in Trenton, but the emergence of New Jersey as a major shipping center did not occur until the natural landscape was transformed through the nineteenth and twentieth centuries by filling of marshlands and dredging of navigation channels.

Inland, geologic conditions had an equally strong influence on settlement. Agriculture was favored where the underlying geologic formations gave rise to good soil: in the northeast on weathered Newark Basin sedimentary rocks and glacial deposits; along the Inner Coastal Plain on Cretaceous and Tertiary formations; and on the limestone soils of the valleys of the Highlands and Valley and Ridge Provinces. Areas less suited for agriculture relied more on their mineral resources: bog iron and glass sand in the Pinelands of the Outer Coastal Plain, and iron and zinc mining in the Highlands.

More recently, New Jersey has become a usually unacknowledged leader in the protection of its environment. Citizen action has repeatedly halted or prevented the destruction of scenery and resources. County reservations established along the Watchung Mountains in the 1890s were among the nation's first recreational parks, and the Palisades Interstate Park, established in large part through the efforts of the New Jersey Federation of Women's Clubs to stop destructive quarrying and logging, soon followed. In the southern part of the state, legislative action in the 1870s to stop the export of Pinelands water to Philadelphia may have saved this unique area from loss of groundwater and dramatic ecologic changes. More recently, citizen protest has been instrumental in preventing Morris County's Great Swamp and a large section of the Pinelands from becoming airports; preventing the construction of the Tocks Island Dam on the Delaware River just upstream from the Delaware Water Gap; preventing uranium mining adjacent to densely populated suburban centers; and salvaging valuable parkland and marsh in the Hackensack Meadows.

Oil in New Jersey?

Through the early years of the twentieth century, the country's oil prospects were poorly known and wildcat drillers tried their luck even in New Jersey. The deepest and most expensive of New Jersey's wildcat wells was drilled in Jackson Township at Jacksons Mills. Here the W&K Oil Company set up a 110-foot derrick and sank the third of three wells they drilled between 1919 and 1930. W&K chose their drilling locations using a newly invented device, the Perry Mineral Indicator. To prove the device worked, they came to New Jersey where no oil had ever been found. Even in the 1920s, geologists familiar with southern New Jersey held out little hope that oil would be found. New Jersey state geologist Henry Kummel noted that at 1,330 feet, the well passed from Coastal Plain sediments into granite gneiss and that commercial quantities of petroleum had never been found in granite gneiss. He denied ever saying, as quoted in the newspapers, "It's all bunk." Despite negative assessments, periodic reports of oil and helium were enough to keep the interest of the principal backer, a Mr. Wright of Worcester, Massachusetts. Wright was well-known for being very rich. According to Kummel, Wright was also on every sucker list in the country and over the years spent $2,000,000 on worthless W&K Oil stock. Drilling continued for several years after the death of Wright in 1923, but eventually, to the disappointment of landowners for miles around, the venture was abandoned in 1930 after the well had been drilled to 5,022 feet. The $50,000 derrick was sold for $10,000, dismantled, and sent to Texas to drill in proven fields.

The complete drilling records were never made public, but well logs and a few samples still held by the New Jersey Geological Survey suggest an interesting sequence in which granitic rocks resembling those of the New Jersey Highlands lie immediately below the Coastal Plain sediments, and sedimentary rocks resembling those of Kittatinny Valley lie below the granitic rocks. If granitic rock overlies sedimentary rock, the likely cause is thrust faulting. The presence of the sedimentary rocks increased oil prospects markedly and accounted for several years of continued drilling.

Whatever the sequence of rocks, a well drilled through 1,330 feet of Coastal Plain sediment, then through rock to a depth of 5,022 feet, would be of considerable scientific interest, particularly in interpreting deep seismic profiles across the continental margin. When it was being drilled, the well would have

Oil drilling at Jackson Mills in 1928. —Photo courtesy of N.J. Geological Survey

been lined with steel piping to the bottom of the Coastal Plain sediments to keep the sand and clay from collapsing in, but may have been open to rock below the loose sediment. Collecting samples of the rock would be difficult, but even without physical samples, cameras and logging devices could be lowered through the well to take pictures; measure the electrical, magnetic, and acoustic properties of the rock; sense any radioactivity; and determine how the rock reacts to radioactive sources built into the logging tools. The results would not be as exciting as rock samples but could suggest at what depths the borehole was in granite, gneiss, schist, marble, shale, limestone, or whatever, and give some idea as to how the rock has been folded, fractured, and faulted.

With this in mind, the U.S. Geological Survey returned to the well in the 1960s and attempted to clean out the borehole. The hole was cleaned out to about 1,000 feet below the surface where it was blocked, probably by pipes and pumping equipment thrown down when the drilling was abandoned. Attempts to remove the debris failed.

The well in Jackson Township failed to find oil, but this was hardly the final attempt to find oil in New Jersey. Most recently, in the 1980s numerous exploratory wells were drilled offshore on the continental shelf, and there has been occasional interest even in the Newark Basin, the New Jersey Highlands, and the Coastal Plain. The Newark Basin interest in the 1980s was in western New Jersey where folds and faults might reasonably create closed structures in which hydrocarbons could accumulate. Composition of hydrocarbon residues in the rock, however, showed that the rock has been heated to temperatures too high for petroleum preservation. According to some, the search was as much for closed subsurface structures in which hydrocarbons might be stored as for hydrocarbons themselves. Heating of the younger Jurassic rocks in the Newark Basin of northeastern New Jersey was within the range in which organic

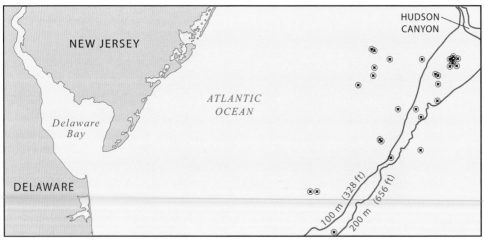

Exploratory wells were drilled on the continental shelf to look for hydrocarbons in the 1980s.
—Modified from Doyle, 1982

matter is converted to petroleum, but there are no closed structures in which oil might be trapped. Recoverable hydrocarbons would have migrated to the surface along permeable layers and fractures and been lost long ago.

Drilling the 10-mile thickness of sediment of the continental shelf in the 1980s was more promising in that the sediment did not appear to have been heated to temperatures at which petroleum would be destroyed; potential traps in which hydrocarbons would accumulate were inferred from seismic profiles; and sediments with enough organic material to generate petroleum likely exist. Hydrocarbons were, in fact, found, but not in sufficient quantities to warrant installing the infrastructure needed for production. It has more recently been suggested that the drilling was not deep enough to evaluate the potential resource. Specifically, rift basin rocks beneath the Atlantic Ocean sediment may have generated oil or gas that remains trapped below the layers drilled in the 1980s.

NEWARK BASIN
Basalt, Sedimentary Rock, and Glacial Lakes

A series of lowlands paralleling the east coast of North America and floored mostly with red sedimentary rocks was known early in the exploration of North American geology and are shown on maps published as early as 1816. They were initially correlated with the Old Red Sandstone of England, but it was soon realized that these were younger and unrelated to the similar-appearing English rocks. Later, the basins, from South Carolina along the eastern seaboard into Canada, were grouped as the Piedmont Lowlands on account of their subdued topography and their location at the foot of the Appalachian Mountains. They were eventually called basins because the red rock appeared to have been deposited where the land surface had dropped downward due to faulting. The faults along which the basins dropped are known as the border faults.

The basins were named individually by their location. The basin covering much of northeastern New Jersey, including Newark, is the Newark Basin. Close by are the Gettysburg Basin to the southwest in Pennsylvania and the Hartford Basin to the northeast in Connecticut.

By the 1960s, it was clear that the basins had a common origin as a series of rift valleys active in the initial phases of the breakup of the supercontinent Pangea. Though the rocks are similar in many respects from basin to basin, they are different enough that different formations and formation groups have been assigned for each basin. The Newark Basin is the one of the largest of the basins and is centrally located, and the rocks are well exposed. It has thus been accepted as the type example of the eastern North American rift valleys of the Triassic and Jurassic Periods. The formations and formation groups in the rift basins from South Carolina into Canada are accordingly grouped as the Newark Supergroup.

FLOOD BASALTS

Three sequences of lava flows are exposed in the Newark Basin: Orange Mountain Basalt of the First Watchung Mountain, the Preakness Basalt of the Second Watchung Mountain, and the Hook Mountain Basalt of the Third Watchung Mountain, called Long Hill along much of its length. The Watchungs are made of volcanic rock but were not exploded from volcanoes. The Watchung magmas poured out as flood basalts, which flow more easily than most magmas and spread horizontally into sheets more like lakes of molten rock than cone-shaped volcanoes. After the lavas cooled and had been covered by additional layers of sediment washing into the Newark Basin, both the lava flows and the enclosing sediment layers were tilted westward. Still later, erosion sculpted valleys along the belts of softer sedimentary rock and left ridges along the harder Watchung basalt flows. The Watchung Mountains are the exposed edges of the tilted layers of basalt. Some magma intruded between layers of sedimentary rock and cooled at depth into diabase sills. The Palisades Sill along the Hudson River is the best exposed.

The original volume of igneous rock in the Watchung flows was immense. Most of the volcanic rock still preserved is in an area of a hundred or so square miles near the center of the Newark Basin, but much has eroded away. Small areas of the Orange Mountain Basalt, in particular, are preserved at widely scattered locations, and it appears that the lava initially covered almost the entire Newark Basin, over 2,500 square miles. As voluminous as they are, the Palisades and Watchung magmas are only a small part of a vast outpouring associated with the rifting of continental plates just before the breakup of the supercontinent Pangea. The magmas have been grouped as the Central Atlantic Magmatic Province (CAMP) and extend across much of eastern North and South

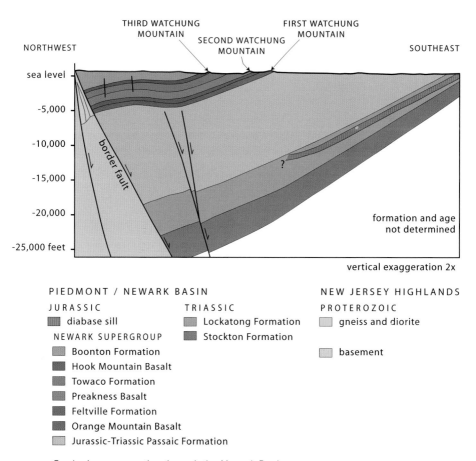

THIRD WATCHUNG MOUNTAIN
SECOND WATCHUNG MOUNTAIN
FIRST WATCHUNG MOUNTAIN

NORTHWEST
SOUTHEAST

sea level
-5,000
-10,000
-15,000
-20,000
-25,000 feet

border fault

?

formation and age not determined

vertical exaggeration 2x

PIEDMONT / NEWARK BASIN

JURASSIC
diabase sill
NEWARK SUPERGROUP
Boonton Formation
Hook Mountain Basalt
Towaco Formation
Preakness Basalt
Feltville Formation
Orange Mountain Basalt
Jurassic-Triassic Passaic Formation

TRIASSIC
Lockatong Formation
Stockton Formation

NEW JERSEY HIGHLANDS

PROTEROZOIC
gneiss and diorite

basement

Geologic cross section through the Newark Basin. —Modified from Drake and others, 1996

America, northwest Africa, and smaller areas of Spain and France. By some estimates there are 500,000 cubic miles of lava flows and intrusions. The CAMP outpourings are unusually voluminous but are not unique in Earth's history. Similar massive floods of basaltic lava at different times covered thousands of square miles each in the Deccan Plateau of India, central Siberia, and the Columbia River basin of the Pacific Northwest. The largest areas of flood basalt, like those of the Central Atlantic Magmatic Province, are usually associated with crustal rifting and produce their huge volumes of lava in a short period of time. The CAMP rocks were emplaced over about 500,000 years, and most of the activity appears to have occurred in five short pulses lasting only a few hundred years each.

The curvature of the Watchung Mountains and exposures of the Hook Mountain Basalt and Towaco Formation west of the primary occurrence of Hook Mountain Basalt in the Third Watchung Mountain are the result of folding of the rock into the broad, gentle Watchung Syncline. Synclines and other folds are most common in compressional environments, and the existence of the large though very gently folded Watchung Syncline in the Newark Basin would not intuitively be expected. The basin was formed by extensional rifting and ever since has been on the Atlantic passive margin. Clearly, though, there has been compression. There are similar folds in other Atlantic rift basins up and down the East Coast, and in addition to the syncline, evidence of compression in the Newark Basin includes small reverse faults and reptile tracks deformed by compression. The likely cause is ridge push early during the widening of the Atlantic. Ridge push is caused by the movement of newly formed oceanic crust away from the mid-oceanic ridges on which it forms. Early in the widening of the Atlantic Ocean, ridge push eastward and westward would have caused compression along passive margins on both sides of the narrow ocean.

Watchung Copper Mines

From the mid 1700s to the earliest 1900s, there were attempts to mine copper at locations across the Newark Basin, including North Arlington, New Brunswick, Edison, Somerville, Griggstown, Flemington, the Watchung Reservation, and numerous places along the base of the First Watchung Mountain. The primary ore mineral was chalcocite (copper sulfide), which would not have attracted the attention of the early miners. It was the colorful secondary minerals, formed by weathering of the chalcocite, and native copper that led to the recognition of the deposits. Some ore was rich and even contained traces of silver and gold, but the deposits were small. In 1901, the remains of twenty-one mines and prospect pits and three furnaces were counted along the base of the First Watchung. There is little likelihood that any of the operations were profitable. Only the Schuyler Mine in North Arlington had enough ore to generate substantial profits. The mines now are almost all collapsed and grown over. They come to attention most often when tunnels are encountered in excavations.

There is little agreement as to exactly how the ore formed, but most workers seem to agree that traces of copper from the Newark Basin rocks were concentrated by heated water, possibly superheated brine. Native copper has been found periodically at base of the Orange Mountain Basalt at the Chimney

Secondary copper minerals, mostly chrysocolla, from a mine in the Chimney Rock area, Bridgewater Township. —Photo by D. Harper

Abandoned copper mine at Flemington found during excavation.
—Photo by Gregory Herman, N.J. Geological Survey

Rock Quarry in Bridgewater and in other, similar deposits along the base of the mountain. The native copper has been attributed to the chemical reduction of dissolved copper by iron minerals. By contrast, the host rock at the Schuyler Mine has less iron and native copper is absent.

SEDIMENTATION IN THE NEWARK BASIN

Sedimentation in the downdropped rift basins of Mesozoic eastern North America followed a three-part sequence. In the first part, when the basins first began to drop, they were small and there was more than enough sediment eroded from the surrounding land to keep them full. At this stage, the floors of the basin were crossed by rivers. Sand, gravel, and silt were the predominant sediments. In the Newark Basin, this phase of basin development is represented by the Stockton Formation, well-known for the sandstone of its brownstone quarries. A number of small, abandoned quarries in the Stockton Formation lie within the Delaware and Raritan Canal State Park, along the Delaware River, within walking distance upstream from Pralls Mills.

Stockton Formation in an abandoned brownstone quarry along the Delaware and Raritan Canal. Sandy beds were used for brownstone. Shaly beds were waste or used for fill. —Photo courtesy of N.J. Geological Survey

Conglomerate beds within the Stockton Formation. —Photo by D. Harper

As the basins deepened and the border faults lengthened, the valleys became wider and longer. At some point sedimentation could no longer keep up with downdropping. The top of the sediment fill dropped below the rim of surrounding uplands, and deep lakes filled the basins. In this second part of the three-part sequence, alluvial fans, floodplains, and deltas were deposited around the shores. Fine-grained silt and clay were deposited on the lake bottoms. Deep lakes of this stage are represented in the Newark Basin by fine-grained, lake-bottom beds of the Lockatong Formation.

As basins further widened and lengthened there eventually came a point, depending on climate, at which the water coming into the basin could not keep up with evaporation and seepage through aquifers. In this third part of the

Lockatong Formation along the Delaware River bluffs north of Byram. —Photo by D. Harper

Passaic Formation along the Delaware River bluffs. —Photo by D. Harper

sequence, the lakes became shallower, sometimes even drying up entirely. In the Newark Basin the shallow-water lake deposits are part of the Passaic Formation sediments. The Passaic Formation sediments are typified by mudstone, shale, and sandstone colored red by iron in an oxidized state.

As might be expected from the gradual evolution of the basin, transitions between formations are gradual rather than abrupt. From the Stockton Formation into the Lockatong, conglomerate and sandstone become less abundant and finer-grained rocks formed from silt and clay become more abundant because less of the sediment was deposited by rivers and more was deposited on lake bottoms. Going from the Lockatong into the Passaic, shallow, more oxygenated lakes are increasingly represented in the sediments. There are fewer black and gray beds and more beds colored red by iron oxide.

The three-part sequence—deposition initially by streams and rivers, then in deep lakes, then in shallower lakes and mudflats—is well represented in the Newark Basin because it was in an area of semiarid climate about 7 degrees north of the equator in Mesozoic time and because it was large. Illustrating the effect of climate, basins to the south were closer to the equator, at the latitude of today's equatorial rain forests. In the Triassic and Jurassic Periods, they were wetter even though they were in the interior of a large continent. The deep lake phase is predominant, and there are coal seams in the shallower-water parts of the sequence. Basins to the north were farther from the equator, at the latitude of today's desert belts, and the shallow lake phase is predominant even to the point that, in the Fundy Basin of Nova Scotia, the lakes resembled Utah's Great Salt Lake and thick salt beds were deposited.

Geologists have known since at least the 1940s that rock layering in the Newark Basin follows complex cycles. Through much of the thickness, the rock was deposited in lakes. The beds pass repeatedly and cyclically, every few feet to every few tens of feet, from deeper-water beds to shallower-water beds, sometimes even to beds deposited on dry land, then back into deeper-water beds. Further, this is a cycle within a cycle. Within the middle part of the basin fill, the deepwater lake sediments of the Lockatong Formation switched back and forth every few thousand feet between cycles in which most of the sediment was silt and clay, and cycles in which the sediment contained substantial amounts of the zeolite mineral analcime and other substances that appeared to have precipitated from mineral-laden waters rather than being carried in as stream detritus.

By the 1960s, sediment cores from deep ocean basins had shown that, for much of the Cenozoic Era, climate followed cycles coincident with cyclic variations in the Earth's orbit. Astronomers know the Earth's orbital cycles have not changed much in the past few hundred million years, but it was not known whether the close match between orbital cycles and climate was unique to the Cenozoic or common through geologic history. The answer was important to the understanding of climate and possible human impacts on climate, and Paul Olsen of Columbia University became convinced that, at least for the Triassic Period, the answer could be found in the complex bedding cycles preserved in the Newark Basin rocks. The Triassic cycles are closely related to climate, especially to rainfall, which caused lakes toward the center of the basin to cycle between deep and shallow water. Similar to deep-sea sediments, there was continuous deposition uninterrupted by erosion.

Instead of relying on outcrops to test the idea, Olsen and many coworkers assembled a complete and consistent record by coring through the entire thickness of the Newark Basin sedimentary rocks below the Orange Mountain Basalt. Rather than attempt to recover a single 15,000-foot core, six overlapping cores between 2,400 and 3,000 feet long were collected. The bedding in the overlapping sections of the cores was correlated tree-ring style, and the cores were logged inch by inch as to color, bedding thickness, particle size and sorting, mud cracks, coprolites (fossil dung), roots, radioactivity, magnetic

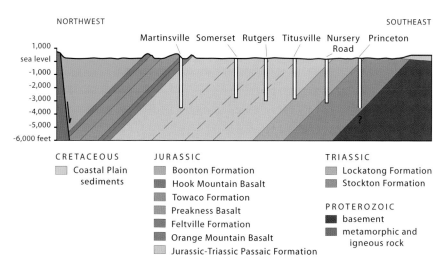

A complete cross section through the Newark Basin sedimentary rocks below the Watchung ridges was obtained by drilling six overlapping cores rather than trying to drill a single 15,000-foot core. This cross section is a composite from multiple locations and is nonlinear. —Modified from Olsen and others, 1996

polarity (measuring the Earth's periodic reversals of the north and south magnetic poles), and a myriad of other characteristics. The logs were then analyzed statistically without reference to the astronomic cycles. Amazingly, cyclic bedding in the rock matched cyclic variations in the Earth's orbit perfectly. The 30-million-year record included cycles at 20,000 years, 100,000 years, 400,000 years, and 2,000,000 years.

Extinction at the End of Triassic Time

While sedimentary conditions at this particular place on Earth did not change between the Triassic and Jurassic Periods, life on Earth did. The end of the Triassic saw one of the five greatest mass extinctions in the fossil record. More than half the species known to have been alive went extinct in a geologically instantaneous moment. The causes of mass extinctions are one of the more contentious issues in geology today. The most widely known extinction, the demise of the dinosaurs and many other creatures at the end of the Cretaceous Period, is widely accepted as the result of a well-known meteorite impact at Chicxulub in the Yucatán Peninsula of Mexico, but even this seemingly well-founded explanation is not accepted by all competent investigators. The cause of the Triassic extinctions is far more uncertain, and the Newark Basin of New Jersey has turned out to be a good place to investigate the extinctions and the life before and after for two reasons. First, cyclic patterns of layering in the sedimentary rocks allow geologic history to be studied in increments of as little as 1,000 years, an exceptionally small time span for rocks over 200 million years old. Second, while skeletal fossils other than fish are limited, plant spores, pollen, and animal footprints, including dinosaurs, are abundant. Footprints have been collected by the hundreds at several places, and most New Jersey museums with natural science exhibits have at least a few Newark Basin footprints. The best-known footprint trackway, several dozen prints on a single slab of rock, are at the Rutgers Geology Museum. The slab was collected in the 1870s in a quarry at the base of Towaco Mountain in Montville.

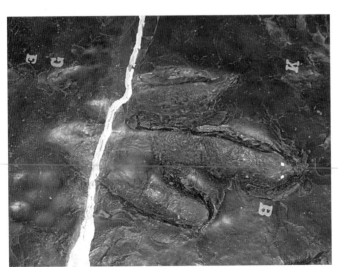

Jurassic dinosaur footprint from Montville housed at the Rutgers Geology Museum. The track is 17 inches from heel to toe.
—Photo by D. Harper

After considerable searching with a number of colleagues, Paul Olsen of Columbia University was able to find four places in the Newark Basin where Passaic Formation exposures spanned the Triassic-Jurassic boundary and satisfied the following criteria: the position of the boundary could be pinpointed using the distinctive cycles of layering in the sediments, there were no breaks in sedimentation above and below the boundary, and fossilized spores and pollen were common. At each of the locations, spores and pollen from plants that went extinct at the end of the Triassic are abundant immediately below and absent immediately above the boundary. Spikes in iridium content and fern spore abundance coincide with the pollen disappearances. The suddenness of the extinctions and the iridium and fern spore spikes point enticingly toward a meteorite impact similar to the one that likely wiped out the dinosaurs. Iridium is a common metal in some meteorites but scarce in most rocks of Earth. In the impact of a large meteorite, much of the meteorite is vaporized and blown back into the atmosphere. An iridium spike from the Chicxulub impact has been found in rocks widely spaced around the globe. Ferns recover more quickly from natural disasters than other plants and would be expected to flourish after the widespread devastation of a large impact. Again, fern spore spikes mark the Chicxulub impact at widespread locations.

To date, however, no smoking gun confirming an impact at the time of the extinctions has been found. Either shocked quartz or a closely dated impact scar could be the smoking gun. Shocked quartz is quartz whose crystal structure has been deformed under extremely high pressures. It is known only from meteorite impacts and nuclear blasts. Shocked quartz from the Late Cretaceous Chicxulub impact is widely distributed around the world, but none has been found in rocks deposited at the time of the Triassic extinctions. A possible explanation for the scarcity of shocked quartz might be that the meteorite fell in an ocean. Oceanic crust has little quartz, and an impact might not produce detectable volumes of shocked quartz. Similarly, impact in an ocean would explain why no impact scar has been found. Oceanic crust is continually being overridden by encroaching crustal plates and recycled down into the Earth's mantle. There is no longer any oceanic crust remaining from the Triassic Period. The scar from an impact in an ocean would have been destroyed along with the surrounding crust.

In another explanation, the extinctions may be due to the massive, short-lived eruptions of basaltic magma of the Central Atlantic Magmatic Province. The outpourings of hundreds of thousands of square miles of lava could well have been accompanied by the release of enough carbon dioxide, sulfur dioxide, and other gases to cause dramatic changes in climate and widespread extinctions. Also, while there is far less iridium in basaltic rocks than in nickel-iron meteorites, there is more than in most continental crust. It has been convincingly shown that iridium spikes similar to those from large meteorites can also be caused by large eruptions of basalt. Further, if it is confirmed that the eruptions came in short bursts of a few hundred years, this would account for the geologically instantaneous suddenness of the extinctions.

As with the impact hypothesis, there is a substantial problem with this explanation. The igneous activity, at least in North America, *follows* the extinctions. The Orange Mountain Basalt, the oldest basalt in the Newark Basin, is above the layer in which the extinctions are noted and therefore postdates the extinctions. The same is true for other North American flood basalts. While these eruptions could not have played a part, other CAMP eruptions may be the culprit. According to some interpretations, some North African volcanic rocks are older than the North American basalts and may have erupted at higher rates and with higher concentrations of gases capable of disrupting climate.

Whatever their cause, the extinctions at the end of Triassic time were followed by a radiation of new species into the vacated ecologic space. Reptile tracks from New Jersey show how quickly this can occur. True dinosaurs existed long before the extinctions but remained smaller than nondinosaur reptiles with which they were in competition. Worldwide, the large nondinosaur reptiles, with the exception of crocodiles, died out at the end-of-Triassic extinction. In the Newark Basin, tracks have been found in sedimentary rocks deposited within 50,000 years before and 10,000 years after the extinctions. The earlier tracks show a wide diversity with the largest animals being nondinosaur reptiles. Tracks from 10,000 years after the extinctions have little diversity and lack nondinosaurs. The dinosaurs are all carnivorous. The largest tracks, *Eubrontes*, are 14 inches long, 20 percent larger than the largest Triassic dinosaur tracks. Higher in the rock record, trackways in younger rocks, within 100,000 years of the extinctions, include herbivores and are more diverse, similar in diversity to trackways through the following 135 million years of dinosaur history. The 20 percent increase in dinosaur track size within only 10,000 years has been attributed to the reduction of competitive pressure and is similar to well-documented increases in reptile size on islands where the reptiles lack competitors. Temporary dominance of carnivores similar to that recorded in the New Jersey tracks has been seen following other mass extinctions in the geologic record and has been attributed to the relative ease of digesting meat in comparison with vegetation. Herbivores faced a greater evolutionary challenge, and their evolution and increase in size to where they could survive on the open lakeshore mudflats where the tracks were preserved is interpreted as taking longer. The lakes were large and fish remains are abundant in rocks older and younger than the extinctions. The fish, rather than the usual land-based herbivores, may have been the food base for the carnivore-dominated ecosystem.

Brownstone

The red and brown, iron-cemented sandstones of New Jersey were recognized as a good building stone early in the colonial era, and brownstone is informally the state rock of New Jersey. The sandstones were deposited in the Newark Basin in late Triassic to early Jurassic time and then cemented with iron from circulating groundwater. The sandstones are from the Stockton and Passaic Formations. A request to the New Jersey Geological Survey for a New Jersey rock will get you a piece of brownstone.

Brownstone was widely used as a building stone throughout the northeastern United States during the nineteenth century and earlier. Nassau Hall at Princeton University, built with brownstone fieldstone, was the largest stone building in the colonies when it was completed in 1756. The Steuben House in New Bridge Landing, River Edge, is one of numerous Dutch-style brownstone

Geological Hall, on the campus of Rutgers University in New Brunswick, was built with New Jersey brownstone in 1871–72. —Photo by Zehdreh Allen-Lafayette, N.J. Geological Survey

houses in Bergen County. In the Revolutionary War, the Steuben House stood at a strategic crossing on the Hackensack River and served as an intelligence gathering point, an encampment, a headquarters, and a battleground. Today it is a state historic site. Old First Presbyterian Church in Newark, dedicated in 1791, is a magnificent example of brownstone architecture and was for many years the largest church in New Jersey.

During the first half of the nineteenth century, most brownstone quarries were adjacent to canals and railroads. Quarries along the Delaware and Raritan Canal in Princeton and from Trenton northward to Raven Rock supplied thousands of tons annually but could not keep up with demand. Quarries along the Morris Canal at Belleville, Little Falls, and elsewhere were similarly productive. The Little Falls quarries produced a superior, fine-grained, deep-hued, rock,

Brownstone quarry in the 1800s. —Photo courtesy
of N. J. Geological Survey

called "liver rock" by local workmen. Liver rock was the preferred stone for mansions and churches in Paterson, Newark, and New York City.

Beginning in the middle of the nineteenth century, many quarries, especially in and around Newark, were abandoned as cities expanded and land became more valuable. Further, brownstone was falling out of fashion as a building material. Public buildings continued to be built of brownstone, but new residential brownstones were no longer common. By 1900, only a small amount was still being quarried, mostly for foundations and the windowsills and cornices of brick buildings.

WISCONSIN GLACIATION OF THE NEWARK BASIN

Glaciers are commonly thought of as powerful agents of erosion, scouring and shoving everything in their path to a moraine at their farthest advance. In fact, they are more like water and wind, eroding rock and sediment in some places and depositing it elsewhere, a few feet, a few miles, or hundreds of miles farther along their path. Also like water and wind, glaciers give distinct shapes to the surfaces they move across. Where streams commonly shape sand and gravel into ripples and bars, and wind commonly shapes sand into dunes, ice can streamline either rock or unconsolidated sediment into small hills known as drumlins. Where glaciers move across larger, flatter areas of easily sculpted, unconsolidated sediment, drumlins can be 200 feet high and over a mile long. The Newark Basin provides a good surface for drumlin formation.

Some drumlins are shaped from rock and covered by a thin layer of postglacial soil. Others are made entirely of unconsolidated glacial till. Whether

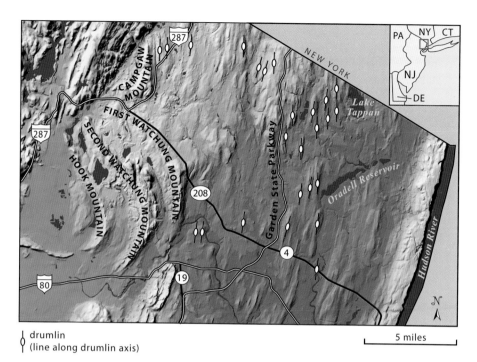

drumlin
(line along drumlin axis)

5 miles

There are dozens of drumlins in northeastern New Jersey. Only the largest are marked here. Many are not visible at this scale.
—Shaded-relief image from EROS Data Center, U.S. Geological Survey

made of rock or sediment, the shape of a well-developed drumlin is the same: a streamlined teardrop with the blunt nose facing into the oncoming ice and a longer, more gently sloping tail trailing in the direction the ice is headed. Most of the New Jersey drumlins are not well developed into the teardrop shape, but they are clearly streamlined and clearly oriented parallel to ice movement. Many are composed of glacial sediment as much as 250 feet thick and are the result of glacial sculpting rather than erosion parallel to resistant beds of rock.

The drumlins composed of till typically have two layers. An upper layer of brown or gray till was deposited during the most recent ice advance. Below this is an older, red till that is deeply weathered to soil. A similar sequence of two tills is common through much of southern New England. The age of the older till has been controversial for many years. Whatever its age, the shaping of this lower till into drumlins and plastering of newer till on top of older till confirms that the glaciers were not simply an overpowering erosional force. If they were, both the younger till and the older till would be gone.

Hundreds of striations and gouges made by larger rocks have been found on the crest of the Palisades, many weathered, but many also perfectly preserved beneath soil and exposed in building projects. They are consistently oriented northwest-southeast. Together with the arc-shaped terminal moraine centered between the Watchungs and Staten Island, orientations of drumlins through-out northeastern New Jersey, and Palisades diabase erratics scattered across much of New York City, the striations show that at the height of glaciation, the ice covering northeastern New Jersey and New York City did not flow directly down the Hudson Valley. Instead, it crossed over the Hudson Highlands, then formed a lobe flowing southward and outward from the lowland between the Palisades and the Watchungs.

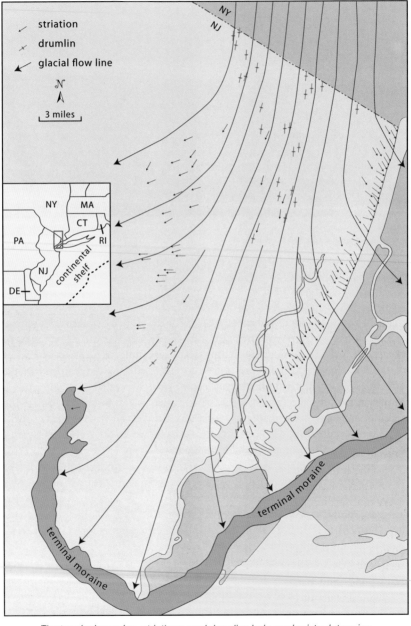

The terminal moraine, striations, and drumlins help geologists determine the direction of ice flow between the Watchungs and the Palisades.
—Modified from Stanford and Harper, 1991

Glacial Lakes Bayonne and Hackensack

At the end of the ice age, as the Wisconsinan ice retreated northward, seaward flow of meltwater was blocked by the terminal moraine. Glacial Lake Bayonne ponded between the moraine and the ice. Meltwater cut through the unconsolidated sediment of the moraine within a couple of thousand years and hit diabase bedrock at Tremley Point along the Arthur Kill and between Bayonne and Staten Island along the Kill van Kull. Downcutting slowed to negligible, and the lower-elevation lake, Glacial Lake Hackensack, lengthened and covered New Jersey's Hackensack Meadowlands as the ice continued to recede. To the east, Glacial Lake Hudson formed when the ice melted back past Hell Gate, opening a spillway through which water flowed eastward into the Long Island Sound lowland. Glacial Lake Hudson stood about 40 feet lower than Glacial Lake Hackensack.

Glacial Lake Hackensack continued to drain through the Kill van Kull until about 17,000 years ago when ice melted back past Sparkill Gap through the Palisades ridge. The gap, just north of the New York border, bottoms roughly 500 feet below the crest of the ridge. Because of glacial rebound, it is now about 60 feet higher than bedrock at the Kill van Kull and would not serve as an outlet for water in the Meadowlands. During the ice age, however, the load of ice had tilted the Earth's crust northward. A thousand feet of ice loads 2,000 million pounds per square mile onto the crust, and the glaciers were as much as 2,000 to 3,000 thousand feet thick in northernmost New Jersey.

We can tell that the ice weighed down the crust about 100 feet more at Sparkill Gap than at the Kill van Kull from the heights of deltas along the shore of Glacial Lake Hackensack. As with any lake, the surface of Glacial Lake Hackensack was flat, with all the shoreline features at the same elevation. After the weight of the ice lifted, the crust rebounded, and over several thousand years the land returned to its preglacial elevation. Shoreline features to the north rose farther than those to the south because the crust had been pushed farther downward. The most common shoreline features of glacial lakes are deltas built by meltwater streams overloaded with sand and gravel. Most of the sand is carried to the edge of the delta and avalanches into deeper water, building the delta outward by adding sloping foreset beds. Some sand and much of the gravel is usually deposited on the top of the delta as gently sloping topset beds. The water level of the lake is at the contact between the foreset and topset beds.

In Glacial Lake Hackensack, ice age deltas are now about 3.5 feet higher for every mile farther north. Deltas are about 40 feet above sea level at Hackensack, 65 feet at Westwood, and 75 feet just south of Sparkill Gap. When the gap was uncovered, the water level dropped to the 40-foot level of Glacial Lake Hudson. Sediment had filled much of the Hackensack lowland even before the glaciers melted past Sparkill Gap, and large areas stood dry after the lake drained. Small lakes, ponds, and marshlands remained where the land surface was below the gap.

Beginning about 13,000 years ago, because the Earth's crust was rising faster to the north where there had been more glacial downwarping, Sparkill Gap rose above the Kill van Kull. Drainage through the ponds and marshlands shifted gradually, over hundreds of years, from Sparkill Gap back toward Kill

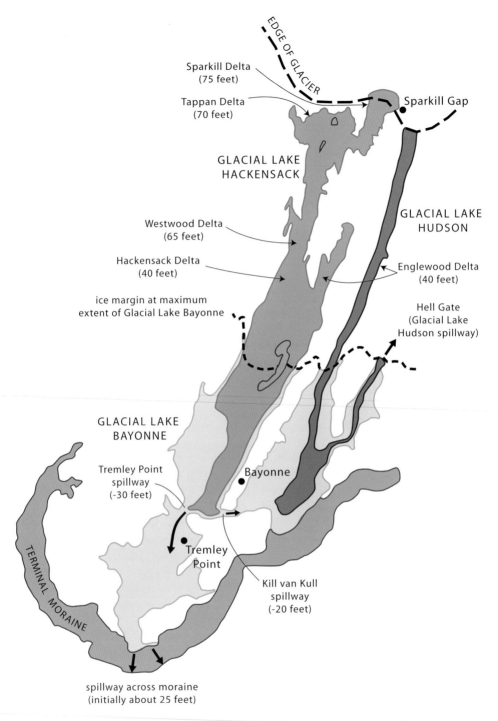

EDGE OF GLACIER

Sparkill Delta
(75 feet)

Tappan Delta
(70 feet)

Sparkill Gap

GLACIAL LAKE
HACKENSACK

GLACIAL LAKE
HUDSON

Westwood Delta
(65 feet)

Hackensack Delta
(40 feet)

Englewood Delta
(40 feet)

ice margin at maximum
extent of Glacial Lake Bayonne

Hell Gate
(Glacial Lake
Hudson spillway)

GLACIAL LAKE
BAYONNE

Tremley Point
spillway
(-30 feet)

Bayonne

Tremley
Point

TERMINAL MORAINE

Kill van Kull
spillway
(-20 feet)

spillway across moraine
(initially about 25 feet)

*Glacial Lakes Bayonne, Hackensack, and Hudson. Postglacial tilting of the Earth's surface
after the weight of the glaciers was lifted is measured using present-day elevations of spillways and deltas. Outlet streams and deltas in any lake are at roughly the same elevation
while the lake is full of water. Because of postglacial uplift, elevations of shoreline features
at the northern end of Glacial Lake Hackensack are now about 100 feet higher than those
at the spillway about 40 miles to the south.* —Modified from Stanford and Harper, 1991; Stone and others, 2002

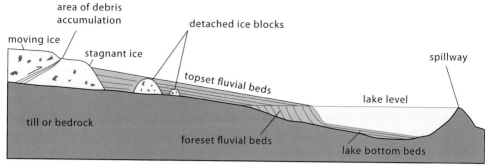

Cross section of a delta. —Modified from Koteff, 1974

Delta built into a glacial lake. Topset beds are above the man. Foreset beds are to his right. The lake level was at the elevation of his head. —Photo courtesy of N.J. Geological Survey

van Kull. Still, the Hackensack lowland was not a tidal marsh. Large volumes of water were still held in glaciers and the shoreline was still miles to the east. About 6,000 years ago, the rising oceans finally flooded the lowland. The Meadowlands changed from a river valley to an estuary, filling in to the high tide level and building a flat expanse of marsh and swamp southward into Newark Bay.

Glacial Lake Passaic

Glacial lakes are common in north-draining valleys, and numerous lakes were created in New Jersey in front of the advancing and retreating glaciers. Glacial Lake Passaic was the largest of the lakes entirely in New Jersey. It filled the lowland between the bathtub-shaped curve of the Watchung ridges and the New Jersey Highlands not once, but twice, first during the Illinoian glaciation about 150,000 years ago, then during the Wisconsinan glaciation about 25,000 years ago. Before the glaciations, the area behind the Watchungs was drained by two separate river systems: the Ancestral Passaic and Pompton Rivers. The Ancestral Passaic flowed through gaps across the First Watchung Mountain at Millburn and the Second Watchung Mountain at Short Hills, then to the Ancestral Raritan River. The Ancestral Pompton River drained through gaps at Little Falls and Paterson. Between the two glaciations, the rivers probably reoccupied their preglacial drainages, but after the Wisconsinan, the Passaic was unable to reoccupy its preglacial route because the gap at Short Hills was blocked by

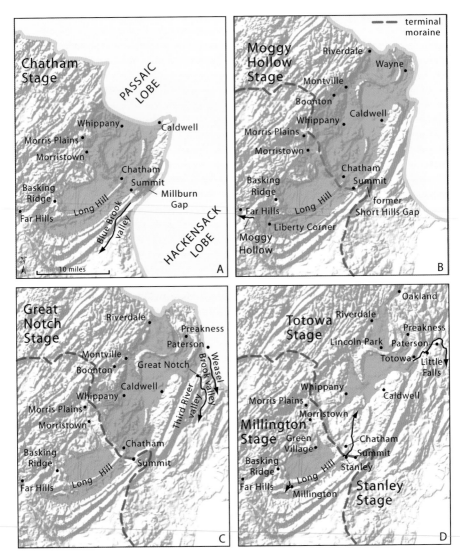

Glacial Lake Passaic underwent several distinct stages during its life span. A. Glacial Lake Passaic before ice deposited the terminal moraine. The lake drained along Blue Brook. B. Glacial Lake Passaic at its maximum extent after ice began to recede and the terminal moraine blocked the former Short Hills Gap. Drainage was through Moggy Brook. C. Glacial Lake Passaic after outlets at Great Notch and Weasel Brook were uncovered. D. Small lakes left in the Passaic basin after the outlet at Little Falls was uncovered. —Modified from Stanford, 2007

the terminal moraine, up to 250 feet thick. The Passaic was forced northward to join the Pompton River at Fairfield and now crosses the Watchungs at Little Falls and at Great Falls in Paterson.

At its maximum, the ice stood across the lake between Morristown and Chatham and deposited a hummocky terminal moraine fringed to the south by a flat-topped delta built into the lake. The moraine in this area is relatively thin and sits atop deltaic sand. Kettle holes in the moraine here do not hold ponds or marshes as they do along most other sections of the moraine because the water drains into the underlying deltaic sand. Many kettle holes along the moraine have been filled for development, but some are still visible, including the large Punch Bowl on the Drew University campus, which is usually completely dry, and the even deeper kettles at the College of St. Elizabeth, which are wet only at the very bottom where they likely intersect the water table. Smaller kettles in Drew's arboretum used to be dry but were lined with clay to convert them to ponds.

No lake can fill above the lowest point on its rim. As the ice advanced southward, Glacial Lake Passaic drained briefly through the Blue Brook valley in the Watchung Reservation. The glaciers continued to advance, and soon ice between Summit and Chatham cut off the Blue Brook spillway. The lowest point across rock surrounding Glacial Lake Passaic was then at Moggy Hollow, between Liberty Corner and Far Hills.

The ice stood at the terminal moraine for perhaps 1,000 years before it began melting northward. Because the moraine blocked the preglacial course of the river at Short Hills, the Passaic River could not return to its preglacial bed. Instead, the lake expanded northward as the ice melted back. Flow continued across the Moggy Hollow spillway until the ice melted past Great Notch, about 80 feet lower than the outlet at Moggy Hollow, then further lowered to small, shallow lakes when the gap at Paterson was uncovered. Most of the lakes were held back by sediment ridges that eroded fairly quickly, draining out the water and leaving Troy Meadows, Hatfield Swamp, Great Piece Meadows, and Dead River Swamp. The Millington stage of Glacial Lake Passaic was held back by the basalt ridge of Long Hill and lasted longer than the sediment-dammed lakes. The basalt was fractured and relatively easily eroded, however, and by about 1,400 years ago had eroded to form Millington Gorge. The lowering of the outlet drained the Millington stage lake, leaving today's Great Swamp.

Wide areas of wetland remained after Glacial Lake Passaic drained and are now some of the most flood-prone areas of the state. In the southern part of the basin the wetlands are crossed by small rivers carrying little sediment. Low areas have filled with muck and peat and remain low-lying and swampy. The Great Swamp south of Morristown is the largest, but low-lying areas of Washington Valley near Morristown and marshes along the Dead River near Millington are similar.

The swamps flood, but there is little damage because they are largely uninhabited. Low-lying areas in the northern part of the basin, on the other hand, were crossed for a time after Glacial Lake Passaic drained via large meltwater rivers still fed by active glaciers in the northern part of the drainage basin. Active glaciers produce enormous amounts of ground-up sediment, and the

Great Swamp in winter. —Photo by Scott Stanford, N.J. Geological Survey

low areas in the northern part of the basin were mostly overspread with sand and gravel outwash deposits. Glacial outwash deposits and floodplains along the Passaic, Pequannock, and Pompton Rivers are flat, most of the time dry, easily developed, and prone to flooding. Despite major floods as long ago as 1811 and continued periodic flooding, sometimes several major floods per decade, the area was built up during postwar suburbanization and even now continues to attract development.

Efforts to control the flooding date to the 1870s, but costs and anticipated adverse impacts have prevented most plans from being carried out. By the 1990s there was, on average, $116 million in flood damage per year in the Upper Passaic basin. Most recently, the basin has seen protracted disagreements between proponents of hard and soft approaches. The favored hard approach centered on 21 miles of flood emergency tunnels, most 40 feet in diameter, draining to Newark Bay. Inlets were planned near confluences of the Passaic and Pompton Rivers at Two Bridges and the Pequannock, Wanaque, Ramapo, and Pompton Rivers a few miles to the north. Major objections to the tunnels were expense, impacts to water quality and ecosystems, and the possibility that tunneling might, instead of solving the flood problem, make it worse by encouraging development. After many millions were spent in planning, investigation of soil and rock along the route, environmental impact studies, and public presentations, the project has been shelved for the foreseeable future. Current plans focus more on channel improvements, flood hazard zoning, removal of buildings from floodways, and rehabilitation of the Great Piece Meadows, which have been degraded by decades of mining the glacial sands and gravels.

ROAD GUIDES IN THE NEWARK BASIN

I-78
Holland Tunnel—I-287
40 miles

Unlike the George Washington Bridge and Lincoln Tunnel, which cross from the metamorphic rocks of Manhattan onto igneous and sedimentary rocks of the Newark Basin as they cross the Hudson, the Holland Tunnel exits to New Jersey within a sliver of metamorphic rock that runs for a few miles along the east side of the Bayonne peninsula. The metamorphic rocks west of the Hudson are mostly beneath marsh sediments, fill, and buildings and are known primarily from borings and excavations. About a mile north of the tunnel, however, metamorphic rock is exposed for several blocks along the Hudson River at Castle Point. At the top of Castle Point, Stevens Institute of Technology stands on a 30-foot-high bluff of green serpentinite, colored green by the mineral serpentine. Serpentinite is a metamorphic rock that usually forms from basaltic igneous rock but can also form from silty or clayey limestone or dolomite with the same overall percentage of iron, magnesium, silica, and calcium as basalt. It can be almost impossible, in some cases, to tell by looking whether the serpentinite was originally igneous or sedimentary, but not at Castle Point. Here the serpentinite is studded with pinhead-size, black crystals of the mineral chromite. Chromium would not be expected in limestone but is common in seafloor basaltic rocks. The serpentinite rocks here and in a much larger area along I-278 in Staten Island are remnants of oceanic crust pushed up onto

Castle Point serpentine at Castle Point in Hoboken. —Photo by D. Harper

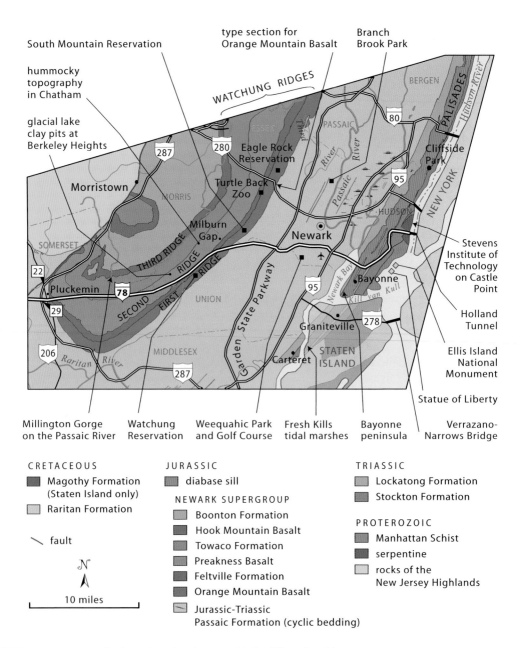

South Mountain Reservation

type section for
Orange Mountain Basalt

Branch
Brook Park

hummocky
topography
in Chatham

glacial lake
clay pits at
Berkeley Heights

WATCHUNG RIDGES

BERGEN

ESSEX

PASSAIC

PASSAIC

PALISADES

Hudson River

287

280

Eagle Rock
Reservation

Peckman River

Passaic River

80

Cliffside
Park

Morristown

MORRIS

Turtle Back
Zoo

95

NEW YORK

Milburn
Gap

Newark

HUDSON

SOMERSET

THIRD RIDGE

SECOND RIDGE

FIRST RIDGE

Stevens
Institute of
Technology
on Castle
Point

22

Pluckemin

78

UNION

Garden State Parkway

95

Newark Bay

Bayonne

Kill van Kull

Holland
Tunnel

29

206

Raritan River

MIDDLESEX

287

Carteret

Graniteville

STATEN
ISLAND

278

Ellis Island
National
Monument

Statue of Liberty

Millington Gorge
on the Passaic River

Watchung
Reservation

Weequahic Park
and Golf Course

Fresh Kills
tidal marshes

Bayonne
peninsula

Verrazano-
Narrows Bridge

CRETACEOUS

■ Magothy Formation
(Staten Island only)

☐ Raritan Formation

╲ fault

N

10 miles

JURASSIC

▨ diabase sill

NEWARK SUPERGROUP

☐ Boonton Formation

■ Hook Mountain Basalt

■ Towaco Formation

■ Preakness Basalt

■ Feltville Formation

■ Orange Mountain Basalt

▨ Jurassic-Triassic
Passaic Formation (cyclic bedding)

TRIASSIC

☐ Lockatong Formation

■ Stockton Formation

PROTEROZOIC

■ Manhattan Schist

■ serpentine

☐ rocks of the
New Jersey Highlands

Geology along I-78 between Holland Tunnel and I-287. —Compiled from
the USGS's Preliminary Integrated Geologic Map Database for the United States, 2006

North American continental crust in the Taconic Orogeny. The chromite in the New Jersey rocks is too sparse to be mined as ore, but similar deposits in southeastern Pennsylvania were worked in the nineteenth century, and had enough chromium to weather to chrome barrens, areas of soil poisonous to most plants.

The Hoboken serpentinite is not very compact but has seen limited use on building exteriors. The Weehawken Public Library, visible near the top of the helix at the Lincoln Tunnel entrance, is attractively trimmed with this stone.

Chromium was never mined in New Jersey, but some areas close by the tunnel entrance do have an unfortunate legacy of chromium. At the time of colonization much of the Hudson River waterfront along the Bayonne peninsula was mosquito-infested marshland. Malaria and yellow fever, while not endemic, were problematic. Through the nineteenth and early twentieth centuries, the land was gradually filled to rid the area of disease and allow development. Most of the fill was innocuous: cinders, soil from hills that were being leveled elsewhere, trash, and the like. Other fill materials, most notably waste from chrome ore processing plants, which used ore from around the world, have come to be serious public health problems. Some toxic chromium compounds in the waste are water-soluble and crystallize on basement walls when water seeps through walls and evaporates.

Palisades Sill and Kill van Kull

About a mile west of the tunnel, the road begins a climb up the Palisades Sill, only about 120 feet tall here as opposed to 350 feet at the George Washington Bridge. The rock here is just as resistant to erosion, and the sill is about as thick as at the bridge. The ridge is lower in part because the land has subsided to the south and in part because to the south of Cliffside Park it was planed lower by the Pensauken River, which flowed southwest from the Long Island Sound area from about 8 million years ago to about 2 million years ago. At the Kill van Kull the rock surface drops from 40 feet at Bayonne to 30 feet below sea level across the half-mile-wide Kill van Kull, then rises back to 40 feet in the Graniteville neighborhood of Staten Island, inappropriately named for its diabase quarries. The Kill van Kull gap was cut by an east-flowing precursor to the Raritan and Passaic Rivers. It occupied the gap after it had been abandoned by the much larger and wider southwestward-flowing Pensauken River. From Graniteville, the diabase ridge continues to decrease in elevation for about 4 miles across Staten Island until it drops below sea level west of the Fresh Kills tidal marshes. The diabase does not end where it drops below sea level but curves southwestward beneath a cover of Coastal Plain sediment and returns to the surface in New Jersey near Princeton.

Liberty and Ellis Islands

In early colonial times, Liberty and Ellis Islands were piles of oyster shells on morainal deposits that were barely exposed above the waters of Upper New York Bay. They are now largely artificial islands. Ellis Island in particular has been greatly expanded by fill.

Newark Bay

Newark Bay was part of Glacial Lake Hackensack between about 20,000 and 18,000 years ago, then became dry land after the retreating glaciers melted back past Sparkill Gap in New York and the lake drained. The area became bay and marshland when rising sea levels flooded the seaward parts of the Hackensack lowland.

Branch Brook and Weequahic Park

In their advance and retreat across the land, continental glaciers leave a variety of landforms and soils, some of which are well suited to particular uses. Orchards do well on well-drained, sandy uplands, and many of northern New Jersey's orchards are on sandy deltas. Many cemeteries also are in well-drained, sandy soils. Newark's two largest parks, Branch Brook and Weequahic, owe much of their character to their underlying glacial topography. Branch Brook Park is on the bed of a small glacial lake, Glacial Lake Watsessing, ponded in the north-draining Branch Brook valley when glaciers stood just south of its confluence with the Second River. The southern part of the park was built on an area of marshy lake-bottom sediment known as Old Blue Jay Swamp. The swamp was a dismal, unattractive place used for both sewage disposal and water supply for the surrounding tenements and was the source of periodic cholera outbreaks. In the park design, the swamp was deepened and dammed in some places for open water, and cleared and drained elsewhere for ball fields and broad, open meadows. The northern section of the park, toward the ice front, has a hilly aspect from deposition of sands and gravels against the ice, deltas built into the lake, and downcutting by Branch Brook after the ice melted back. This area was left more to woods and trails and has some of the most scenic of the cherry tree plantings for which the park is famed.

Weequahic Park was similarly developed where a north-draining valley was flooded by a small glacial lake and left areas of marshy bottomland. Deltas and knob and kettle uplands along the west side of the park were developed to showcase views across low-lying areas now occupied by Newark Airport; lower areas focused on Weequahic Lake. At the Weequahic Park Golf Course, either the original knob and kettle topography was left intact in the design of the course or something closely resembling knob and kettle topography was constructed.

Millburn Gaps

West of Newark Bay, I-78 crosses about 10 miles of mudstone and sandstone of the Passaic Formation before crossing the Orange Mountain Basalt of the First Watchung Mountain at Millburn Gap. I-78 is similar to most of the major transportation routes across New Jersey's upland ridges in being laid out to take advantage of erosional gaps cut by rivers. The Ancestral Passaic River cut the gap at Millburn before the Wisconsinan ice age.

Eagle Rock Reservation

Eagle Rock Reservation, north of I-280 in West Orange, lies along a stretch of the First Watchungs widely known in the late nineteenth century for its traprock

Curvicolumnar jointing in Eagle Rock Quarry, at Orange Mountain near Eagle Rock Reservation. —Photo by J. Volney Lewis, N.J. Geological Survey, 1918

quarries. By the late 1800s, quarry faces over 100 feet high had exposed extraordinary exposures of columnar basalt in the lowermost of the several basalt flows that make up the Orange Mountain Basalt. The columns, similar to the larger columns exposed along the Palisades cliff, formed due to tension in the basalt when it cooled and contracted. In some places, the columns ran straight up and down the entire height of the quarry walls. In others, they traced loops arcing downward, then upward across the quarry face.

The quarry has been graded over and the columns are no longer visible. The curving has been explained as the result of differences in heat loss from place to place across the lava flow. As was the case much of the time in the Newark Basin, there was a lake when the lava flowed outward, and the lava cooled quickly beneath the water. The first fractures to form were widely spaced master fractures. The water percolated into the master fractures, especially where they intersected, creating cold spots within the flow. Cooling did not progress uniformly downward. It also progressed laterally from where the water was cooling the master fractures toward hotter places away from the fractures. The contraction and fracturing followed the cooling, fanning downward and outward from colder places toward hotter places. The curved jointing is characteristic of the lower flow of the first Watchung along the length of the Watchungs. It is no longer visible in the park but can be seen today in exposures along I-78 uphill to the east from the I-287 intersection, along I-287 uphill to the east of the NJ 206 Bedminster exit, and most spectacularly, at the type section of the Orange Mountain Basalt along I-280 uphill to the west of the Orange exit (see page 87).

This retaining wall near Eagle Rock Reservation was constructed by stacking sections of basalt columns horizontally, like logs. The effect is almost like looking downward onto vertical columns at bare rock surfaces in the park. —Photo by D. Harper

The quarries became attractions for day trippers from as far away as New York. A trolley line ran to within walking distance of the quarries. After looking over the columns, the more vigorous could climb to the top of the mountain for a view across the countryside. You can see from the Verrazano-Narrows Bridge north to the George Washington Bridge. In the late 1600s, the overlook was a base station for land surveying to the east.

South Mountain Reservation

Essex County's South Mountain served as a lookout in colonial times. George Washington established outposts along the ridge to forewarn of British advances toward his encampments at Morristown. On June 23, 1780, a signal fire atop Washington Rock in South Mountain Reservation warned of troops advancing toward a gap in the ridge at Millburn. The South Mountain Reservation, north of I-78 at Millburn, spans a valley eroded in the Feltville Formation and includes the summits of the basalt ridges of the First and Second Watchung Mountains. Essex County was a pioneer in park development, and land purchases for its South Mountain and Eagle Rock Reservations began in the 1890s. Though the area was still somewhat rural, quarries were scarring the mountainsides and development was encroaching.

Unlike the Watchung Reservation, where only the northern part of the park was glaciated, glacial remnants are everywhere. Most of the valley floor is covered by thick glacial sediment, and exposures of the Feltville Formation are scarce. Exposures of basalt along ridgetops are rounded into roche moutonnée shapes (gently sloping up-ice side and steep down-ice side) and occasionally show the polygonal pattern of the tops of basalt columns. The patterned rocks are locally known as turtle backs and gave the nearby Turtle Back Zoo its name.

Much of the character of the glaciated valley can be seen in a short hike from the Tulip Springs parking area just north of the intersection of South Orange Avenue and Cherry Lane. The park was designed by the Olmstead brothers, sons of Frederick Law Olmsted, who designed New York's Central Park. The design left most of the park semiwild, with winding carriage roads designed for leisurely rides through bucolic settings. The carriages are gone, but the carriage roads remain as flat, wide trails. From the parking area, cross the South Orange Avenue bridge to a carriage road and a bridge across a small tributary of the Rahway River. To the left of the trail past the bridge are columnar basalt outcrops of the First Watchung's bedrock. To the right, visible through the trees across the Rahway River, is a steep ridge. The ridge is a delta of sand and gravel deposited in a small glacial lake at the edge of the ice. The Rahway River floodplain is choked with small boulders of a bewildering variety. Basalt, gneiss, Newark Basin sandstone, and Paleozoic quartzite are the most common.

Turtle backs at Turtle Back Rock, South Mountain Reservation. —Photo by D. Harper

Gravel and boulders in the bed of the Rahway River in South Mountain Reservation. The boulders are what's left behind after the finer sediments have been eroded from a delta built into a small glacial lake that once existed here.
—Photo by D. Harper

The boulders were brought south by the glaciers and washed from the glacial deposits when the river cut its way through the delta. Boulders were abundant in the delta. Even in the torrential meltwater streams south of glaciers, large boulders did not move far. They now remain on the floodplain because they are moved only slowly downstream even when the Rahway River is in flood.

At one time a municipal water supply well that drew water from the permeable sand and gravel of the delta stood near the top of the ridge. The drilling log for this well shows that the deposits are 75 feet thick, with sand, gravel, and boulders through the entire thickness. Similar valley fill deposits are common throughout glaciated areas and are some of the state's most productive aquifers.

Another hike from the Tulip Springs parking area on another carriage road takes you to the base of Hemlock Falls, which flows over Orange Mountain Basalt. The falls originated as meltwater cascades when glaciers stood just north of here. Of the two waterfalls along the trail, the lower is the most picturesque, but the upper offers a better impression of the conditions during the ice age summer. You are lucky now to see a few gallons per second passing over the falls, but the ice age flow must have been thousands of gallons per second. A climb to the top of the upper falls brings you to a 30-foot-deep channel cut into the rock. The channel is swept clean of soil and rocks toward the lip of the cascade but littered with glacial erratics the size of large beach balls a few hundred feet upstream. Glacial ice tends to flow as lobes within valleys, and the ice here was cast into lobes east and west of the Watchungs. Summertime torrents channeled between the lobes to Hemlock Falls would have been spectacular.

Hemlock Falls in South Mountain Reservation. Columnar basalt is exposed to the left the cascade. The rounded boulder to the right is a glacial erratic of Proterozoic gneiss, probably from the New Jersey Highlands.
—Photo by D. Harper

Rocky channel upstream from the cataract at Hemlock Falls. This section of the channel has been swept clean of glacial boulders. —Photo by D. Harper

Watchung Reservation

West of Millburn Gap, I-78 bends southwestward and for about 1.5 miles passes through Union County's Watchung Reservation. Within the reservation, I-78 follows an erosional valley cut along the Feltville Formation between the Orange Mountain Basalt of the First Watchung Mountain and the Preakness Basalt of the Second Watchung Mountain. For several miles the roadway is cut into the Preakness Basalt. Steep road cuts on the northwest side of the highway display unusual vertical jointing that has been variously described as platy prismatic jointing and splintery columns. The jointing is characteristic of the Preakness Basalt and also the second flow of the Hartford rift basin to the north. The splintery columns do not match any of the several styles of columns common in basalt flows, and their origin remains a mystery.

The abandoned village of Feltville in the Watchung Reservation was built in the 1840s as a company town centered on a paper mill owned by David Felt. The mill and two mill ponds that supplied water power are gone, but several houses, the church, and a carriage house have been preserved as a historic village. Among geologists the town is best known as the type section of the Feltville Formation. The Feltville is similar to the Passaic Formation in consisting predominantly of reddish brown mudstone, sandstone, and siltstone. It is distinguished by having, in addition, calcareous mudstone and limestone beds deposited in lakes when little sediment was being washed in. Limestone beds a few inches thick are exposed along the abandoned millrace at Feltville. They reach thicknesses of 10 feet in the Jacksonwald Syncline to the southwest in Pennsylvania.

Splintery columns in the Preakness Basalt of the Second Watchung Mountain along I-78. —Photo by Michael Flite

A short walk across the Blue Brook valley from Feltville is the Gorge, a narrow, steep-sided tributary valley, with a small alluvial fan where it empties into the Blue Brook valley. The Gorge is conspicuously different from other small valleys in the park. There are many reasons a stream can change dramatically, and dozens of streams in New Jersey are known to have changed. Among the reasons are blockage by glaciers, tilting of the Earth's crust under the weight of ice, stream capture in which a rapidly eroding stream cuts into the valley of a more slowly eroding stream and diverts the water, and even blockage of valleys by beavers. The stream that cut the Gorge likely began cutting its narrow valley during the Wisconsinan ice age. The main stream through the park, Blue Brook, briefly served as the outlet stream for Glacial Lake Passaic and cut its valley wider and deeper because of the increased flow. The deeper valley and steeper walls likely created the conditions for the rapid downcutting at the Gorge.

Long Hill and Lake Passaic Clay

I-78 parallels Long Hill, the Third Watchung Mountain, between Berkeley Heights and Millington. Long Hill was an island in most stages of Glacial Lake Passaic, but during the final, Millington stage, this basalt ridge limited the formerly much more extensive lake to the area to the north. Eventually, a spillway eroded through the basalt, forming the Millington Gorge through which the Passaic River now flows. Clay from the Glacial Lake Passaic lake bed was dug at Berkeley Heights and Gillette.

I-95/I-80
George Washington Bridge—I-287
33 miles

This trip across New Jersey begins at the New York border midway across the George Washington Bridge. Also midway across the bridge, the route crosses from Proterozoic and Paleozoic metamorphic rock of New York City onto Mesozoic igneous and sedimentary rock of the Newark Basin. The Newark Basin was a rift valley that formed when the supercontinent Pangea split apart and the Atlantic Ocean opened. The New York City rock is much older. It began as sediment in the Iapetus Ocean, which closed in the Ordovician Period, long before the opening of the Atlantic, then was strongly metamorphosed during the ensuing collision between North America and an island arc to the east of Iapetus. Ocean-bottom muds were changed to mica schist, and limestones were changed to marble. In northwestern New Jersey, I-80 passes into the Highlands, where more exposures of rocks formed from sediment deposited in Iapetus occur. They were farther from the collision and experienced lower temperatures and pressures.

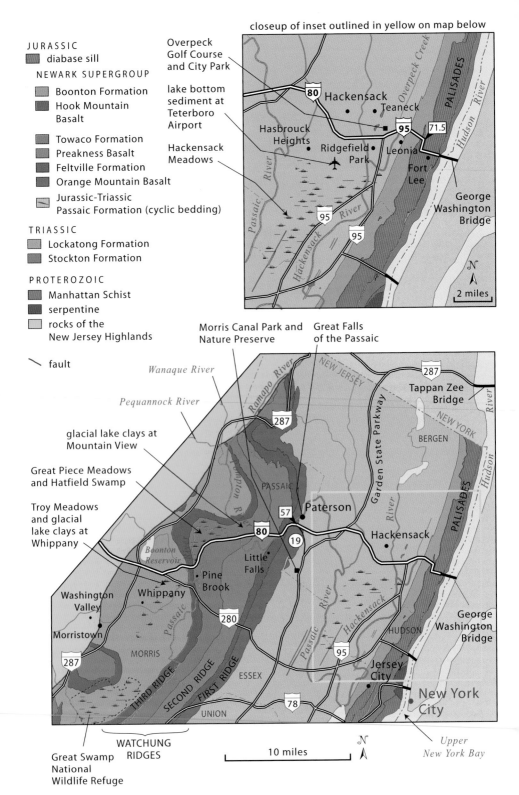

JURASSIC
- diabase sill

NEWARK SUPERGROUP
- Boonton Formation
- Hook Mountain Basalt
- Towaco Formation
- Preakness Basalt
- Feltville Formation
- Orange Mountain Basalt
- Jurassic-Triassic Passaic Formation (cyclic bedding)

TRIASSIC
- Lockatong Formation
- Stockton Formation

PROTEROZOIC
- Manhattan Schist
- serpentine
- rocks of the New Jersey Highlands

- fault

closeup of inset outlined in yellow on map below

Overpeck Golf Course and City Park

lake bottom sediment at Teterboro Airport

Hackensack Meadows

Overpeck Creek

PALISADES

80 Hackensack
Teaneck

Hasbrouck Heights
95   71.5

Ridgefield Park
Leonia

Passaic River

95 River

Fort Lee

Hudson River

George Washington Bridge

95

95

N

2 miles

Morris Canal Park and Nature Preserve

Great Falls of the Passaic

Wanaque River

Pequannock River

glacial lake clays at Mountain View

Great Piece Meadows and Hatfield Swamp

Troy Meadows and glacial lake clays at Whippany

Washington Valley

Morristown

287

MORRIS

Ramapo River

NEW JERSEY

287

Tappan Zee Bridge

287

Hudson River

NEW YORK

BERGEN

Garden State Parkway

PASSAIC

57 Paterson

80

19

Little Falls

Pine Brook

Whippany

Boonton Reservoir

280

Passaic River

THIRD RIDGE

SECOND RIDGE

FIRST RIDGE

ESSEX

UNION

78

WATCHUNG RIDGES

Great Swamp National Wildlife Refuge

10 miles

Hackensack

Passaic River

Hackensack

95

HUDSON

Jersey City

PALISADES

Hudson River

George Washington Bridge

New York City

Upper New York Bay

N

Geology along I-95 and I-80 across the Newark Basin. —Compiled from the USGS's Preliminary Integrated Geologic Map Database for the United States, 2006

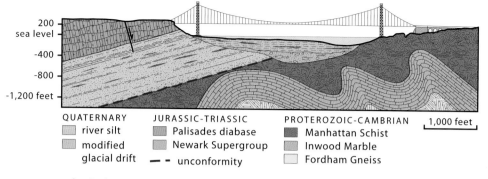

QUATERNARY	JURASSIC-TRIASSIC	PROTEROZOIC-CAMBRIAN	1,000 feet
river silt	Palisades diabase	Manhattan Schist	
modified glacial drift	Newark Supergroup	Inwood Marble	
	— — unconformity	Fordham Gneiss	

Geologic cross section at the George Washington Bridge. —From Berkey, 1933

The Hudson River—A Fjord?

From the George Washington Bridge the Palisades cliffs plunging into the Hudson River call to mind the fjords of Norway. The resemblance is even stronger 30 miles to the north in New York where the Hudson Highlands rise steeply above both banks of the river. Several estuaries, including the Hudson, Somes Sound in Maine, and the Saguenay River in Quebec, have been called the southernmost fjord in eastern North America. While the Hudson fits one of the dictionary definitions of a fjord—"a long, deep, steep-walled, narrow, U-shaped valley bordered seaward by shallower water"—and while it visually resembles the Scandinavian fjords, it differs from the Scandinavian fjords in its origin, morphology, and hydrology.

With regard to origin, the Scandinavian fjords formed where glaciers entered the sea. Characteristically the floor of a fjord slopes landward, rather than seaward, and is bounded seaward by a shallowly submerged moraine or bedrock sill. The shallowing at the mouths of the Scandinavian fjords has been attributed in part to the decrease in glacial erosion where ice from highland valleys flowed directly into the sea. Toward the ends of the valleys, the ice thinned, was buoyed upward by the water, calved icebergs, and lost its ability to erode. The Hudson Valley ice flowed through a valley crossing a highland area, deepened the valley upstream, and thinned as it reached the end of its rock-walled valley. Unlike in Scandinavia, however, seaward calving was never a possibility. When the glaciers were deepening the Hudson Valley, the sea was nowhere nearby. Large amounts of water were locked up in continental ice sheets, and sea level was lower by several hundred feet. The glaciers stood across Staten Island and central New Jersey. The shoreline was about 80 miles to the east.

With regard to morphology, the Scandinavian fjords remain substantially deeper inland than where they meet the sea, some over 1,000 feet deeper inland than at the mouth. They are deep because the glacially overdeepened reaches have not filled with sediment. In the Hudson, on the other hand, much of the glacially overdeepened valley has filled with sediment. Water depth today is related to tidal scour, not glacial overdeepening. In the open waters of Lower New York Bay, water depths away from dredged channels are commonly 20

Palisades cliffs and the Hudson River. —Photo by D. Harper

to 30 feet. From the Battery (the southern tip of Manhattan Island) northward, water is channeled between rock to the east and west. Unable to spread out, the river cuts deeper into river-bottom sediment to accommodate the combined river flow and tidal ebb and flood. Beneath the George Washington Bridge depths are 40 to 60 feet. In the wider Tappan Zee reach north of New Jersey, the river is less constricted and depths are 25 to 30 feet. In the narrowest parts of the valley, New York's Hudson Gorge near Bear Mountain and West Point, depths are 75 to 150 feet. While the overdeepened Scandinavian fjords are continuing to fill slowly with sediment more than 10,000 years after glaciers melted from their valleys, comparison of old and new navigation charts show that the Hudson is deepening. Most of the river north of the Battery is naturally deep enough for shipping, and channel dredging is needed only along parts of the Tappan Zee in New York. The river is not being dredged deeper. It has cut deeper because filling of wetlands to the east and west has forced more flow into the main channel, and the greater flow has eroded the riverbed.

With regard to hydrology, the Hudson it is not a fjord-type estuary. It is often cited as an example of a salt wedge estuary. Estuaries are mixing zones between freshwater from land and salty water from the ocean. They are classified by the pattern of mixing. A fjord-type estuary is one in which a deep inland basin is filled with salt water below a thinner layer of fresher river water. The fresher, lighter river water floats across the top of the heavier salt water with little mixing until it reaches the sea. Salt water is trapped below the fresher water because the shallow sill at the entrance blocks the turbulent ebb and flood of the tides, which mix salt water and freshwater in most estuaries. The result in the Scandinavian fjords is commonly stagnation of the underlying salt water. Without oxygen, organic material like the wood of Viking ships can be preserved for many hundreds of years.

Salt wedge estuaries like the Hudson are often shallow toward the ocean, but the shallowing is less pronounced than in a fjord and does not block a vigorous inflow of salt water with each rising tide. The heavier salt water sinks beneath the lighter freshwater, flows inland along the bottom, and gradually mixes upward. Net flow is landward at the bottom because of the inflowing salt water. Net flow is seaward at the surface because the seawater that came inland along the river bottom mixes upward into fresh river water and, through a number of tidal cycles, returns to the sea. The salt wedge is the triangle of salt water wedging landward beneath lighter, fresher river water.

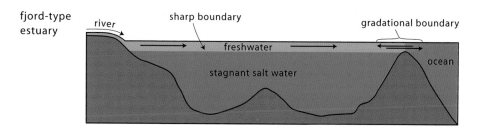

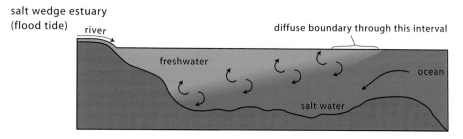

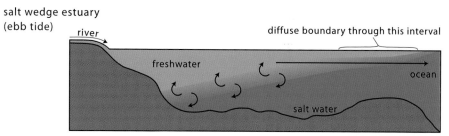

The river is flowing from left to right in these examples of fjord and salt wedge estuaries. In a fjord-type estuary a high sill prevents turbulent ebb and flood currents from mixing oxygen downward into a deep inland basin, and the bottom water stagnates. In a salt wedge estuary a greater volume of water passes in and out in each tidal cycle. Salt water coming in with the flood tide is heavier than the fresh river water. It sinks to the bottom and, through several tidal cycles, mixes upward into the freshwater. The bottom water is replaced often enough that oxygen does not become depleted. —Artwork by Mountain Press

Fort Lee Historic Park

The site of Revolutionary War Fort Lee is in a commercial area a few hundred feet south of the George Washington Bridge. The fort was strategically atop the Palisades directly across the Hudson from Fort Washington. Fort Lee Historic Park is in a forested area between the historic location of the fort and the Palisades cliff. It overlooks the Hudson and has spectacular views of the bridge, the river, and New York City. The park includes reconstructions of gun batteries outlying the fort and a comprehensive museum documenting the military campaigns of 1776.

The British had occupied Boston since 1768, and George Washington concentrated his attention on the defense of New York City and the Hudson River Valley. The British plan was to split the colonies at the Hudson and bring a quick end to the insurrection. Over thirty-one thousand British troops, part of the largest force up to then ever dispatched from England, quickly forced the Continental Army from Long Island, Staten Island, New York City, and Fort Lee and into a bitter, wintertime retreat across New Jersey—the "times that try men's souls" of Patrick Henry. The retreat ended only with Washington's Christmas Day defeat of the Hessian troops at Trenton.

Crossing the Palisades

The Palisades cliffs, which border the Hudson from north of the Tappan Zee Bridge to Jersey City, are spectacular from the Hudson River but do not begin to suggest the volume of rock behind the cliff face. The cliff face is a cross section of a 600- to 1,000-foot-thick sill of diabase, an igneous rock intruded between layers of sandstone and shale. Reportedly gravitational attraction from the mass of rock immediately west of the George Washington Bridge caused enough concern during the bridge building that vertical lines were determined by nighttime observations to the North Star rather than by gravity.

West of the George Washington Bridge, I-95 enters a long road cut carrying the roadway from atop the Palisades down to the Hackensack Meadowlands. Do not stop to look at the rocks. If you do not get killed, you will likely get ticketed. Stopping to look at rocks is illegal on all New Jersey interstate highways and would be an exceptionally bad idea here. Accessible exposures of the Palisades rock are described in the Palisades Interstate Parkway road guide in this chapter.

In geologic terms, the Palisades is a cuesta, a ridge with a steep slope on one side and a gentler slope on the opposite side. Cuestas usually form by erosion above and below a layer of hard rock. The gentle slope (the dip slope) results from the stripping back of overlying softer rock. The steep slope (the escarpment) forms by undermining of the harder layer. Most of the road cut is in diabase, not layered sedimentary rock, and the dip is not easily seen. The only place where layering is at all visible is just west of the Jones Road bridge, where sedimentary rock above the diabase is exposed at the top of the road cut on the south side of the highway. The diabase magma was intruded at a temperature of about 2,200 degrees Fahrenheit between sediment layers about 2 miles below the surface. It could not cool quickly in the atmosphere like a lava flow does after it reaches the surface. Instead, it stayed baking hot for thousands of years. At some places, the Stockton sandstone was in contact with the magma. The sandstone was little affected by the heating and remained a sedimentary rock. At other places, as at Jones Road, the clay-rich Lockatong Formation was in contact with the magma. The clay, in contrast to the sandstone, was baked to a contact metamorphic rock, hornfels, similar to the way soft clay is baked to hard pottery in a kiln. Contact metamorphism affects rocks up to 1,000 feet above and below the Palisades, but the degree of baking decreases with distance. Close to the diabase, the hornfels visible from the road is baked about as hard as the diabase. Farther away it is softer and the rock has been stripped away by erosion.

Farther down the dip slope, past the road cut, grassy embankments mostly covered by a sound barrier along the highway were cut into a till ramp plastered along the base of the Palisades by glacial ice moving southeastward up and across the Palisades. The till is up to 75 feet thick along the base of the Palisades and thins toward the crest. As in many geologic situations, understanding the behavior of water is key to interpreting glacial erosion and deposition at the Palisades. The ice at the southern limit of glacial advance was in a relatively warm climate and was at its pressure melting point. It melted under pressure just as a knife pressed onto a warm ice cube melts its way downward. On the west side of the ridge, the ice was moving southeastward and was melting where

Bedding in hornfels overlying the Palisades diabase west of the arched Jones Road bridge. Arrow points to contact. —Photo by D. Harper

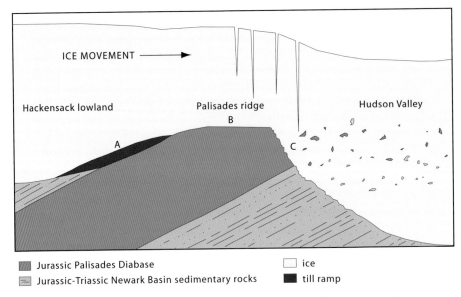

Jurassic Palisades Diabase
Jurassic-Triassic Newark Basin sedimentary rocks

□ ice
■ till ramp

Glacial sculpting of the Palisades ridge: A. Pressure melting of ice on the up-ice slope to the west released sediment embedded in the ice, building up a ramp of till. B. Scouring by sand and stones eroded the top of the ridge, flattening it and carving a roche moutonnée, an outcrop with a gently sloping up-ice side and a steep down-ice side. C. Under lowered pressure on the down-ice slope of the ridge, ice froze onto the face of the Palisades, the underlying sedimentary rocks, and in crevices between diabase columns. The rocks broke loose and were carried southeastward with the ice. —Artwork by D. Harper

it pressed against the ridge. On the east side of the ridge the ice, still moving southeastward, was moving away from the ridge and was not under pressure. Water from the melting ice at the west side of the ridge seeped along the base of the ice and through crevices in the rock, moving eastward to where pressure was lower. Under the lower pressure, it froze hard to the rock on the face of the Palisades and in the crevices between the columns. The till ramp was built up from sediment carried east by the ice and plastered onto the ridge, grain by grain, as the ice melted. The escarpment to the east was steepened by the breaking loose of columns as water froze and expanded in the crevices and by the transport of the broken rock eastward, frozen to the ice. The crest of the Palisades, standing high in the path of the ice, was scoured mostly bare of sediment and weathered rock. This pattern of glacial erosion is not unique to the Palisades. It is repeated throughout northern New Jersey. At the Palisades, the pattern is especially pronounced because it enhances the natural cuesta shape of the Palisades.

Glacial Lake Hackensack

West of the Palisades, I-80 dips below the level of Glacial Lake Hackensack between Leonia and Teaneck and again between Ridgefield Park and Hasbrouck Heights. The flat expanse of lake-bottom and estuarine sediment between Ridgefield Park and Hasbrouck Heights is one of the reasons Teterboro Airport was built here. The area between Leonia and Teaneck, home to Overpeck County Park and Overpeck Preserve, is more visually appealing than the flat industrial and commercial area around Teterboro, but the topography is further from its natural state. The parkland here was reclaimed in the early 2000s by landfill rehabilitation and placement of thousands of truckloads of additional fill. The "natural area" of Overpeck Preserve includes relatively natural tidal wetlands of the Hackensack Meadows along Overpeck Creek and also carefully designed woodlands, swamps, grasslands, open water, and vernal ponds. It has become a year-round home or seasonal refuge for a great variety of wildlife. In the wintertime, bald eagles on the lookout for a meal are commonly seen in trees overlooking open water.

Type Section of the Passaic Formation

From Hackensack to Paterson, the numerous outcrops of red sandstone and siltstone along the roadside are the type section of the Passaic Formation, deposited in the Newark Basin in Triassic to Jurassic time. To a geologist, geologic formations are the units of rock shown on geologic maps. A thick sequence of limestone beds lying between thick shale layers might, for example, be designated as a formation. Designating a geologic formation is somewhat similar to describing a new species in zoology. When a biologist describes a new species, the description must follow specific guidelines. Similarly, a North American geologist describing a new formation must follow the North American Stratigraphic Code. Just as a biologist will designate a type specimen that other biologists can use to help determine if a specimen belongs to the same species, a geologist will designate a type section, described foot-by-foot, for comparison with other rocks that may belong to the same or a different formation. This is not to say that every exposure of the formation must match the type. Returning to the biological comparison, there are many kinds of dogs, but they are all a single species. Similarly, if rocks that appear completely different share a common origin and history, it may be appropriate to include them in the same formation. The Passaic Formation was designated by Paul Olsen of Columbia University in 1980. Much of Olsen's foot by foot description can still be seen along the roadside, but the siltier beds are slowly crumbling to soil, and sound barrier construction has covered over other sections of the outcrop. Even bedrock outcrops are temporary, and a careful description of the type section was especially necessary for the Passaic Formation.

Orange Mountain

As you approach Paterson from the east, the long, low ridge visible ahead is the First Watchung Mountain, locally known as Orange Mountain. The ridge is made of Orange Mountain Basalt, one of three sequences of lava flows exposed in the Newark Basin. Near the NJ 19 interchange, the contact between dark gray basalt of the Orange Mountain Basalt and red sandstone of the Passaic Formation is visible from I-80, when the leaves are down, in an abandoned quarry on the mountainside above the highway. The quarry is now a police target range not open for visit. Most of the Passaic Formation, over 10,000 feet of its thickness, was deposited in the Triassic Period, but the uppermost beds, up to several tens of feet thick including those in the quarry, are Jurassic. There is no reason a geologic formation must be deposited in a single period of geologic time. If sedimentary conditions continue from one period into the next, the rocks will likely be similar, and as with the Passaic Formation, appropriately placed in a single formation. This is one of four places in the Newark Basin where the Passaic Formation spans the Triassic-Jurassic boundary, when the Triassic extinctions occurred.

Contact between red sandstone of the Passaic Formation and black basalt of the Orange Mountain Basalt from I-80. —Photo by Charles Merguerian

Curvicolumnar jointing in the Orange Mountain Basalt of the First Watchung Mountain along I-280. Since this photo was taken the exposure has been covered over with chain link safety netting. —Photo by D. Harper

I-80 crosses the top of Orange Mountain fairly high on the shoulder of the gap through which the Passaic River flows and has views across Paterson. Sandstone of the Passaic Formation and the overlying basalt are exposed in woods to the south. A few miles to the south of I-80, I-280 crosses the ridge of Orange Mountain Basalt by a series of road cuts, one with an outstanding exposure of the curved columns for which the Orange Mountain Basalt is known. This curvicolumnar jointing is further described in the section on Essex County's Eagle Rock Reservation in the road guide for I-78 in this chapter.

Great Falls of the Passaic

At the Great Falls of the Passaic River up to 2 billion gallons per day drop 77 feet. It is the second largest waterfall, after Niagara, east of the Mississippi and the site of the oldest planned industrial city in North America. Great Falls and nearby Little Falls were a destination for colonists and visiting Europeans long before the Revolutionary War. Great Falls is now more dramatic, but Little Falls (upstream from Great Falls), with a drop of 51 feet across two ledges of basalt, was at one time considered by many to be one of the scenic wonders of North America. The ledges at Little Falls were blasted away sometime after 1896 in

Great Falls of the Passaic River flows over Orange Mountain Basalt. —Photo by D. Harper

Great Falls retreats upstream over time as water erodes rock weakened by faulting. —Photo by D. Harper

Little Falls, before it was blasted in an unsuccessful attempt to reduce flooding upriver, flowed over the Preakness Basalt. The painting was done by William Frerichs in about 1875. —Courtesy of Ringwood Manor State Park

an unsuccessful effort to reduce flooding upriver. A large arched stone viaduct carrying the Morris Canal across the Passaic was demolished after the canal was abandoned in 1924.

Great Falls and Little Falls owe their existence to a realignment of the Passaic River during the Wisconsinan ice age. Prior to the Wisconsinan, the Passaic followed a shorter route across the Watchung ridges through a gap at Short Hills. At the height of the ice age, glaciers blocked the Short Hills Gap, ponding the river and forming Glacial Lake Passaic. When the ice melted back, the river could not return to its former course because the gap was filled over 250 feet deep with glacial debris. It now follows a circuitous path north between the Second and Third Watchung Mountains, then east to Little Falls and Great Falls. At Little Falls, the river crosses from west to east across the Preakness Basalt of the Second Watchung Mountain. At Great Falls it crosses the Orange Mountain Basalt of the First Watchung Mountain and is eroding back along a zone of closely spaced faults that have weakened the basalt.

Water mills for grinding wheat and corn, sawing timber, crushing ore, and pumping bellows for ironwork had long been in use in the colonies, but power on the scale possible from the falls was beyond comprehension until the 1790s. In 1791, with the inspiration of Alexander Hamilton and the assistance of New Jersey governor William Paterson, the Society for the Establishment of Useful Manufacturers (SUM), was organized to harness the Great Falls to run a manufacturing center for the new republic. In 1792, a small Dutch village near the base of the falls was renamed Paterson after Governor Paterson. Pierre L'Enfant, designer of the new capitol city at Washington, was commissioned to design the new industrial city. The city was not built as envisioned by L'Enfant, but his design for a three-tiered raceway brought water to a series of mills. SUM, instead of continuing to build the industries, operated more as a real estate brokerage and supplier of water power to entrepreneurs who designed their own factories. SUM extended the raceways in stages. Eventually the water ran sawmills, nail mills, spinning and weaving plants, machine and tool works, paper mills, chemical plants, locomotive factories, and the Colt revolver factory. In 1914, after steam replaced water power at most of the factories, the water was harnessed for one of the nation's first large hydroelectric plants. Flood damage closed the plant in 1969, but it was rebuilt and restored to operation in 1986. One of the four original turbines was left in its historic place. On March 30, 2009, President Obama designated the falls and surrounding area as Paterson Great Falls National Historical Park.

Morris Canal and Paterson Area Quarries

Being the lowest point along the Watchung ridges, Paterson not only became the course of the Passaic River when glacial ice melted; it is also became the route for the Morris Canal in the 1820s. The canal, which crossed New Jersey from Jersey City to Phillipsburg, approached Paterson from the south, along the base of the First Watchung ridge and directly below sandstone and basalt outcrops. Brownstone quarries in the sandstone and traprock quarries in the basalt loaded stone directly to canal boats. The quarries expanded quickly with the growing popularity of brownstone as a building material and a growing demand for crushed basalt for roads, railroad beds, and concrete. Rock quarries were a prominent part of the Paterson area for over 150 years. Even now the Prospect Park traprock quarry, just northwest of Paterson, is an important source of crushed stone, recycled asphalt, and soil that has been cleaned of contaminants.

The Paterson area has long been known for traprock minerals, including amethyst, calcite, prehnite, and zeolites. The zeolites are a group of aluminum silicate minerals formed by chemical reactions between volcanic rocks and alkaline groundwater. Traprock minerals are found in all the igneous rocks of the Newark Basin. One of the zeolites, analcime, is even common in some black lake sediments of the basin, but the black sedimentary rock seldom makes its way into mineral collections. The collectors instead concentrate on crystals deposited from groundwater moving through cracks, fissures, vesicles left by expanding steam bubbles, and spaces between the pillows formed when lava flows into water. The uppermost lava flow of at least two flows making up the Orange Mountain Basalt went into a lake in the Paterson area and has abundant pillows and thick, vesicle-filled zones left from when water quenched the magma before gas bubbles could rise to the top of the flow and escape. Its quarries have yielded a great number of museum-quality specimens. The lower flow, with thinner chilled zones and fewer pillow basalts, has fewer cavities large enough to grow attractive crystals and yields fewer specimens.

Pillow basalt, exposed in the New Street Quarry in Paterson, formed when lava flowed beneath the water of a Jurassic lake in the Newark Basin. —Photo by Jane Alexander of the College of Staten Island–City University of New York

Traprock minerals from the Paterson area: amethyst (top), stilbite (bottom left), and prehnite (bottom right).
—Amethyst and prehnite photos by D. Harper; stilbite by John Dooley

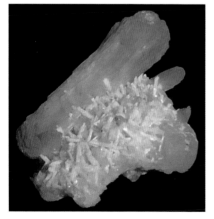

Great Piece and Troy Meadows

Between Little Falls and Whippany, I-80 crosses the bed of extinct Glacial Lake Passaic. Near the village of Pine Brook, the route crosses Hook Mountain, a ridge of volcanic rock known elsewhere along its length as the Third Watchung Mountain, Long Hill, and Riker Hill. At the time Glacial Lake Passaic was full, the ridge was a 50-mile-long line of skinny islands snaking from the north end of the lake almost to the outlet stream at Moggy Hollow. Hook Mountain still stands high and dry today. At lower elevations the road was built across swampland and marshes on lake-bottom and meltwater sediments: Great Piece Meadows east of Hook Mountain and Troy Meadows to the west. Clay from the lake bed was dug at Mountain View and Whippany for making bricks.

I-95/I-295
Trenton Beltway
16 miles

Scudders Falls and Washington's Crossing

The Scudders Falls Bridge crosses, in quick succession, the Pennsylvania Canal, built in the mid-1820s, the Delaware River with Scudders Falls visible just upstream, a nineteenth-century millrace, and the Delaware and Raritan Canal, opened in the 1830s. Both the Pennsylvania and Delaware and Raritan Canals are preserved as parkland. The millrace, which has been mostly filled and developed, ran 7 miles from the upstream end of Scudders Falls to water-powered factories in Trenton. The remaining few hundred feet of the millrace bypasses Scudders Falls and pours several feet down through a sluiceway usually full through the summer with kayakers and kids.

Like other Delaware River falls, Scudders Falls is more of a rapids. Along some rivers, rapids form where tributaries bring in gravel and boulders faster than they can be carried away. Along the Delaware most of the tributaries are fairly small and do not carry even close to enough boulders to choke the river. Instead, rapids form where layers of relatively hard rock outcrop beneath the riverbed. For stretches of up to several miles between rapids, the Delaware is wider, calmer, and deep enough for boats.

Among the rapids in the few miles upstream from the head of tide at Trenton, Scudders Falls is shorter and less chaotic than Trenton Falls, just west of downtown Trenton, or Wells Falls, at the floor of a steep-walled gap just below Lambertville, New Jersey, and New Hope, Pennsylvania. This is not surprising in that Scudders Falls is formed by only moderately hard sedimentary rock of the Lockatong Formation. Trenton Falls and Wells Falls are formed by more durable rock. Trenton Falls flows over a narrow belt of igneous and metamorphic rock, the Trenton Prong, composed of gneiss, schist, and quartzite. Wells Falls flows over diabase of the Lambertville Sill. What is more surprising at first glance is the absence of rapids between the diabase outcrops of Baldpate

Mountain in New Jersey and Jericho Mountain across the river in Pennsylvania. There are no rapids here because the river has cut entirely through the diabase and runs on the underlying, softer sedimentary rock.

Before the construction of bridges in the early to mid-nineteenth century, there were ferries across slackwater reaches every few miles. Even with numerous ferries, however, boats were insufficient for the traffic. Bridges were built because of the long waiting times for ferries, not because the ferries were too expensive.

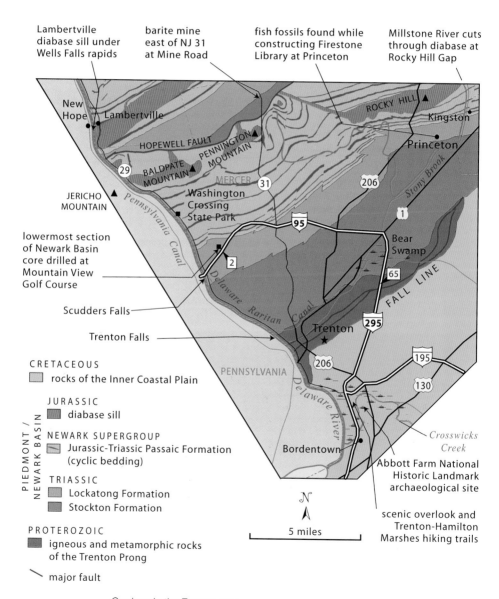

Lambertville diabase sill under Wells Falls rapids

barite mine east of NJ 31 at Mine Road

fish fossils found while constructing Firestone Library at Princeton

Millstone River cuts through diabase at Rocky Hill Gap

lowermost section of Newark Basin core drilled at Mountain View Golf Course

Scudders Falls

Trenton Falls

CRETACEOUS
rocks of the Inner Coastal Plain

JURASSIC
diabase sill

NEWARK SUPERGROUP
Jurassic-Triassic Passaic Formation (cyclic bedding)

TRIASSIC
Lockatong Formation
Stockton Formation

PROTEROZOIC
igneous and metamorphic rocks of the Trenton Prong

major fault

PIEDMONT / NEWARK BASIN

5 miles

Geology in the Trenton area. —Compiled from the USGS's Preliminary Integrated Geologic Map Database for the United States, 2006

At the time of the Revolutionary War, there were two ferries in the slack water reach upstream from Scudders Falls. Scouts preceding Washington in his retreat from New York reported that the little-used crossings were unwatched, and they were chosen for Washington's Christmas Eve 1776 return across the Delaware for his surprise attack and victory over the Hessian garrison at Trenton. Washington had most of the boats up and down the Delaware burned to stop the British advance. Some he kept to allow his army to escape. Others were hidden behind islands on the Pennsylvania side for the return across the Delaware.

Triassic Rocks along the Delaware

In the 2 miles after I-95 crosses the Delaware, it climbs about 200 feet. Toward the top of the climb prominently layered sedimentary rock is exposed along both sides of the road. Only a few tens of feet of layering are exposed here, but the beds are part of a 20,000-foot-thick sequence of sedimentary rock deposited during downdropping of the Newark Basin. Most of the sequence is exposed along the Delaware River bluffs between Trenton and Riegelsville, 36 miles up the river. Probably the most visited of the Delaware River exposures is Pebble Bluffs, upstream from Milford along Spring Garden Road. There, close to the border fault along the northern edge of the basin, River Road and a railroad thread between the rock and the river. The road squeezes to a single lane close by cliffs of pebble and boulder conglomerate. Fortunately, there are pulloffs near the most visited cliffs.

Conglomerate and sandstone in the bluffs are interbedded with shale in a series of alluvial fans built outward from canyons issuing from highlands into the Newark Basin. They were much like the alluvial fans building today along

Lockatong Formation along I-95 at the top of Delaware River bluffs. This same relatively erosion-resistant horizon within the Lockatong is responsible for Scudders Falls on the Delaware River.
—Photo by D. Harper

Interbedded sandstone and conglomerate of the Passaic Formation at Pebble Bluffs. —Photo by D. Harper

the downdropped side of faults in the Basin and Range Province of the western United States, even having been deposited in a similar arid to semiarid climate. For some conglomerate bodies, convex upward profiles, poorly developed internal bedding, poor sorting, and mixtures of angular rocks with well-rounded rocks suggest deposition by debris flows, similar to the thick flows of sand, mud, and rock that move downslope onto alluvial fans in today's Basin and Range. Also similar to today's debris flows, desert plants took hold and caliche soil developed on the debris. The roots have long since decayed, but some have been replaced by caliche infillings. Interlayered with the debris flows are braided stream deposits. In contrast to the chaotic debris flows, the stream deposits are clearly layered, consist predominantly of well-sorted, crossbedded sand and gravel, and have the convex bottoms typical of stream channels rather than the convex tops typical of debris flows. Occasionally, as in today's Basin and Range, wave-rippled sands and mudstones cut by desiccation cracks record moister times when lakes and their surrounding mudflats rose high enough to cover the feet of the alluvial fans. One perplexing aspect is the preponderance of well-rounded, rather than angular, rocks in most of the conglomerates, as though they had been carried for some distance from the edge of the basin to where they are now found. A series of northeast-southwest-trending normal faults west of the border fault may explain the rounded rocks. If these faults were active at the time the Pebble Bluffs conglomerates were being deposited, the basin would have extended farther to the west than it does now, and the rocks would have had ample opportunity to become rounded. Sediments at the western edge of the basin, west of the main border fault, were downdropped less than those to the east and presumably have eroded away.

Arsenic and Radon in the Passaic Formation

We are conditioned to think of environmental problems as the result of human activity, but many potentially hazardous environmental conditions are the result of natural conditions, sometimes the result of conditions tens or hundreds of million years ago. Arsenic and radon hazards from Newark Basin rocks today are the result of deposition in oxygen-poor lake-bottom sediments 225 million years ago. Arsenic is a fairly common natural contaminant in groundwater in wells drilled into gray and black rock in the Trenton area of the Newark Basin. In one study of wells where arsenic was to be expected, it was found at greater than 5 parts per billion, a proposed safe drinking water standard, in twenty-three out of seventy-two wells. The arsenic is there today because it is relatively soluble in oxidizing environments, like the water in streams flowing to the Triassic lakes, and much less soluble in reducing environments, like the mud in the bottoms of those lakes. Arsenic was carried into the lakes a small amount at a time, then built up in the oxygen-poor lake sediments where it remains today.

Radon in wells is mostly from the radioactive decay of uranium. Like arsenic, a small amount of uranium was carried by the Triassic streams and ended up in the lakes. Uranium is adsorbed onto organic matter. Organic matter in the Triassic lakes and the uranium adsorbed onto it settled downward into the oxygen-poor bottom waters and were buried. Like the arsenic, the uranium is still in the rocks today. Fortunately, remediation of indoor radon gas is inexpensive and effective.

Soil in Hopewell

Windblown sediment, much of it from the dry, windy conditions during the Wisconsinan ice age, is common in New Jersey soils but can be difficult to recognize because it may resemble to the underlying bedrock. To the north of Trenton, however, silt blown eastward from the Delaware floodplain is clearly evident because it is yellowish brown, whereas the rock beneath is red. Further,

Windblown silt blown from the Delaware River floodplain overlying red shale weathered to soil, Hopewell Township, Mercer County. —Photo by D. Harper

it is composed of minerals more like those of the Delaware floodplain than the underlying red shale, and the size of the grains is largest close to the river and gradually becomes smaller to the east.

Barite Mine

About 5 miles north of I-95, NJ 31 crosses Mine Road, which leads to a barite (barium sulfate) mine downhill and on the right, just before a railroad bridge. At one time the mine had four or five shafts and went to a depth of 40 feet. By the late 1860s over 2,000 tons of barite had been mined and several tons more were being dug each year using a steam engine and six laborers. As of the 1870 Annual Report of the State Geologist, however, the mine was reported closed and the owner had "left for parts unknown." The shafts have since collapsed, and all that remains today are tailings piles and pieces of barite.

Most barite now mined is used in oil-well drilling muds. Barite is half again as heavy as most other minerals and is crushed and mixed into a mud that is heavier than rock. The mud is pumped down wells, where the weight keeps underground pressure from blowing drilling mud, water, and oil out the top as a gusher. The New Jersey barite mines were active long before barite was used in oil field drilling. Instead, the barite was used as a durable white pigment in paint.

Barite from Hopewell Township. The gray stringers in the barite mass are quartz. — Photo by D. Harper

Rocky Hill and Sourland Mountain

Diabase, the same hard igneous rock that forms the Palisades Sill in northeastern New Jersey, forms ridges north of Trenton. The magma intruded between layers in the sedimentary rock in Jurassic time. It forms ridges now because it is harder than the encasing sedimentary rock. The diabase forms a broken ridge from Rocky Hill west to Pennington Mountain and Baldpate Mountain, overlooking the Delaware River. Another ridge, roughly parallel to Rocky Hill but about 5 miles to the northwest, begins at Sourland Mountain and extends to Lambertville, forming the rapids at Wells Falls. The two parallel diabase ridges are not the result of the magma splitting into two layers as it moved through the Earth.

Rather a single magma layer was offset by the Flemington and Hopewell Faults and then exposed as two linear ridges when the land surface wore down.

Roaring Brook is a particularly interesting feature of Sourland Mountain. Under the permafrost conditions of the ice age, the soil moved downslope and the bare rock was broken into boulders. The stream is invisible, beneath the boulders, but can be heard roaring after heavy rains.

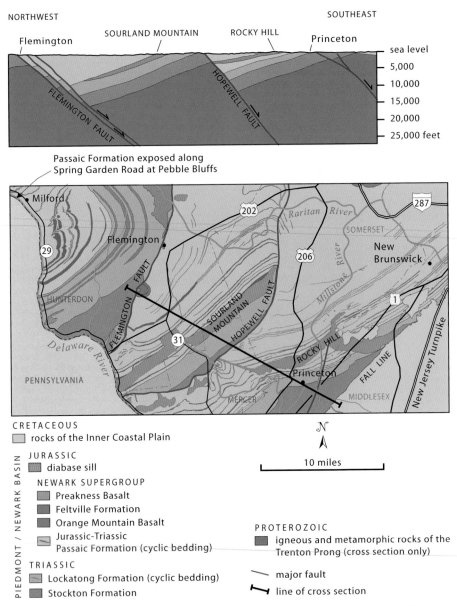

Formations offset by the Hopewell Fault. Erosion has exposed the Stockton, Lockatong, and Passaic Formations and diabase intruding the sedimentary rocks along two parallel belts. —Modified from Drake and others, 1996

Millstone River and a Drainage Divide

Just north of where I-95 becomes I-295 (at the junction with US 1), there is a very subtle drainage divide between the Delaware River basin and the Raritan River basin. The Delaware and Raritan Canal, crossed at the junction, takes advantage of this divide. The Delaware River once flowed north through this low spot. The Millstone River is at the center of this drainage instability in this part of New Jersey. Scott Stanford of the New Jersey Geological Survey has demonstrated that a barbed turn of Stony Brook, which flows into the Millstone River, is related to tilting of the land surface during the pre-Illinoian glaciation. At the onset of the glaciation, the area was on the floodplain of the Pensauken

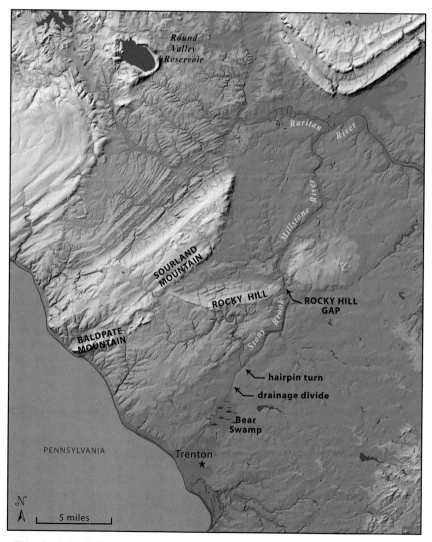

This shaded relief image shows the subtle divide between the Raritan and Delaware watersheds. The Delaware and Raritan Canal cuts through the divide between the hairpin turn on Stony Brook and Bear Swamp. —Image from EROS Data Center, U.S. Geological Survey

River. The Millstone was a tributary of this south-flowing river. By the end of the glaciation, the Pensauken River had been diverted eastward through the New York City area and the Millstone River had established its present course northward across the Pensauken floodplain through the Rocky Hill Gap to the Raritan River. Likely the Millstone shifted initially because the weight of glacial ice tilted the crust enough that the slope of the Pensauken floodplain changed from southward to northward causing the river to reverse direction. By the time the weight of the glaciers lifted, the Millstone had deepened its valley to the Raritan enough that its slope was northward even after postglacial rebound.

Drainage shifted again, this time only partially and temporarily, at some time in the Wisconsinan ice age when sand and gravel up to 50 feet thick were deposited on the Delaware River floodplain. From the glaciers, the sand and gravel were carried downriver between the rock walls of the narrow Delaware Valley upstream from Trenton and, when they reached the wider valley at Trenton, spread outward and built upward. This raised the floodplain to the elevation of the Millstone River, and at least some Delaware River water spilled across into the Millstone River, cutting a channel between the Delaware and the Millstone. Downcutting along the main stem of the Delaware eventually recaptured the drainage, which had gone to the Raritan, but the abandoned channel between the Delaware and the Millstone still exists. Were it not for an embankment that formerly carried Province Line Road across the divide, high water in the Millstone could overtop the low divide and send water southward to Delaware Bay instead of northward to Raritan Bay.

As it is, the nineteenth-century builders of the Delaware and Raritan Canal took advantage of the abandoned channel, routing the canal through the marshy lowland, and reestablished flow from the Delaware watershed to the Raritan watershed. The canal is now used to carry drinking water by gravity from an elevation of 67 feet at Bulls Island on the Delaware across the divide at the Millstone at 56 feet, and almost to sea level at New Brunswick.

Bear Swamp is a good example of this drainage uncertainty. The open area of marsh grass on the southbound side of I-295 just north of Sloan Avenue (exit 65) is a small part of Bear Swamp. Sensitivity of drainage to even minor changes is illustrated by Bear Swamp and Upper Bear Swamp, to the north of Bear Swamp. Both swamps drain northward from their northern ends and southward from their southern ends. Tilting of the Earth's crust even slightly to the north or slight downcutting by the streams to the north would send more water northward. Slight tilting or downcutting to the south would send more water southward.

Delaware and Raritan Canal

The Delaware River scenic overlook along I-295 just south of Trenton, in addition to its view across the Delaware, leads to the head of the Delaware and Raritan Canal and to hiking trails in the Trenton-Hamilton Marsh.

Trenton is one of the East Coast fall line cities established where rivers pass from rock onto sand and clay formations of the Coastal Plain. Many cities grew where ships first encountered rapids and had to be unloaded. This is also where water power was available for mills and often where navigation canals, including the Delaware and Raritan Canal, began. The canal locations were determined by engineering considerations, and for the Delaware and Raritan Canal the optimum location, aside from its being in the mosquito-ridden Trenton-Hamilton Marsh, was at the mouth of Crosswicks Creek. The head of the canal is across the pedestrian bridge from the river and southward along the trail through the woods. The canal ran from here through the Trenton-Hamilton Marsh to Trenton. The remains of abandoned locks, loading facilities, and a canal boat at Crosswicks Creek are best seen at low tide.

The Delaware and Raritan Canal is somewhat unusual in that it did not depend on a lake to supply water to run its locks. Most canals have lakes at their highest points. The Morris Canal, for example, from Jersey City to Phillipsburg, depended mostly on water from Lakes Hopatcong and Musconetcong high up in the New Jersey Highlands. Water ran eastward and westward from water control structures on Lake Musconetcong through locks and inclined planes toward the Delaware River at Phillipsburg and tidewater at Newark. Water for the Delaware and Raritan Canal, by contrast, came down a feeder canal that carried water from upstream on the Delaware. The water to run the canal was diverted from the Delaware at Bulls Island, 20 miles upriver from where it joined the main canal at Trenton. From Trenton the water ran downslope by gravity to locks—southward to the head of the canal at Crosswicks Creek and northeastward through locks to sea level at New Brunswick.

The canal was planned primarily for shipping between Philadelphia and New York, but unforeseen by its builders the feeder canal, rather than the section headed toward Bordentown and Philadelphia, became the primary freight route. Brownstone from quarries along the canal, and especially coal from Pennsylvania's anthracite fields, made this the one of world's most profitable canals through the mid-1800s. The canal was finally abandoned for shipping in 1932 but has remained an important water supply conduit, with some locks replaced by weirs and some removed, carrying Delaware River water from Bulls Island to central New Jersey drinking water intakes. Again, the feeder canal was vital. The branch of the canal from Trenton to Bordentown is abandoned and largely filled or, through the Trenton-Hamilton Marsh, empty of water. The water comes down the feeder canal to its junction with the main canal at Trenton. All but a short section of the water supply route, through a conduit in Trenton, is a state park heavily used for canoeing, hiking, biking, and cross-country skiing.

Abbott Farm National Historic Landmark

Prior to 1872, there was general agreement that Indians were relatively recent immigrants from Europe or Asia, having arrived at most a few thousand years before the present. In 1872, however, Charles Conrad Abbott noted similarities between Paleolithic tools from Europe and implements from gravel terraces above the Trenton-Hamilton Marsh. Abbott became convinced that the gravels dated from the ice age and that the implements proved that North America had been inhabited for far longer than was previously believed. In 1881, he presented a report that polarized the American archaeological and geological communities, and over the next several years the debate became increasingly rancorous.

Harpoon point and hammer- head from the Abbott site.
—N.J. State Museum specimens; photos by D. Harper

Numerous investigations confirmed the Abbott farm as one of the richest archaeological sites in eastern North America. Convincing proof that the site was inhabited in the ice age, however, was not found, and as of an 1897 confer- ence, most had concluded that the implements were made long after the ice age. At his death in 1919, Abbott was one of the few firm believers that the Trenton finds proved that North America was inhabited in the ice age.

The site has been investigated repeatedly since then, most recently in the 1980s preliminary to the construction of I-195 and I-295 across the terraces and through the marshes. The site is ideal for permanent or seasonal living in that rich farmlands are above the mosquito-infested marsh but close enough to the wetlands and Delaware River to allow harvesting of beavers, muskrats, wild rice, edible roots, resident fish, and migratory shad and eels. The Abbott Farm is now a national historic landmark recognized for repeated Indian habitation from over 8,000 years ago into the colonial period.

Among anthropologists, however, the Abbott Farm remains remembered, even now, as the place that inspired the brave act of suggesting that there were people in North America in the ice age. In the words of Frank Roberts Jr., of the Smithsonian Institution, in 1940, "The question of early man in America had become virtually taboo, and no anthropologist, or for that matter geologist or paleontologist, desirous of a successful career would tempt the fate of ostracism by intimating that he had discovered indications of a respectable antiquity for the Indian." A respectable antiquity was demonstrated in 1926 when Folsom points were found together with extinct mammals in New Mexico.

Sedimentation in the Trenton-Hamilton Marsh

Canoeists on the Trenton-Hamilton Marsh sometimes notice the buried remains of roads below high tide along the eroding banks of tidal creeks. Their first thought might be that the roads sank of their own weight or that the marshy sediment has compacted. However, the roads stayed where they were built. The high tide level has gone up and sediment has built the surface of the marsh to the new high tide level. The tide range changed in the 1930s when the Army Corps of Engineers dredged a channel up to 40 feet deep and 300 to 400 feet wide almost to Trenton. Much more water was able to flow through the deep channel than had been able to flow up and down the shallow, gravelly natural channel, and the tide range increased. High tide was higher, and the marsh built up and over the roads. This was possible because the Trenton-Hamilton Marsh has substantial amounts of sediment coming in from the Delaware River and Crosswicks Creek. While the wetlands here have built up, other Delaware River marshes with less sediment coming in have not yet built up in response to the increased tidal range and remain submerged at high tide.

I-287
New York Border—Perth Amboy
70 miles

Interstate I-287 follows the Ramapo Fault, the western edge of the Newark Basin between the New York border and Bernardsville. The highway wanders in and out of the Highlands, but I've put it in the Newark Basin chapter because more of the geology is related to the basin. Interstate 287 crosses into New Jersey after its junction with the New York State Thruway at a steep-walled gap through Proterozoic rocks of New York's Hudson Highlands. Once in New Jersey, the road passes by road cuts in gneiss for a mile or so, then crosses the Ramapo Fault and, at a pronounced lowering of the slope to the west, enters the Newark Basin. The Ramapo River follows the fault southwest to Pompton Lakes, but I-287 curves south for 9 miles around Campgaw Mountain, an upland formed of the Preakness Basalt of Jurassic age. Where I-287 crosses the Ramapo River between exits 58 and 57, it also crosses the Ramapo Fault again and climbs into the Highlands. At exit 57, Skyline Drive heads north into the Ramapo Mountains, home to the Ringwood Mining District, where magnetite was mined. See the road guide for NJ 23 in the Highlands and Valley and Ridge chapter for a discussion of the mining.

Where I-287 is slightly west of the edge of the fault scarp, the highway is bordered by impressive road cuts, mostly in rocks that began as volcanic and sedimentary rocks from the back-arc basin adjacent to the Losee island arc. They were metamorphosed to gneiss under high temperature and pressure during

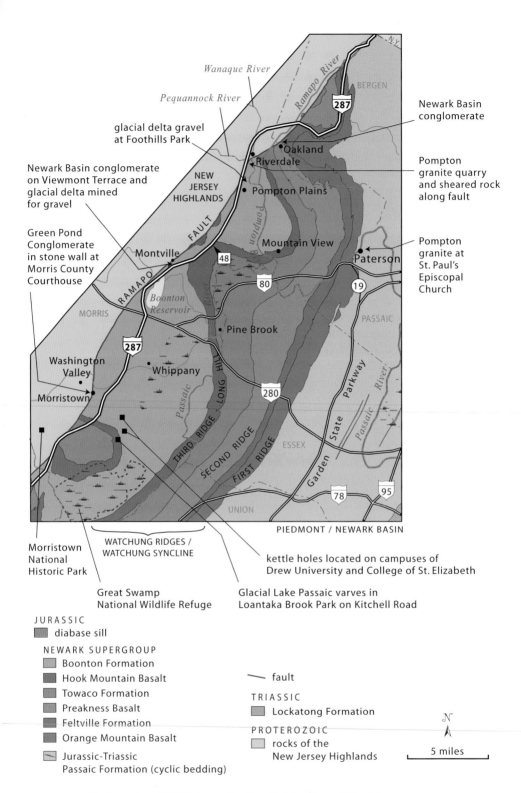

Newark Basin conglomerate

Pompton granite quarry and sheared rock along fault

Pompton granite at St. Paul's Episcopal Church

glacial delta gravel at Foothills Park

Newark Basin conglomerate on Viewmont Terrace and glacial delta mined for gravel

Green Pond Conglomerate in stone wall at Morris County Courthouse

Wanaque River

Pequannock River

Ramapo River

BERGEN

287

Oakland

Riverdale

NEW JERSEY HIGHLANDS

Pompton Plains

Mountain View

Montville

48

Boonton Reservoir

MORRIS

80

Pine Brook

PASSAIC

Paterson

19

287

Washington Valley

Whippany

Morristown

280

Garden State Parkway

Passaic River

ESSEX

THIRD RIDGE – LONG HILL

SECOND RIDGE

FIRST RIDGE

78   **95**

UNION

PIEDMONT / NEWARK BASIN

Morristown National Historic Park

WATCHUNG RIDGES / WATCHUNG SYNCLINE

Great Swamp National Wildlife Refuge

Glacial Lake Passaic varves in Loantaka Brook Park on Kitchell Road

kettle holes located on campuses of Drew University and College of St. Elizabeth

RAMAPO FAULT

JURASSIC
diabase sill

NEWARK SUPERGROUP
Boonton Formation
Hook Mountain Basalt
Towaco Formation
Preakness Basalt
Feltville Formation
Orange Mountain Basalt
Jurassic-Triassic
Passaic Formation (cyclic bedding)

— fault

TRIASSIC
Lockatong Formation

PROTEROZOIC
rocks of the New Jersey Highlands

N

5 miles

Geology along I-287 between the New York border and Morristown.
—Compiled from the USGS's Preliminary Integrated Geologic Map Database for the United States, 2006

the Ottawan Orogeny. Layering is easily visible along many road cuts. Much of the layering is inherited from the original layering of igneous and sedimentary rock. Some is from shearing during the Ottawan Orogeny between 1,045 and 1,024 million years ago.

Just north of Riverdale, I-287 passes near the large quarries where the Pompton Pink Granite was quarried. The Pompton Pink Granite was a solid mass of uniform rock in the quarries but toward the margin of the intrusion was forced *lit-par-lit* (French for "bed by bed") between layers of the gneiss. The intruded granite is completely undeformed, confirming that it intruded between the layers of gneiss after the orogeny, probably between 1,020 and 980 million years ago.

The Pompton Pink Granite of the Riverdale quarries was especially prized because of its pink and green colors and its coarse grain size. It was shipped as far as Washington, DC, where it was used at the south entrance of the Smithsonian Institution. Another notable building, St. Paul's Episcopal Church in Paterson, combines rough-hewn and polished Pompton Pink Granite on the

Pompton Pink Granite injected lit-par-lit between layers of older, darker-colored gneiss at Riverdale. The gneiss is more than 100 million years older than the granite. —Photo by Richard Volkert, N.J. Geological Survey

exterior and, in the interior, a pulpit of the polished granite. The granite was quarried for building stone for nearly a century from a body of rock barely a half mile in area. The rock is now mostly quarried out, but small remnants are visible along NJ 23 and I-287 just north of their intersection.

Other stretches of I-287 are right at the edge of the scarp, where a highway would mar the view from the valley below. These sections are lined with long, high walls of rocks in wire cages. The cages of rocks are known as gabions, from the Italian *gabbione*, for "big cage." The view from the valley is protected, but the view from the roadway, a magnificent panorama across the lowland once filled by Glacial Lake Passaic, then across the Watchungs to New York, is completely obscured.

Newark Basin Conglomerates along the Ramapo Fault

Along most of the erosional scarp along the Ramapo Fault, there are conglomerates deposited by streams and mudflows flowing from the Highlands toward the Newark Basin. Contrasting conglomerate outcrops can be seen in Oakland uphill from US 202 on Post Road and near the corner of River Road and Viewmont Terrace in Montville. The kinds of pebbles and boulders in the conglomerates vary along the length of the border fault depending on the kind of rock in the adjacent Highlands. In some areas the pebbles are largely quartzite, dolomitic limestone, and slate eroded from Paleozoic rocks. In other places a substantial proportion of the rocks are Proterozoic granite and gneiss. The Oakland and Montville outcrops are fairly close by one another, and you would

Conglomerate of the Towaco Formation east of Ramapo Fault at Oakland. None of the pieces here are Proterozoic rock because the Proterozoic rocks of the Highlands still lay beneath Paleozoic sedimentary rocks when these pieces eroded. —Photo by D. Harper

*By the time this conglomerate of the Boonton Formation at Montville was depos-
ited, the Proterozoic gneiss of the New Jersey Highlands had been unroofed.
Many fragments in this exposure are Proterozoic rock.* —Photo by D. Harper

expect the pebbles to be similar, but the Oakland pebbles are predominantly
quartzite, dolomitic limestone, and basalt from the recently erupted flows of
the First and Second Watchung Mountains. Granite and gneiss are entirely
absent. At Montville granite and gneiss abound. In this case, the difference
between the conglomerates has to do with their ages rather than their locations. The conglomerate at Oakland is in the Towaco Formation. When these
conglomerates were deposited, the highland area to the west was covered with
by Paleozoic sedimentary rocks. Erosion had not yet unroofed the Proterozoic
rocks of the New Jersey Highlands. The conglomerate at Montville is in the
Boonton Formation, younger than the Towaco conglomerate. The Proterozoic
rock had been unroofed in the intervening time and was being actively eroded
when the Montville conglomerate was being deposited.

Close by the Montville exposure, a short walk along a municipally owned
drainageway opposite Dahl Road will bring you to conglomerate spectacularly
scoured by ice in some places and fluted and potholed by glacial meltwater
trapped between the ice and the rock in other places. The land was left undeveloped in this heavily residential area in part to preserve the glacial features.
When the edge of the ice stood near here, meltwater flowed beneath the ice,
leaving an esker north of the outcrops near Dahl Road, past the water-scoured
outcrop, and southward from under the ice onto a delta at Montville.

Conglomerate near Dahl Road, Montville, scoured by sand and stones embedded in glacial ice. The ice was moving from right to left. —Photo by D. Harper

Conglomerate near Dahl Road, Montville, scoured by sand and stones in meltwater flowing between the bedrock and the glacier. —Photo by D. Harper

Foothills Park, Pequannock Township

About a half mile south of Riverdale, I-287 passes just west of Foothills Park, near the southern end of West Parkway in Pequannock Township. The park is in a pit left from gravel mining. Gravel was dug down to the bedrock exposed behind the ball fields. The gravel was part of a delta built along the western shore of Glacial Lake Passaic. Meltwater discharging between the ice and the rock wall of the Highlands built the delta along the west shore of the lake. The delta at Foothills Park was only partially excavated. The steep slope past the police target range is deltaic sand and gravel built to the water level of Glacial Lake Passaic. Everything below the top of the slope was underwater.

The rock knoll toward the back of the park is composed of Proterozoic gneiss and is a good example of a roche moutonnée, smoothed and polished on the side facing northward into the moving glacier and plucked to a more ragged surface down-ice to the south where pieces of rock became frozen to the bottom of the glacier and were pulled loose. The polishing was from fine sand, silt, and clay embedded in the base of the glacier. Striations and grooves cut into the polished surface by larger pieces of rock show the direction the ice was moving. The polish is preserved here only because the rock was covered by gravel for the 18,000 or so years since the glaciers melted back. Similar polishing and striation were widespread on Proterozoic rocks of the Highlands at the end of the ice age but have weathered away where exposed to the elements.

The Proterozoic bedrock of the Highlands here is within the Ramapo fault zone, along which rocks of the Newark Basin dropped down relative to rocks of the Highlands. The gneiss is composed of three kinds of rock that are

Gneiss at Foothills Park subjected to multiple episodes of ductile deformation, at least one episode of brittle fracturing, and grooving and polishing by glaciers. The glacier shaped the rock into a roche moutonnée form, smoothed to the right beneath the advancing ice, and plucked to a jagged edge to the left where blocks of rock were pulled loose from the down-ice face. —Photo by Michael Flite

Proterozoic gneiss with mostly smooth folding without breaks from ductile deformation. The sharp break and offset of the thin white bed near the lower right corner of the photo is from brittle deformation. —Photo by Michael Flite

interlayered and intricately folded, showing multiple episodes of deformation. The white, tan, and light green layers are quartz-plagioclase gneiss, the dark gray layers are amphibolite, and the pink layers are granite gneiss. Tracing even a single band of rock across the outcrop is difficult, but with hours of work and considerable argumentative hashing out, geologists looking at the patterns of deformation of the layers have been able to separate out the effects of several distinct events in which this outcrop was deformed. The earliest deformation, from a time of shear when the rock was deeply buried and heated, was ductile shearing. This was followed by ductile folding of the shear planes after they were formed, then by ductile shearing of both the older shear planes and the folds, then finally by brittle fracturing along numerous small faults. The repeated episodes of ductile deformation must have taken place at a temperature and pressure well above anything that would have been expected along the Ramapo Fault when the floor of the Newark Basin was dropping downward about 200 million years ago. The Ramapo Fault is thought to be much older, having been active through several intervals previous to the downdropping of the basin. The fault zone may have been active episodically since the Ottawan Orogeny over 1,000 million years ago. Renewed stress in the Earth's crust will often cause reactivation of faults that have long been dormant.

Montville Delta

Glacial Lake Passaic filled the lowlands east of I-287 from Riverdale to south of Morristown. At Montville, a delta formed where a river entered the lake. The Montville delta was once large with a well-developed, flat top but has been mostly mined for gravel. Just north of Montville, near milepost 48, I-287 begins a descent from the New Jersey Highlands into the Newark Basin. From here southward for about 25 miles, almost to Bedminster, I-287 is within the lowland once occupied by Glacial Lake Passaic.

Jersey City Reservoir and Fossil Fish

Just south of Boonton, I-287 passes west of Boonton Reservoir, built as a water supply for Jersey City in the early 1900s. Long before the reservoir was constructed, quarries in the area now covered by water were known for their fish fossils. During construction of the reservoir, hundreds of fossil fish were found in a single layer of dark-colored shale near the spillway. A similar accumulation, hundreds of fish fossils on a single bedding plane, was found in the 1940s at Princeton University during construction at the Firestone Library. The fish lived toward the top of deepwater lakes in the newly forming rift basin. Because the lakes were in a year-round warm climate and because the water was

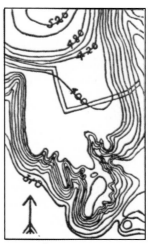

1,000 feet

Contour lines on this 1902 map show the flat surface and steep sides of the Montville delta. Lake Valhalla is just off the upper left side of this map. —Salisbury, 1902

Fossil fish from a quarry at the site of the Boonton Reservoir.
—Photo courtesy of N.J. Geological Survey

most of the time heavy with dissolved solids, there was no turnover of water similar to the seasonal mixing that carries oxygen downward in New Jersey's lakes today, and no way to replenish oxygen in bottom waters. Fish could live only toward the top where waves mixed oxygen downward. After periodic fish kills from natural causes, dead fish would settle onto the bottom. Decay was so slow in the oxygen-poor bottom water that many fish were fossilized intact.

Green Pond Conglomerate Erratics

The Green Pond Conglomerate is an attractive red quartzite that forms a high steep ridge, Green Pond Mountain, in the Highlands west of Montville. Although it is in the Highlands, the conglomerate is of Paleozoic age and is related to rocks of the Valley and Ridge. Millions of boulders of Green Pond Conglomerate were carried southeastward from Green Pond Mountain by glaciers during the ice age and can be found as far south as the terminal moraine at Perth Amboy. Boulders of Green Pond Conglomerate around Montville, Boonton, and Morristown were gathered, shaped, and used for building stone walls, houses, and even churches.

Stone wall at the Morris County Courthouse made from boulders of Green Pond Conglomerate. —Photo by Richard Volkert, N.J. Geological Survey

Lake Passaic Varves

Loantaka Brook Park, near Morristown, is one of the better places in New Jersey to see glacial lake varves. The varves are across the brook a couple of hundred feet downstream from a parking lot on Kitchell Road. Glacial lake varves consist of couplets of sandy silt and finer-grained silty clay. The sandier sediment was deposited during the summer months when density currents carried fine sand and silt underwater to the deepest parts of the lakes. The silty,

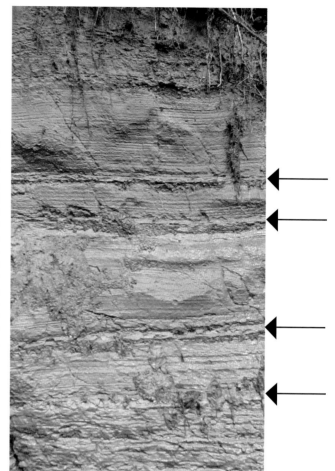

Glacial varves along Loantaka Brook near Kitchell Road in Morristown. The pinkish winter layers (arrows) are thinner: mostly silt and clay that settled from suspension. The thicker summer layers are coarser-grained: fine sand and silt. The fine layering in the summer layers is from deposition by density currents as the currents slowed and sediment settled out. —Photo by D. Harper

clayey sediment settled out through the winter months when there was little or no meltwater. Thickness and sediment composition of varves vary from year to year depending in good part on weather. Because of this, they can be read somewhat like tree rings: counted to determine the number of years a lake existed and correlated from lake to lake. Much of what we know about how fast the ice melted back from the terminal moraine and where the glacier stood at various times in its retreat is based on varves correlated between glacial lakes.

Morristown and the Revolutionary War

Geologic conditions made Morristown a favorable location for overwintering by George Washington's colonial army: close enough to monitor British activities in New York and easily defended. Attack from the west was blocked by the rugged New Jersey Highlands and approaches from the north, east, and south were through easily defended gaps in the Watchung ridges. Approaches to the Watchungs were monitored from the ridgetops. West of the ridges, passage was restricted to narrow corridors by marshlands on the bed of Glacial Lake Passaic. Washington twice took advantage of this strategic location, overwintering at Morristown through late winter in 1777 and the entire winter season of 1779–80. Twice in June of 1780 the British attempted to attack Washington's army at Morristown by advancing through the gap at Springfield. This was the largest of the gaps through the Watchungs and led to a fairly wide corridor along the top of the terminal moraine. Signal fires were lit atop the Watchungs and neither of the attacks was a surprise. Both times the British were unable to advance through the gap even though they outnumbered the defenders and were better supplied.

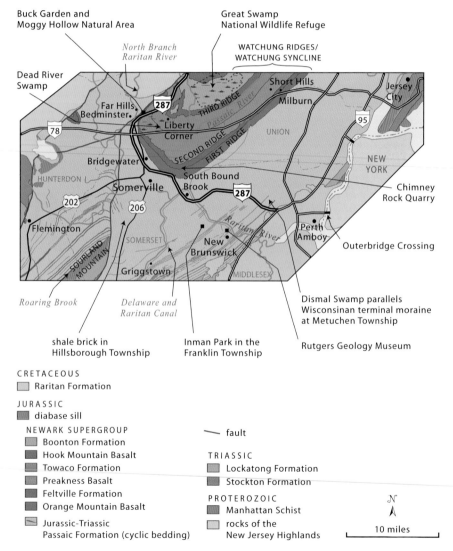

Geology along I-287 between Moggy Hollow Natural Area and Perth Amboy.
— Compiled from the USGS's Preliminary Integrated Geologic Map Database for the United States, 2006

Moggy Hollow Spillway

I-287 crosses the Watchungs at Moggy Hollow, the lowest point along the perimeter of ridges between Millburn Gap and the Highlands. This low point was a spillway for Glacial Lake Passaic. I-287 crosses Moggy Hollow Brook just west of the Liberty Corner bridge and about 2 miles north of exit 24. A small wetland east of the road between basalt outcrops of the Second Watchung widens upstream toward the spillway. The spillway, bordered by a large house, is visible from the road. Before the house was built, the area upstream from the spillway was littered with boulders and cobbles of gneiss that floated to the outlet frozen in ice, then dropped where the ice went aground and melted. Downstream to the west, hidden from I-287 in the woods of Somerset County's Moggy Hollow Natural Area, is an abandoned 25-foot-high waterfall that, through summertime, must have carried far more water than today's Passaic Falls. Downstream from the abandoned falls a short section of a mile-long sluiceway cut by the meltwater is preserved within the natural area. The rest is within Somerset County's Buck Garden. The garden area is cleaned up and landscaped, but before landscaping and development, the sluiceway and a broad flat between the sluiceway and the North Branch Raritan River was littered with basalt boulders washed downstream as the falls eroded. Even now, many rocks in the bed of the North Branch below its confluence with Moggy Brook are basalt. Above the confluence, basalt is a minor component of the bed material.

Chimney Rock Copper Mine

At exit 14, I-287 passes south of First Watchung Mountain, the namesake for the entire ridge. The northeastern slope is the Chimney Rock Quarry, a large traprock quarry in the Orange Mountain Basalt. Long before the quarry existed, the Chimney Rock copper mine was worked intermittently at the same location. The area was likely prospected in colonial times, and a furnace was constructed in 1824. Other than reports of work in 1866, little is known about the mine. Tunnels up to 700 feet long were found during quarry operations, but the rich copper-bearing rock is only a few inches thick. The quarry is absolutely closed to the general public, and trespassers are arrested.

Plainfield Outwash Plain and the Raritan River

At South Bound Brook, I-287 skirts the south end of the 8.5-mile-long Plainfield outwash plain, built southward from the Wisconsinan terminal moraine by gravelly, braided streams. The outwash plain ends here because the sediment being carried southward reached the Raritan River and merged with nonglacial sediment of the Raritan. The Raritan carried less sediment because it was fed in part by meltwater flowing from Glacial Lake Passaic and most of the sediment had settled out in the lake. Unlike the overloaded streams building the outwash plain, the Raritan was carrying less sediment than it was capable of moving. Further, the Raritan below South Bound Brook steepened and flowed within a narrow sluiceway it had only recently cut after being blocked from its preglacial course by the ice. Sediment reaching the end of the outwash plain was picked up by the Raritan and swept downriver past Perth Amboy. In Metuchen, I-287 is just south of the terminal moraine. Dismal Swamp lies between the interstate and the moraine.

Woodland Avenue runs along the base of the moraine for 5.5 miles from Plainfield to the Oak Tree neighborhood of Edison. The ridge is clearly visible to the north as a rise of 40 to 90 feet within a thousand or so feet of Woodland Avenue. Southward, visible sometimes through the trees, the neighborhood is bordered by Dismal Swamp, which parallels the moraine for 2 miles. The swamp may mark a course the Raritan River briefly followed as the ice age glaciers were advancing, after the ice blocked its valley eastward from Bound Brook but before the river established a new route southward through New Brunswick.

Shale Quarry in Franklin

Along with clay, New Jersey's ceramics industries used substantial amounts of red shale quarried from the Newark Basin. In some places the shale was either so weathered or so little hardened since its deposition that it could simply be crushed, moistened, and fired for brick. Inman Park (formerly Quarry Park), in Franklin Township, is one of many places shale was quarried. Pieces of terra-cotta piping and building tile litter the surface wherever the grass is thin, but the size of the quarry is apparent only around the baseball fields, where overgrown slopes rise 20 feet above the 40-acre quarry floor. Historically, much of the crushed shale not directly fired to brick was crushed to pieces the size of rice grains and used for sizing. Sizing is coarser material mixed in with clay before firing to make the final product more resistant to breakage. The coarser grains block the propagation of stresses, which would build up in uniform material. Sizing in brick is commonly sand, which gives brick its gritty feel. Sizing in ceramic pipe and terra cotta is commonly ground shale and shows up as lighter or darker specks in broken pieces. The New Jersey Shale Brick Company in Hillsborough Township, the last brick manufacturer in New Jersey, made brick directly from crushed shale for several decades until it closed in 2008.

Geological Hall and Rutgers Geology Museum

Geological Hall, completed at Rutgers College in 1872, was the first college building in the United States built for the teaching of geology. The Geology Department moved out in the 1970s in a centralization of science departments but left a 14-foot-tall copper relief map of New Jersey in the lobby and the Rutgers Geology Museum upstairs. The relief map was made at the conclusion of a decades-long topographic mapping project in which the New Jersey and United States Geological Surveys completed the nation's first statewide topographic coverage. The map was displayed at the Columbian Exposition in Chicago in 1893.

The Rutgers Geology Museum was included in the building by George Cook, state geologist, to further his goal for the students and the public to have direct and personal contact with scientists. Today the museum continues this tradition with educational programs, periodic lectures by prominent geologists, and, together with the Rutgers Earth and Planetary Sciences Department, a January annual open house with speakers, educational activities, mineral sales, and rock identification.

Outerbridge Crossing

Just south of Metuchen, I-287 crosses onto the Coastal Plain 10 miles before crossing the Arthur Kill on the Outerbridge into New York. This bridge is the outermost crossing between New Jersey and New York. More formally, it takes its name from Eugenius Outerbridge, the first chairman of the Port Authority of New York and New Jersey.

New Jersey Turnpike
Palisades Park—Garden State Parkway
40 miles

Hackensack Meadowlands

The northern 20 miles of the New Jersey Turnpike, through the Hackensack Meadows, the Newark Bay marshes, and tidal marshes along the Arthur Kill, are for many travelers an iconic and lasting impression of New Jersey. On first impression this is a wasteland of oil refineries, airports, sports arenas, truck terminals, and landfills. In fact, the area has been substantially cleaned up from massive air and water pollution in the mid-twentieth century. Although wildlife has returned, eagles are nesting, and recreational use is coming back, few slow their cars to notice the beauty of the meadows. Well-maintained parks have hiking trails, marsh boardwalks, and canoeing trails, and the more adventurous can paddle the Hackensack River. While the improvements are undeniable, the majority of the Meadowlands remains privately owned, and there is unceasing pressure for development.

The inland tidal marshes of the Hackensack Meadows owe their existence to glacial erosion of soft, easily eroded mudstone deposited in shallow lakes of the Newark Basin in Triassic time. To the west and north, away from the center of the basin, the Triassic lakes were shorter lived, and rivers deposited less easily eroded sandstone and conglomerate. To the east is the extremely durable Palisades diabase. To the south, the glaciers eroded into the mudstone almost to the southernmost limit of the Wisconsinan advance at Perth Amboy. Instead of the seaward slope of a stream-cut valley, the glaciers scoured out an irregular bedrock surface, now buried by as much as 300 feet of natural sediment and 100 feet of trash at the largest of the landfills.

Close to 300 feet of silt and clay were deposited in the deepest parts of Glacial Lake Hackensack, and most of it was later covered over by a thin veneer of floodplain and estuarine deposits. The silt and clay are at the surface around Little Ferry because the land in this northern part of the lake rose above sea level after the weight of the ice lifted and the clay was not covered by marsh muck. Sandy, clayey silt deposited in glacial lakes has been used for brickmaking throughout the glaciated northeast. In New Jersey, most of the brick clay from was from Glacial Lake Hackensack and was dug at Little Ferry. The Little Ferry clay supported a substantial brick industry from the 1870s to the 1950s.

In its peak years in the 1890s, one hundred million bricks were fired annually and shipped as far as Providence, Rhode Island. The clay pits were dug well below sea level, most being pumped dry and dug with wheeled equipment. At least one was allowed to fill with water and dug with a floating dredge. A few small lakes are all that remain of the industry.

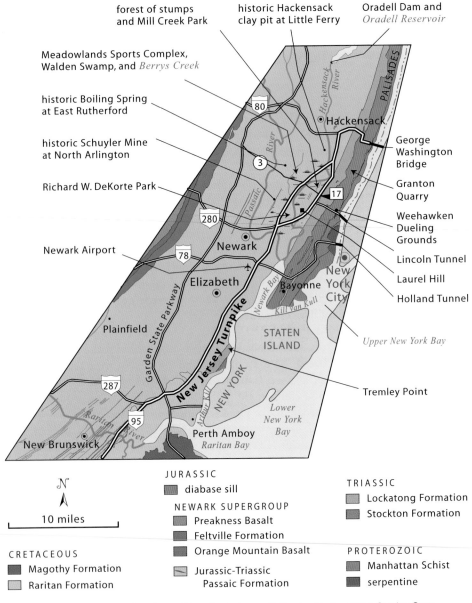

Geology along the New Jersey Turnpike between Palisades Park and the Garden State Parkway. —Compiled from the USGS's Preliminary Integrated Geologic Map Database for the United States, 2006

Boiling Spring

Boiling Spring is today a neighborhood in East Rutherford. Before it was a neighborhood, it was a large, cold-water spring boiling from the ground. Even though the water was only a few inches deep, a stick could be pushed by hand over 12 feet into the churning sand beneath. The spring is here because this is the contact between a sandy meltwater delta on the west shore of Glacial Lake Hackensack and impermeable till and diabase bedrock to the east. Rainwater soaks into the permeable sand and flows underground toward the Hackensack River. If the sediment filling the valley were sandy all the way to the river, the water would flow underground to springs close by the river or beneath its bed. The valley floor is mostly impermeable till and bedrock, however, and the water is forced to the surface at the edge of this barrier.

By the mid-nineteenth century, the water was being piped to nearby railroads to be used in steam engines. In 1882, a spring-fed pond, Glen Waters, was constructed as the centerpiece of a residential development. The lake was short-lived, soon being filled in to prevent malaria, which occasionally struck the Meadowlands area. The spring and its outlet stream are now culverted over, but the oversaturated, unstable boiling sand, capable of flooding construction sites, undermining streets and buildings near excavations, and causing collapses, is well-known to those who build and maintain underground structures in the area.

Cedar Swamps and the Mill Creek Forest of Stumps

At low tide, the forest of stumps comes into view in a pond in Mill Creek Park, west of the Lincoln Tunnel spur of the Turnpike just north of the NJ 3 exit. The stumps are all that remain of cedar forests that covered about half of the Meadowlands at the time of European colonization. The stumps can best be seen from walking trails in the park.

The cedars had only recently colonized the Meadowlands. From the start of widespread peat accumulation in the Meadowlands following glaciation, pollen studies show a sequence of forest types beginning with black ash swamps, followed by northern bog forests of larches and black spruce, then by Atlantic white cedar swamps. Firs, better adapted to the cold, are prominent in early postglacial pollen profiles elsewhere in the northeast, but at this time the Meadowlands was still dry. Accumulation of the peat in which the ash, larch, spruce, and cedar pollen is preserved had not yet begun because sea level was still low and the Meadowlands had not yet flooded. As early as 1949, Calvin Heusser, finding cedar pollen only at or near the surface of the peat, suggested that the cedars became abundant only six hundred years ago. At the time of colonization, the cedar swamps, intolerant of salt, were already shrinking because rising sea level was bringing brackish water farther inland. By 1750 the cedar swamps had been further decimated by uncontrolled logging. Peter Kalm, a Swedish naturalist touring North America on behalf of Carl von Linné (Linnaeus) reported of the Meadowlands that "the inhabitants here are not only lessening the number of their trees, but are even extirpating them entirely. . . . By these means, many swamps are already quite destitute of cedars."

Forest of cedar stumps with the Manhattan skyline in the background, Mill Creek Park.
—Photo by D. Harper

The Meadowlands cedars may have been decimated at the time of Kalm's visit, but cedar swamps are resilient and can come back to be logged again within half a century. By the 1790s, possibly because of decreased logging during the Revolutionary War and the ensuing economic slump, the cedars had recovered enough to provide a safe haven to Newark Bay pirates. In 1791, about 10 square miles were burned to destroy cover. The cedars may again have recovered but eventually fell victim to resumed lumbering, loss of peat by oxidation, browsing of young seedlings by muskrats, brackish water from rising sea level, and ditching for drainage and mosquito control. The last of the cedars succumbed to increased salinity soon after freshwater inflow from the Hackensack River was reduced by construction of the Oradell Dam in 1921. Much of the Meadowlands today is dominated by the common reed *Phragmites*, a magnificent, 8- to 12-foot-tall invasive plant. *Phragmites* thrives in disturbed environments and is ideally suited to the Meadowlands marshes.

Weehawken Dueling Grounds

From the Lincoln Tunnel, the Turnpike connector crosses about one-quarter mile of low-lying flat land, then climbs a spiral loop, the helix, to bring it up about 200 feet to the top of the Palisades cliff. At the top of the cliff, on Hamilton Avenue a few blocks north of the Turnpike, a monument is inscribed "Here in the King Estate, Weehawken, NJ, July 11, 1804, Alexander Hamilton was mortally wounded in a duel with Aaron Burr. His son, Philip Hamilton, had been killed in 1801 in the like manner in the same spot." The spot is scenic, but the location of the duel is misleadingly described. A nearby, more recent plaque better describes the location as "somewhere below this site, on a wooded ledge about 20 feet above the Hudson River." At the time of the duel, most of the area east of the Palisades from Bayonne northward past the Lincoln Tunnel was marshland, not filled until the late nineteenth and early twentieth centuries. The ledge was a preferred spot for the illegal activity of dueling: easily accessible by boat, above the mosquito-infested marsh, and out of sight of the farming village of Weehawken at the top of the cliff.

Granton Quarry

The Granton Quarry is a few miles north of the Turnpike connector to the Lincoln Tunnel along Tonnelle Avenue in North Bergen. The quarry was active for decades until the 1960s, producing road stone, construction stone, fill, and an abundance of fossils. The site is now occupied by shopping plazas and warehouses, but several quarry faces remain accessible. Fossils are still occasionally found despite poison ivy, and there are good exposures of the 60-foot-thick Granton diabase sill. The quarry is most often visited, however, to see cyclic bedding in lake sediments of the Lockatong Formation. The best exposures are at Seventy-ninth Street in a block of rock left between two shopping centers. Bedding is exposed on the south, east, and north sides of the block. The west side is an outstanding dip slope exposure of the top of the Granton Sill.

At the time the Granton Quarry sediments were being deposited, the Newark Basin was subsiding more quickly than it could fill with sediment.

Cyclic bedding in the Lockatong Formation from alternation of deepwater lakes (dark gray layers) and shallower lakes (light brown to white layers), Granton Quarry, North Bergen. —Photo by D. Harper

Consequently, it was a closed depression suited, if there was enough rain, to fill with water and become a lake. New Jersey was, at the time, however, at the center of the continent of Pangea and about 500 miles north of the equator. The climate was semiarid, and lakes filled when rainfall was abundant and dried when there was less rain, somewhat similar to Utah's Great Salt Lake basin today. The abundance and scarcity alternated in cycles of about 20,000 years in response to a 20,000-year-cycle in the tilt of the Earth's orbit. In the wettest of times, the lake was at least 250 feet deep and even the largest waves could not be felt on the bottom. The water did not turn over seasonally as in temperate climate lakes, and the water at the bottom was quiet, deprived of oxygen, and almost devoid of life. Without scavengers and burrowers, the thin layering of fine-grained mud and dark-colored organic material settling down from the surface waters was preserved intact. These are the dark mudstone layers on the quarry walls. Occasionally when fish living in the oxygenated surface waters died and fell to the bottom, their perfectly articulated skeletons were preserved lying flat on the mudstone layers.

In drier times, the water level dropped enough that waves moved sand across the bottom and mixed oxygen through the water column. Life returned, dead fish were disarticulated or completely decomposed, and the organic materials that contribute to the dark color of the deepwater muds were scavenged or decomposed by burrowers and microorganisms. The sediment from these times became the sandier, lighter-colored layers. Many layers include mud-cracked surfaces from times the lakes either dropped to a remnant near the center of the basin or dried completely. About 5 feet of sediment was deposited in each of the 20,000-year cycles. Eleven cycles can be counted in the quarry walls.

Through the period it was active, the Granton Quarry was one of the richest sites in North America for Triassic fossils. Not surprisingly, the fossils are most abundant and best preserved in the black, finely laminated beds deposited when the lake-bottom water had little or no free oxygen and there were no scavengers or burrowers. Shells of ostracod crustaceans, preserved as thin films the size and shape of small beans, are the most common fossils, but articulated fish are still occasionally found. Going upward from the dark-colored beds into sediments deposited in progressively shallower, more oxygenated water, fish are commonly found as disarticulated groupings of bones. In beds deposited in the shallowest water and in the mud-cracked beds exposed above the water, the only fish remains are isolated scales and the heavier bones from skulls. Interestingly, the greatest variety of fish is not from the deepwater deposits where the fish are best preserved, but from shallower-water deposits in which the skeletons are usually disarticulated. This is reasonable in view of the greater variety of habitats in shallower water. Bottom-dwelling fish, for one, could not live in the deeper, oxygen-deprived parts of the lakes.

In addition to the ostracods and fish, numerous reptile fossils have been found at the Granton Quarry, some the only known specimens for a species. Without a doubt, the best-known specimen is a nearly complete skeleton of the gliding reptile *Icarosaurus seifkeri*. The fossil was found in the early 1960s by three boys. One of them, seventeen-year-old Mark Seifker for whom the species was named, gave the others a telescope and a few other small things for the fossil, then took it to the American Museum of Natural History in New York. The specimen was cleaned of its matrix under a microscope using a miniature sandblasting device. The cleaning was done from both sides, took three months, and left the fossil almost paper thin. At some places between bones the rock was entirely removed and light can be seen through pinholes.

The creature's elongated ribs supported a thin membrane that allowed it to glide from tree to tree like today's flying squirrels. While older gliding vertebrates have since been found, *Icarosaurus* was the oldest for many years and pushed back the age of the oldest known airborne vertebrates by about 10 million years. Unlike birds and bats, which fly using wings developed from forelimbs, and flying squirrels, which glide on skin stretched from forelimbs to hind limbs, *Icarosaurus* and the unrelated flying dragons now living in Southeast Asia glided on a widened, flattened torso. A look at the fossil may convince you that the arms were not wings. Instead, elongated ribs separate from the main rib cage supported the gliding surface.

Unlike the carefully negotiated Fort Lee phytosaur (described in the Palisades Interstate Parkway road guide in this chapter), the museum did not formally acquire ownership of the *Icarosaurus*, and in 1989 Mr. Seifker, beset by health problems and without resources, reclaimed the fossil through lengthy court action and placed it for auction. Paleontologists feared the fossil would

The Icarosaurus seifkeri *fossil was prepared from the bottom as well as the top and left almost paper-thin.* —Photo by Mick Ellison, American Museum of Natural History

pass into private ownership and be lost to the public and to scientific study, but a California businessman, Dick Spight, bought the fossil for $167,000 (about half the appraised value) and donated it back to the American Museum. Fortunately, the fossil was protected from rough handling through its travels and is still intact.

Berrys Creek

Berrys Creek south of the Meadowlands Sports Complex was at one time known as the most polluted waterway in the Meadowlands because of waste from a mercury refining plant. The waste was dumped in a marshy area known as Walden Swamp, and as recently as the 1980s it was possible to dig a hole in the worst parts of the dump and watch mercury seep in. The swamp and creek became one of the country's highest priority Superfund sites and have been in good part been cleaned up and no longer remain hazardous. There is still mercury waste in the area, but it is deep within the sediment, away from contact with people and the plants and animals that live there.

Laurel Hill

What remains of Laurel Hill, still widely known as Snake Hill despite a name change in 1926, rises 150 feet above the meadows just west of the George Washington Bridge spur of the Turnpike. The rock is a pipelike intrusion of diabase, probably an offshoot of the Palisades Sill. For many years, from 1855 to 1962, this isolated island in the Meadowlands was home to hundreds of people at a time in Hudson County's almshouses, penitentiaries, contagious disease hospitals, tuberculosis sanitariums, and mental hospitals. Quarrying here dates from prison labor of the late nineteenth century but expanded greatly in the 1960s and into the 1970s when the county leased much of the hill to be leveled. About 80 percent of the hill and 50 feet of its height were taken down and became crushed stone. Through the time it was being quarried, Laurel Hill became well-known for its museum-quality minerals. In 1982 a specimen collected by Nicholas Facciolla was recognized as a new mineral and named Petersite after the brothers Thomas and Joseph Peters, curators of minerals at the Paterson Museum and American Museum of Natural History, respectively. Much of the area is now Laurel Hill County Park.

Schuyler Copper Mine

The Schuyler Mine opened in about 1719 in the 100-foot-high slopes along the west side of the Meadowlands in North Arlington. It is one of the oldest mines in the United States and one of the few copper mines in New Jersey to ever turn a profit. The first owner, Arendt Schuyler, reportedly became a rich man from the mining. Because the fine-grained chalcocite ore mineral was difficult to separate from the country rock and because of laws prohibiting the refining of ores in the colonies, the ore was initially shipped to Holland, then to Bristol, England, for smelting. The ore was dug and dressed by slaves. About 100 tons of dressed ore was sent overseas in some years.

Through the first decades of mining, water was drained through horizontal tunnels leading to the Meadowlands, and mining was restricted to rock above the sea level marshes. In the 1750s, however, the mine was expanded. The first steam engine in the colonies was brought from England to dewater levels below the marshlands. This Newcomen engine generated power by the condensation of steam, opposite to later steam engines powered by the expansion of steam. It allowed the Schuyler Mine to reportedly become the first deep mine in the English colonies, eventually reaching 347 feet below the surface.

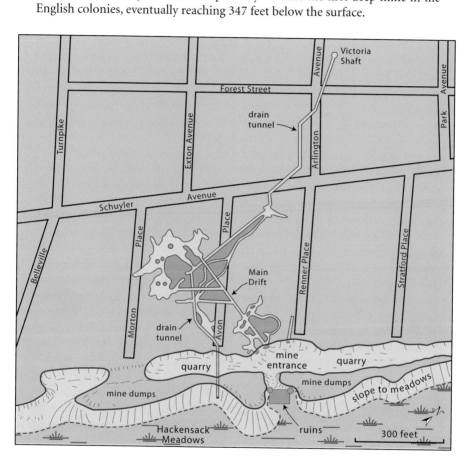

- Jurassic diabase of the Arlington Sill
- Jurassic-Triassic Passaic Formation
- Passaic Formation altered by intrusion of the Arlington Sill

Schuyler copper mine map and generalized cross section. Unlike the Watchung copper mines that followed the base of the Orange Mountain Basalt, the Schuyler Mine worked ore in the altered sedimentary rock at the top of a body of igneous rock, the 20-foot-thick Arlington Sill. Numerous chambers and tunnels are not shown on the map. —From Woodward, 1944

The mine was operated sporadically, in prosperous times and when the price of copper was high, until 1903, but was seldom profitable after the first few decades of operation. Water, fires, robbing of support pillars for ore, labor disputes, and sabotage led to numerous shutdowns. After mining stopped, the horizontal tunnels were used for a few years for storage and mushroom growing, but by 1927 the tunnels were collapsing, dangerous, and abandoned. The vertical shafts were covered over soon after the mines closed and largely forgotten until the Victoria Shaft, the deepest of about 40 shafts, collapsed in November 1989. The collapse left a hole 20 feet across and 70 feet deep in a homeowner's backyard and apparently triggered a surge of water along a 1,300-foot drainage tunnel. There were smaller collapses at several shafts directly above the tunnel. Near the tunnel entrance the water was moving with enough force to burst upward through the reinforced concrete floor of a factory, flooding the building and pushing aside heavy industrial machinery.

Twelve additional shafts were soon found by drilling where cracked pavement or surface depressions suggested subsurface voids. Drilling numerous holes in a residential neighborhood is challenging, however, and there was no guarantee even with closely spaced holes that all the shafts shown on sometimes contradictory historic maps would be found. Further, vibration of the drilling machinery could, itself, cause collapses. Finding a better way to locate shafts so they could be stabilized became an immediate priority of the New Jersey Geological Survey. Numerous geophysical techniques were evaluated, with gravity surveying to detect the slightly lower gravity above a subsurface void being the most successful. Locations of twenty-one shafts shown on historic maps were surveyed. Nineteen locations where gravity anomalies suggested that there might be an underground void were drilled. Fifteen shafts were found, filled with stone, and capped with concrete. The maps showed other shafts below houses, but gravity surveying would not have worked within the buildings.

Richard W. DeKorte Park

Richard W. DeKorte Park, home of the New Jersey Meadowlands Commission, is an award-winning example of transformation of an environmentally abused wasteland into a rich and varied wildlife habitat. Changes to the Meadowlands ecosystem began with the Indians and accelerated with the diking of rivers and draining of marshes by the earliest European colonizers. Today only 13 of the more than 30 square miles of marsh that existed at the time of European colonization remain. Much of the loss of marshland took place through the mid-twentieth century when the meadows was regarded as wasteland and treated as such. Uncontrolled dumping was a long-standing practice in the meadows. By the 1950s the Meadowlands was arguably the largest dump in the world. In addition to household waste, thousands of tons of chemical and industrial waste, sand and mud dredged from shipping channels, World War II munitions, and debris from the Battle of Britain shipped as ballast were dumped. Much of the trash was simply trucked to illegal dumps and emptied onto the marshes. Construction of the Turnpike only accelerated the loss of wetlands by creating easier access for trucking terminals, warehousing, horse tracks, and stadiums.

The Hackensack Meadowlands Development Commission, now the New Jersey Meadowlands Commission, was established in 1968 to facilitate economic activities and stem the environmental degradation. Its headquarters, environmental center, and bird observatory in DeKorte Park are open to the public, as are parkland trails developed by teams of landscape specialists, wildlife scientists, and solid waste engineers. The Kingsland Overlook section, originally called the Experimental Park on a Landfill, was one of the first landfill parks in the country and the first landfill to be capped with a synthetic plastic rather than clay. The cap was made from 400,000 used soda bottles, covered with soil, and planted with upland native species. The plantings have thrived, and the 100-foot-high hill has become home to an increasing variety of animals and birds.

The Lyndhurst Nature Reserve, on an illegal and abandoned landfill in the park, is larger and presented larger challenges. A properly designed landfill has a liner at the bottom to catch the tea-colored, contaminated leachate from rainwater seeping through the waste, an impermeable cap to prevent rainwater from reaching the garbage, a leachate collection and treatment system because no cap is perfect, and a system to collect the explosive methane given off by the waste. The gas is either vented safely to the atmosphere or burned to generate electricity. The Lyndhurst landfill had none of these safeguards. Fortunately, much of the Meadowlands has impermeable silt and clay rather than sand beneath its peat and muck. Here and at numerous other abandoned landfills in the meadows, the silt and clay has been used as a natural liner. Impermeable walls were constructed by trenching to the silt and clay and backfilling the trench with clay. Leachate collection systems were added by trenching and backfilling with crushed stone. The landfill cap at DeKorte Park's Lyndhurst Nature Reserve was designed as an outdoor classroom, sculpted to hills and valleys, and planted to illustrate natural succession and habitats. Elsewhere in DeKorte Park, trails follow access roads and boardwalks into marshlands and mudflats preserved by the Meadowlands Commission. A World Trade Center Memorial includes two piers suggesting the shadows of the towers. Each pier is constructed of 110 boards for the 110 stories of the towers.

At other landfills in the Meadowlands, small methane-powered generating stations are visible from the Turnpike. Still other landfills were in the path of the Turnpike when it was built between 1950 and 1952. In what must have been a truly unpleasant task, the waste was dug down to native soil and moved to landfills outside the right-of-way. The larger landfills in the meadows are truly impressive, and an often repeated suggestion is to use them for ski hills or sledding runs. A number of large landfills in the cold upper Midwest have become ski slopes, but in New Jersey's milder climate the heat from the decaying waste would likely melt off the snow before it could get much use.

Electric Power Plants at Elizabeth

Two electricity generating plants are visible from the Turnpike at Elizabeth, an older plant at the edge of Newark Bay to the east and a newer cogeneration plant (which combines waste incineration and electricity generation) to the west. The plants produce electricity but were built here more to produce steam for oil refineries. Gasoline contains more hydrogen and oxygen than crude oil. The extra hydrogen and oxygen come from steam (H_2O) as part of the refining process.

Ice Margin Positions

South of Newark Airport, the land rises gradually and irregularly from the tidal marshes toward the Wisconsinan terminal moraine. In the heart of the Meadowlands, the topographic features left behind when the glaciers melted back are now mostly under sea level and buried by postglacial sediment. South of the airport, the retreating ice left a series of poorly defined ridges and valleys paralleling the terminal moraine. The ridges were left where the ice stood in one place long enough for sediment to build upward. Tidal marshes between the ridges fill subdued valleys left from times when the ice was retreating more rapidly and sediment had less time to build up. Elizabeth was built on the widest and highest of the ridges. Refineries and tank farms were built on lower ridges to the south. The Turnpike climbs onto the terminal moraine just south of the Garden State Parkway interchange. See the continuation of the Turnpike road guide in the Coastal Plain chapter.

Garden State Parkway
New York Border—New Jersey Turnpike
32 miles

From the New York Thruway to Woodbridge, the Parkway passes through glaciated terrain. Along the first few miles in New Jersey, east of the Ramapo Mountains and west of Oradell Reservoir, the roadway passes by numerous glacially streamlined hills known as drumlins—a drumlin field. The first drumlin visible from the Parkway is to the east about a mile past the state line. This hill, like most New Jersey drumlins, is fairly small, only about 50 feet high, and does not have a name.

Atkins Glen

Atkins Glen, off Bear Brook Road at the southern end of Glendale Road in Washington Township, is a picturesque gorge carved by Bear Brook. When the Wisconsinan glaciers were retreating northward through Bergen County about 15,000 years ago, Bear Brook drained a mile or so of the edge of the ice sheet. Summertime flow along ice-marginal Bear Brook would account for the glen's steep, scoured walls and large boulders. Unlike now, when surface runoff flows to streams all year, runoff to ice age streams slowed in the coldest months when ice and snow remained frozen and rose to a torrent in midsummer.

The gorge may owe its boulders and steep walls to ice age meltwater, but the crossbedded gravelly sandstone in the walls is much older. The sandstone is part of the Passaic Formation, deposited in the Triassic Period in the Newark Basin rift valley. The edge of the valley was at the Ramapo Fault, about 8 miles to the west. Flats covering the floor of the valley began a few miles to the southeast,

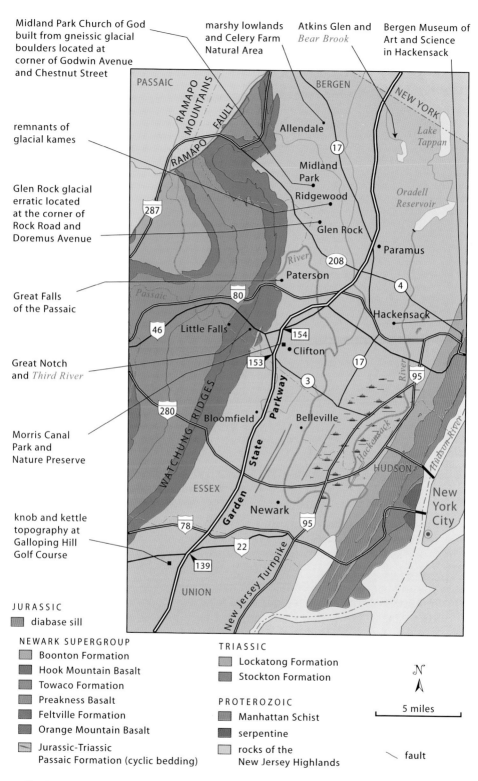

Midland Park Church of God built from gneissic glacial boulders located at corner of Godwin Avenue and Chestnut Street

marshy lowlands and Celery Farm Natural Area

Atkins Glen and *Bear Brook*

Bergen Museum of Art and Science in Hackensack

remnants of glacial kames

Glen Rock glacial erratic located at the corner of Rock Road and Doremus Avenue

Great Falls of the Passaic

Great Notch and *Third River*

Morris Canal Park and Nature Preserve

knob and kettle topography at Galloping Hill Golf Course

PASSAIC

RAMAPO MOUNTAINS

RAMAPO FAULT

BERGEN

NEW YORK

Allendale

17

Midland Park

Ridgewood

Glen Rock

287

Paramus

208

Paterson

River

Passaic

80

4

Hackensack

46

Little Falls

154

Clifton

153

17

95

3

River

280

Bloomfield

Belleville

Garden State Parkway

WATCHUNG RIDGES

ESSEX

Newark

95

Hackensack

HUDSON

New York City

Hudson River

78

22

139

UNION

New Jersey Turnpike

Lake Tappan

Oradell Reservoir

JURASSIC
- diabase sill

NEWARK SUPERGROUP
- Boonton Formation
- Hook Mountain Basalt
- Towaco Formation
- Preakness Basalt
- Feltville Formation
- Orange Mountain Basalt
- Jurassic-Triassic Passaic Formation (cyclic bedding)

TRIASSIC
- Lockatong Formation
- Stockton Formation

PROTEROZOIC
- Manhattan Schist
- serpentine
- rocks of the New Jersey Highlands

N

5 miles

fault

Geology along the Garden State Parkway between the New York border and the New Jersey Turnpike. —Compiled from the USGS's Preliminary Integrated Geologic Map Database for the United States, 2006

Crossbedded gravelly sandstone in Atkins Glen, Washington Township. —Photo by D. Harper

extending from the Hackensack Meadowlands southwestward across central New Jersey and into Pennsylvania's Bucks County. Highlands rose steeply west of the fault, and swift mountain streams and mudflows carried bouldery gravel down into the valley. These are preserved as conglomerates along the west edge of the basin. Flats toward the center of the valley, by contrast, were usually covered by lakes and mudflats. The sedimentary rock is predominantly mudstone, siltstone, and shale. Atkins Glen was toward the narrowing, shallowing northern end of the Newark Basin distant from the steep slopes and swift streams at the border of the basin but not at the lakes and mudflats at the center of the basin. Streams were unable to carry the large pebbles or boulders common along the Ramapo Fault, but still fast enough to form sand and fine gravel into the crossbedded sandstone of the walls of the gorge.

Ridgewood Kames

Kame in Scottish is a long, steep-sided ridge. In geology it is a poorly defined term referring to mounds or small hills of sand and gravel deposited against or below a glacier. The Ridgewood kames are small hills, one of which stands between the Parkway and the northbound exit lane at exit 165. These are probably moulin kames, *moulin* being French for "mill." Mills are holes straight down through glaciers where meltwater and the sand, gravel, and boulders it carries swirl downward into the ice with a roar like that of a large water mill.

The forested hill is the remnant of a kame at Ridgewood. Before gravel mining the kame was about twice as high. —Photo by D. Harper

The Ridgewood kames were larger, 77 feet high rather than their present 40 or so feet, in 1902 when they were described by Rollin Salisbury in *The Glacial Geology of New Jersey*. They were also made of coarser sediment. Before the Parkway was built, gravel was mined from the kames, leaving them smaller and composed predominantly of the less valuable sand.

Oradell Reservoir and the Lake Hackensack Jökulhlaup

Oradell Reservoir was originally built for water supply in 1923. Excavations at the northern end of the reservoir in the 1970s uncovered a mastodon skeleton, now in pieces at the Bergen Museum of Art and Science, and evidence of a sudden, immense flood from the draining of Glacial Lake Hackensack. Floods are common in glacial environments and are called *jökulhlaups*, Icelandic for the floods that issue periodically from their glaciers. Jökulhlaups must have repeatedly scoured the valleys of northern New Jersey as the retreating glaciers released lakes dammed by ice. Locations of dozens of glacial lakes are known. The places where floods may have run can be inferred from positions of valleys, but physical evidence for the floods is elusive. Some of the clearest examples of flood effects in New Jersey are from the drainage of Glacial Lake Hackensack.

Glacial Lake Hackensack was 30 miles long and drained southward through spillways along the Arthur Kill and Kill van Kull until Sparkill Gap, just north of the New York line, was uncovered. When the gap was uncovered about 18,000 years ago, the water level in Glacial Lake Hackensack dropped 30 feet, probably as an immense jökulhlaup. Draining of glacial lakes can be sudden and dramatic. Flow may start as a trickle near the edge of the thinning ice, but the energy of flowing water melts ice quickly and a trickle can grow to a flood in a matter of hours. The excavations at Oradell Reservoir uncovered a series of channels cut into Glacial Lake Hackensack bottom sediments. At the bottom of one channel, a 9-foot-diameter boulder came to rest and a 30-foot train of smaller boulders collected in the lee, downstream to the north. The channels are filled with sand and capped by peat, which has been radiocarbon dated as 12,870 years old. The channels cut into lake-bottom sediment, the north-flowing currents capable of moving a 9-foot boulder, and the timing (between the deposition of the lake-bottom deposits and the deposition of the 12,870-year-old peat) are consistent with flood drainage of the 30-mile-long lake and hard to explain otherwise.

Paramus Shopping Centers and Glacial Lake Paramus

The shopping centers along NJ 17 and NJ 4 around Paramus owe their location in part to sedimentation in and around Glacial Lake Paramus, northwest of Glacial Lake Hackensack. Lake Paramus formed between the receding ice to the north and a dam of glacial sand and gravel in a narrow reach of the Passaic Valley between Newark and Lyndhurst. It was bordered to the north and east, toward the retreating but still active glaciers, by bedrock hills and meltwater deltas built from sand and gravel carried into the lake.

When NJ 17 was built in the 1930s, the upland hills and deltas surrounding the lake basin were already well on their way to becoming today's residential neighborhoods and village centers. The glacial topography that invited development remains visible at Bergen Pines Hospital. The hospital was built on a delta of sand and gravel carried to the edge of Glacial Lake Paramus by glacial meltwater. The flat top of the delta and the steep slope where sand carried to the edge of the delta avalanched westward into deeper water are unmistakable. Lake-bottom areas directly to the south and west of the bedrock hills and meltwater deltas, especially where they were covered by lake-bottom muds, were marshy and less densely and less prosperously developed. This left them open for the construction of NJ 17 in the 1930s and shopping centers in the decades after World War II.

The pattern of well-drained, flat sandy uplands on deltas and poorly drained marsh on adjacent lake-bottom sediments is common everywhere in the glaciated northeast and is the result of the different behaviors of sand and gravel as opposed to silt and clay in running water. Sand and gravel are carried downstream by the force of water at the streambed. They settle quickly when the stream enters the quiet water of a lake. As more and more sand and gravel are carried into the lake, a delta grows outward with a flat, sandy or gravelly delta plain standing just above the water level. By contrast, silt and clay travel suspended through the entire water column and settle out over days or months.

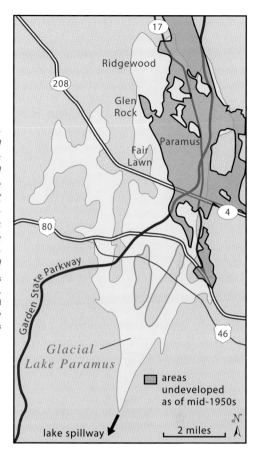

Much of the northeast-ern part of the Glacial Lake Paramus basin was marshy and remained undeveloped well into the twentieth century. This left it open for the construc-tion of NJ 17 in the 1930s and the Garden State Parkway, NJ 4, and shop-ping centers after World War II. —Glacial Lake Paramus modified from Stone and others, 2002; Developed areas modified from historic U.S. Geological Survey 7.5-minute quadrangle maps

Meltwater streams issuing from glaciers commonly carry so much silt and clay that they appear milky. Because of the suspended mud, the stream water is often heavier than the clean water of the lake. Instead of coming to rest when it flows into the still water of the lake, it sinks and flows downslope across the lake bottom as a density current, fast enough in some cases to keep even fine sand moving. If it contains enough suspended silt and clay, gravity carries it downslope to the deepest part of the lake, where the silt and clay settle out. Glacial lakes thus fill simultaneously from the shore outward as sand and gravel build onto deltas and from the bottom up as density currents carry silt and clay to the deepest parts of the lake.

While the older suburban area around Glacial Lake Paramus has residen-tial and town center development on upland deltas and roadways and newer commercial development on lowlands, this is not always the pattern of devel-opment. Many deltas were mined for sand and gravel. The worked-out gravel pits have become commercial or industrial more often than residential. Also, many marshy lowlands remaining from the glacial lakes are more remote or more difficult to develop than those of Glacial Lake Paramus and were as yet undeveloped when environmental regulations protecting wetlands were enacted. Some are now preserved as parkland, wildlife refuges, and muckland farms like the Celery Farm Natural Area in Allendale. Even along NJ 17, a surprising amount of the lake-bottom lowland remains either undeveloped or in parkland, golf courses, and other low-density uses.

Glen Rock

The town of Glen Rock is named for one of the state's largest glacial erratics. The rock, at the intersection of Rock Road and Doremus Avenue, was known as Pamachapura (Stone from Heaven) by the Lenni Lenape Indians. It was recognized as from somewhere else long before geology was a science. The rock is granite gneiss, and the nearest gneiss bedrock is 8 miles northwest of Pamachapura.

Millions of smaller gneiss boulders litter northeastern New Jersey and are widely used for stone walls and buildings. The Church of God in Midland Park, at the corner of Godwin Avenue and Chestnut Street, is a good example. The Church of God stones are from the New Jersey Highlands but were harvested from areas of sandstone and shale bedrock well to the east of the Highlands. Most of them are undoubtedly glacial erratics, but rivers also carried rocks eastward from the Highlands onto the red sandstone and shale of the Newark Basin long before the glaciers entered New Jersey. Pamachapura is far too large to have been moved by New Jersey's rivers and is unquestionably a glacial erratic.

Pamachapura, also called Glen Rock, is a large glacial erratic. —Photo by D. Harper

Church of God in Midland Park is constructed with boulders of gneiss, carried here by either ice or water. —Photo by D. Harper

Great Notch Outlet of Glacial Lake Passaic

South of where Glacial Lake Paramus stood, the Parkway crosses a higher area never covered by glacial lakes. At mile 153, four radio towers to the west and a golf course to the east mark a meltwater channel that, for a short time, carried meltwater eastward, then southward from Glacial Lake Passaic. Through most of its existence, Glacial Lake Passaic drained through Moggy Hollow in Somerset County. Great Notch, along US 46 west of the Parkway here, is at a lower elevation but was filled with ice through most of the lake's existence. When ice melted from Great Notch, the lake level suddenly dropped by about 80 feet, releasing about 2.5 cubic miles of water. The water carved the channel beneath the towers, then spread southward through the golf course east of the Parkway toward Bloomfield and the Third River. The sandy bottomlands along the extinct Great Notch drainageway were less developed than areas to the east and west and, before the golf course was built, were known locally as the sand wastes. New Jersey Transit's Montclair-Boonton railroad passes through Great Notch, taking advantage of the low crossing.

Eventually the outlet across the Watchung Ridges at Little Falls and Great Falls was uncovered, and this is where the modern Passaic River now flows.

Morris Canal

Between a half mile south of Interchange 151 and Interchange 154, the Parkway follows the bed of the Morris Canal, which connected the Hudson River and the Delaware River in the early 1800s. A small section of the canal is preserved in Clifton's Morris Canal Park and maintained in garden style by local volunteers.

Belleville Brownstone

Quarries at Belleville supplied more brownstone building fronts than anyplace else in the country. The sides and backs of the buildings were made from less expensive material, commonly brick. Old Queens, the emblematic heart of Rutgers University, was built in 1809 with Belleville brownstone. The brownstone was from the Passaic Formation. The Morris Canal passed close to Belleville so stone was easily shipped.

Union's Knob and Kettle Topography

To the west of the Parkway along mile 139, the Galloping Hill Golf Course preserves an area of up-and-down hillocks, sandy slopes, ponds, and marshy swales. This kind of landscape, knob and kettle topography, is common near the edges of retreating ice sheets, and in Scotland became the first upland golf courses. Other courses were played near the coast where a similar kind of hillocky, sandy topography from the edges of ice sheets, "linksland," was created beneath sea level, then rose up to become dry land after the weight of the glaciers had lifted. Many golf courses of glaciated northern New Jersey, similar to the upland Scottish courses, were laid out with little modification of glacial topography. The knob and kettle terrain at Galloping Hill Golf Course is largely natural and is pronounced because the preglacial valley of the Ancestral Passaic River trends northeastward through the golf course. The ice was thicker in the valley than to the north and south, and blocks of ice remained in the valley after the thinner ice to the north and south had melted. Sand and gravel washed around and across the abandoned blocks. When the ice melted, the landscape collapsed into the knob and kettle topography.

Palisades Interstate Parkway
New York Border—Fort Lee
11 miles

For 14 miles from the George Washington Bridge to the New York border, the Palisades Interstate Parkway runs along the crest of the Palisades Sill. In Jurassic time, magma intruded between layers in the sedimentary rocks of the Newark Basin. It cooled into the igneous rock diabase, similar in composition to basalt. The preeminent geologic feature of Palisades Interstate Park is the sill, but the area also has good exposures of Triassic sedimentary rocks underlying and overlying the diabase, glacial erratics, and so many fossils that Yale University for a time had a fossil quarry in sedimentary rocks at the base of the sill at Weehawken.

The Palisades have impressed visitors since at least the time of the Italian explorer Giovanni da Verrazzano. In 1524 his sailors named the Palisades after the palisade forts of vertical logs of the local Indians. In 1983, they were designated a National Natural Landmark as "the best example of a thick diabase sill in the United States." We owe their preservation in good part to action by the New Jersey State Federation of Women's Clubs. The Palisades, with their

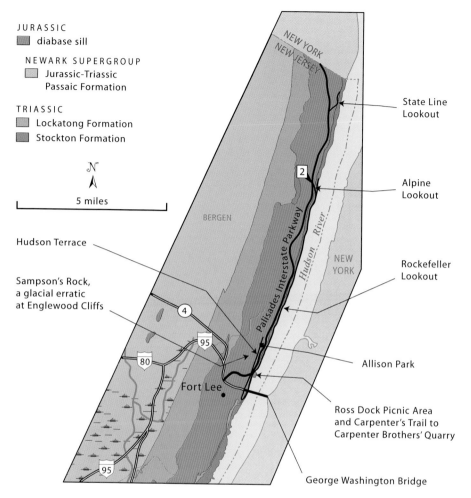

Geology along the Palisades Interstate Parkway. —Compiled from the
USGS's Preliminary Integrated Geologic Map Database for the United States, 2006

volume of rock and access to water transport, were ideally situated for quarrying, and quarries were operating up and down the length of the Palisades by the early 1800s. By the 1890s the invention of dynamite and improvements in steam-operated rock crushing and earth-moving equipment made it possible for the first time to open quarries directly on the cliff faces. Quarries were quickly destroying the natural beauty of the cliffs. Blasting of landmark features became public spectacles advertised weeks ahead. Opportunities to push the plunger to set off the blasts were raffled. In response to citizen action calling for a halt to the uncontrolled quarrying and destruction of forests for firewood, the Palisades Interstate Park Commission was established in 1900. Gifts from the Rockefellers, Harrimans, Morgans, and others went to the purchase of property from Fort Lee into New York.

Quarries along the Palisades about 1900. —Photo courtesy of N.J. Geological Survey

Completion of the George Washington Bridge in 1931 was followed by a real estate boom that threatened properties not yet managed by the commission. The Parkway we know today was built to channel development to appropriate areas and protect areas more appropriately included in the park. Numerous properties, including several mansions overlooking the Hudson, were purchased through condemnation. Many of the park's trails, roads, and picnic pavilions were built in the 1930s as federal public works projects. The elaborate stonework in some places almost overshadows the natural beauty of the park.

There is parking and trail access along the crest of the Palisades along the Palisades Interstate Parkway at the Rockefeller, Alpine, and State Line lookouts and at Allison Park off Hudson Terrace in Englewood Cliffs. All have cliffside overlooks of the Hudson River and New York City that will bring sweat to the palms of your hands. They are also good places to see roche moutonnée outcrops, scoured and streamlined by ice on the up-ice side and plucked to ragged surfaces down-ice. With a bit more searching, you may also find glacial erratics, the weathered remnants of gouges made by rocks embedded in the ice, and crescentic fractures where the rock broke under the pressure of the ice. Most of the erratics are red sandstone from the Newark Basin, banded gneiss from the Highlands, or red or white Paleozoic quartzite. Usually they are more rounded than the angular blocks of Palisades diabase littering the ground away from landscaped areas. Some have been built into the walls constructed to keep people back from the cliffs. Others are along woodland trails that head north and south along the cliff top from the overlooks.

Roches moutonnées along the crest of the Palisades. Some Palisades roches moutonnées are streamlined knobs (top). More often they are scoured flat and plucked to a right angle on the down-ice side (below). The ice moved from left to right across both rocks.
—Photos by D. Harper

Crescentic fractures at the crest of the Palisades. The fractures were caused by flaking of the rock under the pressure of the ice. —Photo by D. Harper

Sampson's Rock and Glacial Sculpting of the Palisades Ridge

Sampson's Rock is a large glacial erratic on the front lawn of an Englewood residence. The 9-foot-tall rock is red sandstone and weighs about 32 tons. It must have been carried at least 1.5 miles from the nearest sandstone outcrop, but is far from the largest or farthest-traveled New Jersey erratic. Few, however, show glacial and postglacial processes more clearly, and none have the same significance to the study of glaciation in New Jersey. In addition to illustrating the power of glaciers and the effects of weathering, Sampson's Rock is historically significant as the first place at which glaciation was convincingly shown to have affected New Jersey.

Large rocks in geologically improbable locations are common by the thousands in northern latitudes, and through much of the nineteenth century were seen as evidence of gigantic floods inundating entire landscapes, or even the whole world. In New Jersey, large rocks are common southeast of the nearest similar bedrock outcrops and were interpreted by Henry Rogers in his 1840 *Description of the Geology of the State of New Jersey* as one of several lines of evidence that at least one immense flood had crossed the state from northwest to southeast. This was not Noah's flood. By 1840, consistency between science and sacred history remained important, but strict biblical literalism had fallen out of favor. Most natural scientists had abandoned the idea of a single Noachian deluge several decades before.

Sampson's Rock. —Photo by D. Harper

Also by the 1840s, geologists realized that many deposits now recognized as glacial were difficult to explain as the result of floods. Flooding did not, for example, explain the restriction of the deposits to northern latitudes, the presence of house-sized erratics consistently southward from where they originated, and the absence of sorting in deposits we now know as glacial till. Continental glaciation was proposed for European deposits by Louis Agassiz in 1837, and by the 1860s there was growing acceptance that New England and much of New York had been glaciated. However, convincing evidence had not been found in New Jersey.

One of those seeking evidence was William B. Dwight of Vassar College. Dwight knew that the scoured outcrops atop the Palisades resembled the glacial roches moutonnées of Manhattan Island and that their shaping, smooth to the northwest and steep to the southeast, indicated the same northwest-to-southeast ice flow as affected the New York rocks. Until he came across Sampson's Rock in 1860, however, he was unable to find the polishing and fine striations cut by stones at the base of the moving ice he needed to convince himself that the "great Hudson Valley glacier" reached the top of the Palisades. The exposed diabase had weathered, and the grooving and polishing prominent on the New York exposures was gone.

Sampson's Rock sits atop a low-profile roche moutonnée. The rock is concave across its base, with several inches of open space between the bottom of the rock and the bare surface of the diabase underneath. Here, protected from the elements by the rock above, the glacial striations are perfectly preserved.

Their northwest-southeast orientation matched the direction of ice movement in New York and confirmed, at least to Dwight, that ice had overtopped the Palisades.

Ice flow across the Palisades undoubtedly accentuated the already steep eastern face of the Palisades. As the ice moved southeastward, sections of diabase columns frozen to the base of the glacier were plucked from the cliff face and carried along by the ice. These jagged, dark blocks of diabase can still be seen in the less developed areas of many New York City parks.

Rockfalls

The Palisade cliffs are continuing to evolve today. Some blocks of rock in the great aprons of talus along the bottoms of the cliffs may date from the ice age, some may have been blasted in quarry operations, and some are from recent, natural falls. The falls are most common through the winter and spring. Water freezing in the fractures between columns can exert a horizontal push of 2,000 pounds per square inch. Crumbling of a poorly consolidated olivine zone near the base of the columns undermines the cliffs and is a contributing factor to some falls. In some years, thousands of tons of rock cascade downward. A number of climbers have been killed in rockfalls.

This rockfall from the Palisades occurred in 1938.
—Photo courtesy of the Palisades Interstate Park Commission

Base of the Palisades Sill

Henry Hudson Drive, along the base of the Palisades, can be reached from Hudson Terrace in Fort Lee, Palisade Avenue in Englewood Cliffs, exit 2 off the Palisades Parkway, or any of several footpaths scaling the ridge. Talus fields of immense blocks can be seen at numerous places along trails, but the rocks are best seen in place near Ross Dock at the base of the George Washington Bridge. From the Ross Dock parking area, walk south toward the boat launch, then up the stone steps of the Carpenter's Trail and through the tunnel to the Ross Dock traffic circle. The abandoned quarry at the circle was part of the Carpenter Brothers' Quarry, the largest along the face of the Palisades. It was bought for parkland in 1900 with a donation from J. P. Morgan and shut down as a quarry.

There is no question that the Palisades is an outstanding example of a sill, but it is not a simple layer of igneous rock intruded between sediment layers. For many years, based on work published by Frederick Walker in 1940, the Palisades was used in elementary geology courses throughout the country to illustrate the differentiation of magma during cooling. Chill zones of quickly cooled, fine-grained rock formed at the top and bottom of the sill when it first intruded into the cooler sedimentary rock. Above the lower chill zone, there is an olivine-rich layer in some places about 30 feet thick. Olivine is heavier than most of other minerals in diabase and was held to have settled downward while the sill was still molten. In apparent confirmation of this, mineral composition of chill zone samples had the average composition for the sill as a whole and samples above the olivine zone had less olivine than the overall average for the sill.

As with many things in the natural world, reality has turned out to be more complex. In a closer look in 1969, K. R. Walker noted that the olivine had too much iron in its composition to have crystallized from melt with the composition of the chill zones and that the olivine crystals were too small to have settled through the magma in the few tens of thousands of years it took to cool and solidify the sill. He proposed a second injection of olivine-rich magma into the partially cooled sill for the origin of the olivine zone. As more workers examined the Palisades, the complexity of the sill only became more apparent. It now appears that there may have been at least four closely timed pulses of magma from at least three distinct magma sources.

The face of the Carpenter Brothers' Quarry exposes most of the lower chill zone and extends upward through the olivine zone and into the prominent columns for which the Palisades is named. The lower chill zone is fine-grained at the contact with the underlying sedimentary rock and becomes progressively coarser-grained upward toward the olivine zone. The olivine zone is visible about 25 feet up the cliff as an interval through which the columns become less distinct and the spalling off of the loosely aggregated crystals has left rounded, dark gray patches interrupting the flat, reddish-brown-weathering vertical faces of the columns.

The base of the sill and thermally metamorphosed mudstone and sandstone of the underlying Lockatong Formation are well exposed from the Ross Dock traffic circle south past the George Washington Bridge. The mudstone remained remarkably undisturbed while the sandstones appear to have

At the Carpenter Brothers' Quarry in Palisades Interstate Park, you can see the olivine zone within the Palisades Sill at the break in the columns about halfway up the cliff. —Photo by D. Harper

Contact between Palisades diabase (above) and thermally metamorphosed sedimentary rock (below), Palisades Interstate Park. —Photo by D. Harper

fluidized and become chaotically intermixed with the intruding diabase, sometimes even appearing to have exploded upward from beneath mudstone and into the magma.

Continuing south along Henry Hudson Drive past the dizzying view up to the bridge brings you uphill to a curve approaching the park gate and a weathered, crumbly exposure of the olivine zone rock. The olivine in the most weathered part of the outcrop is so highly decomposed as to be almost unrecognizable, but dark green grains of the mineral can be seen in unweathered rock just above and below. This same mineral, transparent and lighter green, is peridot, the birthstone for August. You will not find any gem-quality olivine crystals at the Palisades.

Looking south from the olivine zone exposure, the crest of the Palisades is visibly offset several hundred feet to the west. The offset was caused by a normal fault cutting diagonally across the Palisades. Rock to the north dropped downward relative to rock to the south. River Road takes advantage of a prominent cleft created by erosion along the fault. There are numerous similar places where erosion along faults cutting the Palisades left gentle inclines now used by roads.

A walk from the olivine zone exposure down the path to the river and back along the riverbank to the parking area will bring you past several outcrops of the Stockton Formation. The Stockton Formation is well-known for its architectural brownstone, but the rock here, near the transitional contact with the Lockatong, has too many mudstone layers to be a useful building stone.

Fort Lee Phytosaur

The Fort Lee phytosaur, a crocodile-like reptile, *Clepsysaurus* (formerly *Rutiodon manhattanensis*) was found in 1910 by Columbia University geology students about one-quarter mile south of where the George Washington Bridge now stands. Curators from American Museum of Natural History concluded, according to an article in the *New York Times* on December 21, 1910, that the fossil was "a prehistoric monster of the dinosaur class . . . something of a cross between a crocodile and an ostrich on a greatly exaggerated scale." A full-page Christmas day follow-up article in the *New York Times Sunday Magazine* titled "When the Giant Dinosaur Walked Down Broadway" suggested that the animal would "frighten the wits out of any man not a paleontologist," and would cause any partygoer who encountered the beast to "anchor himself to the water wagon for evermore."

The find was on private property in sandstone similar to the Stockton Formation sandstone along the Hudson at the south end of Palisades Interstate Park. There were months of negotiation before the museum became the rightful owner of the bones. After ownership had been secured, a 5,000-pound block of rock encasing the skeleton was cut loose and ferried intact across the Hudson so that the fossil could be dried and prepared for display under carefully controlled conditions. The bones are still on display, partially embedded in rock, in the museum's Hall of Vertebrate Origins. It was the first proof beyond footprints that large creatures inhabited the northeast during Triassic time and is still the largest Triassic fossil from New Jersey. The species name, *manhattanensis*, seems odd for a New Jersey fossil. Soon after it was recovered, the fossil was sent to Friedrich von Huene of Tubingen, Germany. Von Huene named more dinosaurs in the early twentieth century than any other European and assigned the formal name for the Fort Lee phytosaur. He may have chosen *manhattanensis* because it was sent from a Manhattan museum or because he was familiar with Manhattan but not Fort Lee.

Remains of the Fort Lee phytosaur, Clepsysaurus *(formerly* Rutiodon*)* manhattanensis, *from the base of the Palisades.* —Photo by Carl Mehling, American Museum of Natural History

HIGHLANDS AND VALLEY AND RIDGE
Gaps through Hard Rock

New Jersey's mountains are divided into two physiographic provinces, the Highlands and the Valley and Ridge. The types of rocks in each province and their geologic histories, as discussed in the book introduction, are very different. Gneiss and granite of 1,300 to 980 million years of age outcrop in the Highlands. The Valley and Ridge features sedimentary and metamorphosed sedimentary rocks of 540 to 400 million years of age. The Highlands stretch from the Ramapo Fault at the western edge of the Newark Basin west to thrust faults, such as Jenny Jump Thrust Fault, along which Proterozoic rocks of the Highlands were thrust west over Paleozoic rocks of the Valley and Ridge. I've combined the two provinces into one chapter here because their erosional history over the past 100 million years is quite similar and worth discussing together. In addition, the contact between the two provinces is complex, and within large areas of older rock of the Highlands are faulted pieces of younger Paleozoic rocks.

Dozens of faults have been mapped in New Jersey's bedrock. Most can be traced for only a few miles and have seen little movement. A few, like the Ramapo Fault along the eastern border of the Highlands, can be traced, with offsets and changes in name, for tens of miles and have moved thousands or tens of thousands of feet vertically. Some have moved far greater distances, possibly hundreds of miles, horizontally. These large faults are old, and movement on them during the breakup of Pangea was not their first activity. Faults become active whenever there is tension, compression, or lateral shear in the Earth's crust, and once faulting creates a break in the rocks, the break remains a weakness until it is completely annealed, usually during high-temperature metamorphism. The most recent time the rocks in New Jersey were subject to such metamorphism was during the Ottawan Orogeny, a continental collision and mountain building event near the end of the Proterozoic Eon. Since then, there have been tensional stresses during several rifting events and compressional stresses during several mountain building events. Each event likely reactivated many faults in the older rocks of the Highlands.

MINING IN THE HIGHLANDS

The rocks of the Highlands contain iron and other ore, including zinc. Numerous explanations have been proposed for the origin of the Highlands iron ore, and it is clear that not all the ore was formed in the same way or at the same

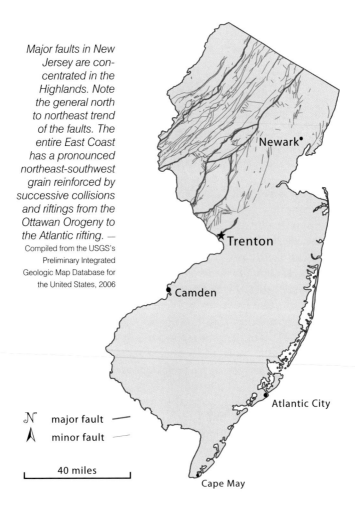

Major faults in New Jersey are concentrated in the Highlands. Note the general north to northeast trend of the faults. The entire East Coast has a pronounced northeast-southwest grain reinforced by successive collisions and riftings from the Ottawan Orogeny to the Atlantic rifting. — Compiled from the USGS's Preliminary Integrated Geologic Map Database for the United States, 2006

time. Iron is soluble in superheated water charged with chlorine and fluorine, and the conditions for generating such water existed at several times during the formation of the rocks. Some iron appears to have been emplaced during magmatism along the Losee magmatic arc and within the back-arc basin. This includes magnetite deposited in back-arc basin rocks by water moving through limestones that were later metamorphosed to the Franklin Marble. Some was released from minerals with iron and water in their crystal structures as the rock was heated and metamorphosed or melted during the Ottawan Orogeny. Some was emplaced during magmatism that followed mountain building.

The New Jersey Highlands was a favorable place for iron production in the 1700s. Ore is common and was mined from open pits, limestone for flux was quarried nearby, and there was wood for charcoal. Water power was plentiful for the bellows and pumps used to force air through the white-hot melt where ore and limestone flux react to produce iron and slag. The industry prospered

Magnetite veins in gneiss (one with magnet attached). From the Weldon Mine in Jefferson Township. —Photo by D. Harper

until, by the early 1800s, the area had been stripped of the trees used to make charcoal. In 1823, thirty-nine of Morris County's ninety-three iron forges were idle from lack of charcoal. Anthracite coal had been discovered in Pennsylvania in 1701, but there was no way to get enough coal into the Highlands to fuel an industry. The rivers were not navigable and the roads were poor. Without cheap transportation, the mines and furnaces could not compete with inexpensive iron goods from England, Sweden, and Russia.

By 1822, George Perot Macculloch, a Morristown businessman and president of the Morris County Agricultural Society, was calling for a canal across northern New Jersey. Similar to iron mining, profitable farming was hindered because there was no cheap way to move goods to market. Macculloch's primary interest may have been farming, but the idle iron mines, furnaces, and forges were highlighted to raise funds. Mining along the canal was projected to drop the price of iron ore from 90 dollars per ton to 55 dollars per ton. Construction of the canal was begun in the mountains near Ledgewood in 1825, and navigation along the entire route between Phillipsburg on the Delaware and Jersey City on the Hudson began in 1831. In contrast to the Delaware and Raritan Canal, which was primarily a long-distance shipping route across New Jersey, especially for coal, the Morris Canal also served as a central artery within the New Jersey Highlands. Iron ore reached the canal from the Ringwood Mines in the Ramapo Mountains by way of a feeder canal and railroad, from mines in Sussex County and the northern part of Morris County by way of Lake Hopatcong, and from the Mine Hill area by rail. Before steam locomotives were common, the railcars were horse-drawn. Anthracite brought to the Highlands by canal went to ironworks at Boonton, Ringwood, Long Pond, and Pompton. New Jersey iron ore was shipped to mills in Pennsylvania as well as New Jersey. Mining again flourished in the New Jersey Highlands because of the canal, and then because of railroads. For several years in the 1890s, New Jersey was the leading producer of iron ore in the United States.

By the late 1890s, however, large, easily worked, easily shipped iron ore deposits near Lake Superior were in full production. The New Jersey mines once again could not meet the competition and fell into decline. Even though the New Jersey ores had a higher iron content, all but the largest mines had closed by 1900. A few of these mines, with their rich ore and well-established transportation links, continued production to the mid-twentieth century.

Uranium and Rare Earths

Depending on the composition of the rock, the first magma to melt out when rock is heated has the composition of granite: mostly feldspar, quartz, and iron and magnesium silicates. Along with the predominant minerals, most granites have a small percentage of accessory minerals composed of elements that are scarce in the country rock into which the granite intrudes but mobilize easily and are concentrated in the mix of magma and superheated steam of granitic melts. One of the accessory minerals in granite is allanite, a rare earth mineral that commonly includes the radioactive elements uranium and thorium in its crystal structure. Individual grains are sparsely distributed through the rock and tiny. Most are so small that they are spotted most easily by a surrounding zone a few tenths of an inch thick at most in which the rock has been discolored and fractured in a radial pattern by over a million years of radiation exposure.

Granites slightly enriched in uranium and rare earths are widespread in the New Jersey Highlands. The rocks enriched in uranium and rare earths have been dated as 990 to 940 million years old and may have melted from the slightly enriched rocks following the continental collision of the Ottawan Orogeny of 1,045 to 1,024 million years ago. Uranium and rare earths are enriched to minable levels in some younger granites and a few magnetite deposits. One mine,

Granite showing radiation damage, Buckwheat Pit, Franklin zinc mine. The radial fractures surrounding the small, black, radioactive grain to the left of the pencil are from over 1 billion years of radiation. —Photo by Richard Volkert, N.J. Geological Survey

the Charlotte Mine in Morris County, was briefly active in the late 1950s as a uranium mine but could just as easily been mined for rare earths. Drill holes showed that the deposit did not extend downdip, however, and the mining was abandoned after the shipment of a small quantity of ore. Granite pegmatite associated with iron ore at the Scrub Oaks iron mine, one of New Jersey's most productive for iron, was rich in rare earths but closed down in the 1960s before the value of rare earths was fully recognized.

Other occurrences were large enough and rich enough to attract the attention of major energy companies. By the 1970s, a number of companies, including Pennzoil, Exxon, Sohio, and Chevron, were evaluating uranium prospects and leasing land in Jefferson Township in anticipation of mining. By all accounts, the companies fully anticipated strong public support in view of the jobs and tax revenues that would be generated and were unprepared for the statewide storm of public protest that met the first mining proposal. Regulations were soon passed, first by the municipality, then the state, virtually prohibiting uranium mining.

SCHOOLEYS MOUNTAIN AND THE SCHOOLEY PENEPLAIN

There is little at Schooleys Mountain to suggest it has been at the center of a geologic controversy that has raged since the 1890s and still excites strong emotions today. Beginning in the 1880s, William Morris Davis of Columbia University, possibly inspired by looking across the Hudson to the level crest of the Palisades, proposed a cycle of landform development in which uplift of the land is followed by three phases: youth, in which steep, fast-flowing streams are cutting into the uplifted surface; maturity, in which the streams have thoroughly dissected the upland surface and the landscape is dominated by slopes; and old age, in which the land has been reduced to low hills and broad valleys, a peneplain. Davis chose Schooleys Mountain for naming the Schooley Peneplain, which he believed extended across much of the Appalachians. In his interpretation, the peneplain reached old age some time during the Cretaceous Period, then was uplifted, higher to the northwest, not as high to the southeast, and is now being dissected.

New Jersey's upland surfaces were held to reflect the summit level of the peneplain. They define a relatively even surface of durable rock sloping gently to the southeast and staying at the level of the peneplain while softer rock was eroded. Where the belts of resistant rock were narrow outcrops of single formations, as along Kittatinny Mountain, the Watchungs, and the Palisades, the Schooley Peneplain was represented by long stretches of nearly level ridgetops. Where belts of resistant rock were several miles wide and separated by belts of less resistant sedimentary rock, as in the New Jersey Highlands, gentle topography on upland surfaces at the tops of the ridges was held to be a remnant from the Schooley Peneplain, and the gently rolling topography in the valleys was held to be a more recent peneplain that was developing following uplift of the Schooley Peneplain. Cascading streams along the mountainsides were held to be dissecting the uplifted peneplain.

youth

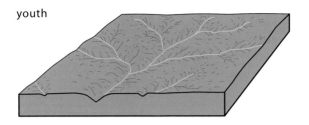

maturity

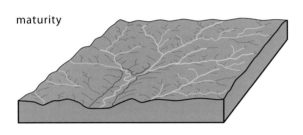

In the 1880s, William Davis proposed the cycle of erosion, which follows uplift of the land. Drainage systems progress from youthful streams to mature and then old rivers. The erosion of the uplands of New Jersey, however, began when sea level fell between 15 and 10 million years ago.
—Modified from Strahler, 1951

old age

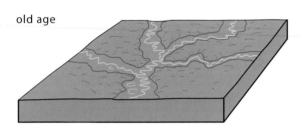

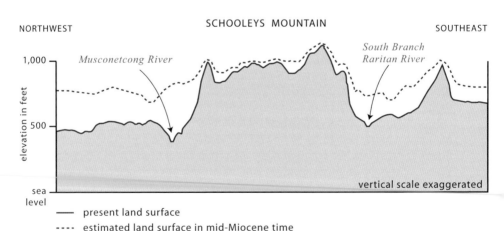

Profile across Schooleys Mountain. Topographic relief was increased by erosion of the valley floors following the mid-Miocene drop in sea level, not by uplift of the granite gneiss of the uplands. —Modified from Stanford, 2010

The idea was controversial from the beginning. Two of the primary objections were that there was not enough time in the Earth's history to reduce a landscape to a peneplain and that no good examples of peneplains exist today. Still, the cycle of landform development was appealing and an irresistible teaching tool, and the immensity of geologic time became apparent with radioactive dating of rocks. There is no question that the concept was overused, with peneplains being projected across broad areas and numerous peneplain levels being proposed based on correlating sometimes widely separated level areas to infer histories of repeated uplift. By the mid-twentieth century, however, admitting to the possibility of peneplains could get one dismissed as a fuzzy thinker. Still, the peneplain concept remained entrenched, and the Schooley Peneplain in particular continued to be presented even in educational publications of geological surveys.

More recently it has become clear that the mid-Atlantic region has seen little abrupt tectonic activity over at least several tens of millions of years. A long period of relative sea level stability provided the time and conditions needed to form an erosion with the elevation and extent of the Schooley Peneplain. The land surface had eroded to a surface that was gentle even in comparison with the subdued topography of modern New Jersey. Highlands stood only 100 to 300 feet above the valleys rather than 500 to 1,000 feet as they do today. At numerous places rivers ran directly across belts of harder rock rather than around them as most do now. Southern New Jersey was much of the time submerged beneath relatively shallow water as it had been since the Coastal Plain sediment wedge began accumulating in the Cretaceous Period. While this more recent interpretation is conceptually removed from the progression through youth, maturity, and old age envisioned in the 1890s, it does explain the relatively flat upland surfaces of the Highlands and the level summit lines of ridges as the result of erosion through a protracted time in which the base level to which streams could erode remained fairly stable.

Sea level changed toward the middle of Miocene time when, between 15 and 10 million years ago, Antarctica's glaciers grew from local ice caps to a continental glacier covering much of the continent with ice thousands of feet thick. As water evaporated from the oceans and became ice in Antarctica, sea level fell between 150 and 250 feet. The shoreline that previously skirted the Palisades, the Watchungs, and Sourland Mountain receded eastward, exposing the Coastal Plain. As sea level fell and rivers flowing across the plain deepened their valleys, the base level to which the rivers of northern New Jersey could cut their valleys also lowered. Erosion to the lowered base level increased the height of northern New Jersey's mountains above the valleys, not by uplifting the mountains, but by deepening the valleys. The effects of the downcutting are particularly notable in the Valley and Ridge and Highlands Provinces where the rivers shifted their flow from southeastward directly across ridges of relatively hard quartzite and granitic rock to southwestward along belts of more easily eroded sedimentary rock. Downcutting was fastest along the softer, southwestward-trending sedimentary rock belts, and the rivers shifted to new, deeper valleys, leaving wind gaps and abandoned valley segments as much as several hundred feet above today's rivers.

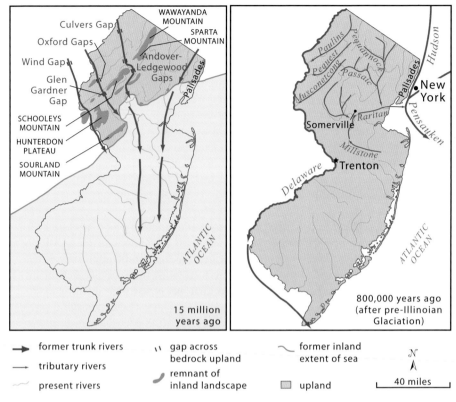

The wind gaps in New Jersey's uplands were the valleys of southeasterly flowing rivers until about 15 million years ago. —Modified from Stanford, 2005; Stanford, 2009

ROAD GUIDES IN THE HIGHLANDS AND VALLEY AND RIDGE

I-78
I-287—Phillipsburg
31 miles

For about 10 miles west of I-287, I-78 is still technically in the Newark Basin. However, it crosses over a number of faults, and the New Jersey Highlands are not far to the north of the highway. I-78 passes over the Ramapo fault zone near where the highway crosses the North Branch Raritan River. The Highlands to the northwest here are bordered by the Flemington Fault, which branches off the Ramapo Fault near Morristown and trends southwest toward Flemington. I-78 crosses the Flemington Fault near Lebanon.

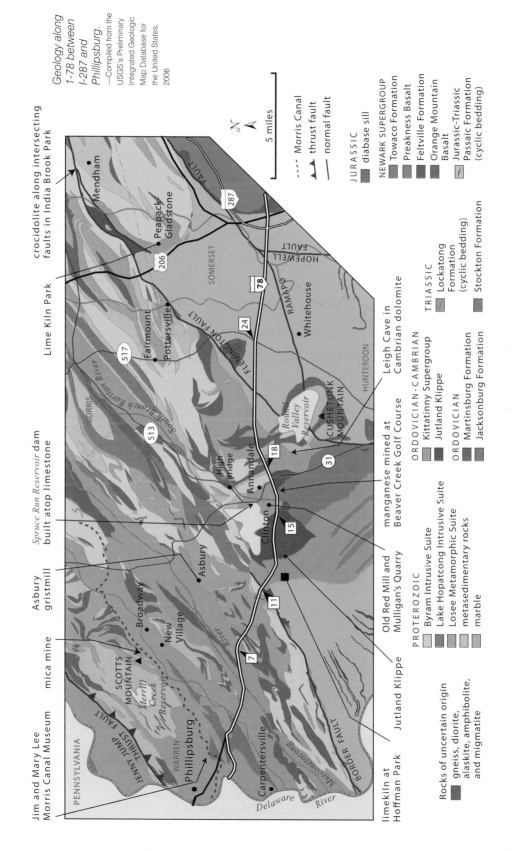

Geology along I-78 between I-287 and Phillipsburg.
—Compiled from the USGS's Preliminary Integrated Geologic Map Database for the United States, 2006

N
5 miles

- - - - Morris Canal
◄▲◄ thrust fault
——— normal fault

JURASSIC
diabase sill

NEWARK SUPERGROUP
Towaco Formation
Preakness Basalt
Feltville Formation
Orange Mountain Basalt
Jurassic-Triassic
Passaic Formation (cyclic bedding)

TRIASSIC
Lockatong Formation (cyclic bedding)
Stockton Formation

ORDOVICIAN-CAMBRIAN
Kittatinny Supergroup
Jutland Klippe

ORDOVICIAN
Martinsburg Formation
Jacksonburg Formation

PROTEROZOIC
Byram Intrusive Suite
Lake Hopatcong Intrusive Suite
Losee Metamorphic Suite
metasedimentary rocks
marble

Rocks of uncertain origin
gneiss, diorite, alaskite, amphibolite, and migmatite

crocidolite along intersecting faults in India Brook Park

Lime Kiln Park

Spruce Run Reservoir dam built atop limestone

Asbury gristmill

mica mine

Jim and Mary Lee Morris Canal Museum

Old Red Mill and Mulligan's Quarry

Jutland Klippe

limekiln at Hoffman Park

Leigh Cave in Cambrian dolomite

manganese mined at Beaver Creek Golf Course

Mendham
Peapack-Gladstone
206
287
SOMERSET
HOPEWELL FAULT
RAMAPO FAULT
78
Whitehouse
HUNTERDON
24
Fairmount
Pottersville
517
FLEMINGTON FAULT
MORRIS
South Branch Raritan River
513
Round Valley Reservoir
CUSHETUNK MOUNTAIN
18
31
High Bridge
Annandale
Clinton
15
Asbury
Broadway
New Village
7
11
SCOTTS MOUNTAIN
Merrill Creek Reservoir
JENNY JUMP THRUST FAULT
WARREN
PENNSYLVANIA
Phillipsburg
Carpentersville
Musconetcong
BORDER FAULT
Delaware River

Fibrous minerals like asbestos are common on fault surfaces. Where the Peapack-Ralston Fault and the Flemington Fault intersect at India Brook Park in Mendham, soft, blue coatings, some of which may include the asbestos mineral crocidolite, are spectacularly well developed. Crocidolite with inclusions of the granite country rock extends along about 300 feet of outcrop across the brook from the recreational fields. Collecting of the attractive blue rock is not recommended as crocidolite is recognized as a particularly dangerous carcinogen even among asbestos minerals. Crocidolite has also been found in sediment of India Brook and in water from nearby public water supply wells. Water from the wells meets a seven million fibers per liter Environmental Protection Agency maximum contaminant level based on the risk of developing benign intestinal polyps.

Round Valley and Spruce Run Reservoirs

Round Valley and Spruce Run Reservoirs were built primarily to supply water through the periodic droughts that affect the northeast. Round Valley Reservoir is in an ideal location for retaining water. It is surrounded on three sides by a horseshoe-shaped diabase ridge, Cushetunk Mountain. The mountain is visible to the south of I-78 west of the Whitehouse exit. The diabase intruded in Jurassic time during the rifting that split apart Pangea. The fourth side of the reservoir, to the west, backs up against Proterozoic gneiss of the Highlands. All that needed to be done was to build dams across three gaps through Cushetunk Mountain and get water into the bowl-shaped depression. Getting water in was a problem because the water level is 150 feet above the surrounding

A sinkhole, the gap filled with boulders and soil between layers in dolomite, was found during construction of I-78. —Photo by Don Monteverde, N.J. Geological Survey

countryside and has almost no drainage basin. Instead of being filled in the usual way, by streams, the water is pumped upward from the South Branch Raritan River, over 3 miles away.

Spruce Run Reservoir, just to the north of the highway at the Clinton exit, was somewhat controversial in that the main dam was constructed on limestone. Limestone is soluble in water and forms caves. New Jersey is not well-known for its caves, but sinkholes leading to underground cavities are common in its limestone areas. An entire house in Phillipsburg dropped into a sinkhole up to its second story when the ground collapsed. Leigh Cave, with 800 feet of passageway, is in Round Valley Recreation Area, west of Round Valley Reservoir and only a few miles from the Spruce Run dam. Leigh Cave is in Cambrian dolomite just below Proterozoic granite gneiss that was thrust over the dolomite. (The entrance to Leigh Cave is gated and the cave is accessible to only bats. Humans may visit by special arrangement.) Some contended that the proposed reservoir would drain to underground passages and be unable to hold water. Before dam construction was begun, the entire footing area was drilled to evaluate conditions. Openings were found and sealed with cement. The dam has not leaked.

The Old Red Mill and Mulligan's Quarry

The Old Red Mill at Clinton is one of the icons of New Jersey tourism, photographed for countless calendars, brochures, and postcards. It is now a historical museum, but the bucolic setting belies its past industrial history. The mill was larger than the gristmills built on almost every New Jersey stream and powerful

The Old Red Mill at Clinton. The cliff in the background is the wall of Mulligan's Quarry. —Photo by Ted Pallis, N.J. Geological Survey

enough to mill quarry products. In the 1800s, the mill and the adjacent Mulligan's Quarry in limestone were noisy, dangerous workplaces. In one example from the museum exhibits, the mill was at one time grinding talc and covering the town of Clinton in fine, white powder. Complaints from the citizens ensued, and the mill stopped milling talc. Instead, for a time, the mill switched to milling graphite, which coated the town in a fine, black powder.

Mulligan's Quarry has become known as more than a historic site where limestone was mined and burned for plaster and agricultural lime. In the 1980s, radon entering houses from rock below their foundations was increasingly recognized as a local public health hazard. Radon, which is emitted from uranium, was anticipated in the granitic rocks of the Highlands. There is enough uranium in some Highlands rock to mine as ore. The uranium was not anticipated in dolomitic limestone areas, and it came as a surprise in 1986 when some of the highest levels in New Jersey were found in Clinton in an area with limestone bedrock. The radon was discovered only because a worker at a nearby plant where radioactive materials were being used set off alarms. The radioactivity was traced to his home, then to other homes in the neighborhood, which was close by the quarry. An investigation in the quarry rock soon revealed that the rock had been severely fractured at some point after the limestones were deposited. The fractures had healed with phosphate minerals that, unlike limestone, are widely known to contain uranium impurities.

Based in part on the unexpected levels in the Clinton neighborhood, an evaluation of indoor radon was expanded to the entire state. Houses with problem radon levels were found throughout the state, even in the sandy Outer Coastal Plain where they were least expected. Fortunately, remedial action is usually inexpensive and effective. For radon in water, a charcoal filter is usually sufficient. For radon in indoor air, the problem can usually be fixed by venting air from beneath the house.

Jutland Klippe and Clinton Point Manganese Mine

Eastern North America was fringed by a bank of carbonate rock, mostly dolomite with some limestone, in the Cambrian and Ordovician Periods. Seaward of the bank, mud and sand were deposited in deeper water. The entire area from the easternmost carbonate bank deposits to the edge of today's continental shelf is covered by more recent sediments, and we cannot look to the east to find out what sediments were being deposited offshore from the carbonate banks. We can, by a quirk, look above the carbonate bank dolomite. In the Taconic Orogeny some offshore rocks were thrust upward and westward above the carbonate bank deposits. They are preserved today as a klippe, an erosional remnant of a thrust sheet in which older rocks are surrounded by and above rocks of the same age or younger. The rocks of the Jutland Klippe, named for exposures in Jutland just to the south of I-78, are mostly shale and sandstone with thin beds of limestone and dolomite. The kinds of rock and sedimentary structures in the rock suggest deposition on the outer continental shelf or upper part of the continental slope. There are few easily accessible, good exposures of the Jutland Klippe rocks. A few beds of the shale and limestone are exposed on the west side of NJ 31 just south of its intersection with I-78.

Trench of a manganese mine near Clinton circa 1918. —Photo by Henry Kummel

Manganese is one of several commodities that occur in New Jersey but too impure, in amounts too small, or in a form too difficult to refine to be profitably mined. Manganese mining was attempted only at one deposit, in Jutland Klippe rocks between Clinton and Annandale. The manganese ore was initially mistaken for iron but had been identified as manganese by 1868. At the time, one railroad car loaded with ore was sent to blast furnaces at Bethlehem, Pennsylvania. The ore was not satisfactory, and the mining apparently ceased until World War I, when the price of manganese more than quadrupled. Once again, the mines opened briefly. This time two carloads of ore were shipped. As of 1918, two additional carloads remained along the tracks and everything at the mine had been abandoned. Only a few shallow depressions on the Beaver Brook Golf Course remain as evidence of the mining.

The origin of the manganese minerals is unclear. For many years it was attributed to leaching of manganese from overlying rocks by groundwater and deposition in the fractured shale host rock. The deposit at Clinton and elsewhere in the Jutland Klippe rocks, however, follows bedding rather than fractures. This suggests that the manganese was related to environmental conditions when the rock was initially deposited rather than to later weathering. In one intriguing possibility, Donald Monteverde of the New Jersey Geological Survey has suggested that the manganese, similar to other manganese deposits, may have accumulated in stratified ocean water. Today most of the ocean is oxygenated from top to bottom, but this has not always been the case. Oxygen-starved water can develop in deep, narrow basins where oxygenated surface water does not circulate. Also, at numerous times in the geologic past, ocean water did not circulate from top to bottom as it does now. At these times the deep ocean became devoid of oxygen.

We know the Jutland rocks were deposited in the ocean because there are fossils of graptolites, an ocean-dwelling organism. Layering in the host shale beds is alternately red and green, indicating that the water alternated between oxygen rich, when oxidized iron colored the rock red, and oxygen poor, when chemically reduced iron colored the rock green. Manganese is soluble in oxygen-poor water and insoluble in oxygen-rich water. In a stratified ocean, manganese in the oxygenated water toward the surface precipitates and sinks toward the bottom. Manganese in the oxygen-deficient water toward the bottom dissolves and mixes upward. Accumulation of manganese to a richness suitable for mining occurs where the ocean bottom is at the interface between waters rich and poor in oxygen. Alternatively, Monteverde suggests that the manganese may have accumulated below the sediment surface at a depth at which conditions went from oxidizing to reducing.

Asbury Mill

A few graphite deposits were mined in New Jersey. The mines are largely collapsed and forgotten, but at least three mills in which rock was ground to free the graphite still stand. The Red Mill in Clinton is the best maintained, and the other two are decrepit but structurally sound. An 1863 gristmill in Asbury, converted to process graphite in 1895, was home to the Asbury Graphite Company until the company moved to a larger building in the 1930s. The company still operates from the 1930s building, within sight of the old mill, and is today one of the world's largest processors of graphite, none of it mined in New Jersey. The old mill may at some point be open as a historic site. The Black Mill in Bloomsbury has been vacant for many years. The exterior design is protected as a historic structure; the interior is being converted to apartments.

Broadway Mica Mine

About 5 miles north of the Bloomsbury exit from I-78, winding county roads bring you to the village of Broadway, at one time a stop on the Morris Canal. Mica was never particularly important among New Jersey's mineral products, but several mines were opened. The mica was used mostly for windows on stove doors. The largest of the mines was about a mile north of Broadway toward the crest of Scotts Mountain. The mica was in granitic veins cutting the gneissic bedrock. Crystals were reportedly more than a foot across through a vein 200 feet long, 30 feet wide, and 30 feet deep. Other mines were opened west of Morristown, south of Mendham, and on Scotts Mountain at a location now flooded by the Merrill Creek Reservoir. The mines were closed from the late nineteenth century until increased demand during World War I allowed several mines to reopen briefly.

This 1863 mill was used by the Asbury Graphite Company from 1895 until the 1930s
—Photo by D. Harper

Merrill Creek Reservoir

Merrill Creek Reservoir is unusual in being built to provide water to make up for water removed from the Delaware River to use for cooling at fourteen power plants belonging to seven different utility companies. Water is piped from the Delaware through a 3-mile-long, 5-foot-diameter tunnel through the springtime when the river is high and returned to the river through the summer. There would otherwise be unacceptably low flow in the Delaware due to the combination of naturally low flow and increased evaporation at the power plants due to high summertime electricity usage.

Portland Cement Quarries in the Musconetcong Valley

Portland cement is made by roasting a mixture of limestone and clay and is used mostly as a binder in concrete. The limestone quarried in the Musconetcong Valley is especially convenient for cement production. It comes from the upper part of the Jacksonburg Formation, informally known as the Cement Rock Member. The member is unusually thick in the valley and consists of about two-thirds pure, fine-grained calcium carbonate and about one-third kaolinite clay from sediment and volcanic ash washed into the basin. With the addition of a small amount of calcium carbonate, this member of the Jacksonburg was ideal for manufacturing portland cement.

Cement was produced in New Jersey beginning in the 1890s but not in large amounts. The production methods were inefficient, cement was not a widely used building material, and most cement was brought from Europe cheaply as ballast. This had begun to change by the early twentieth century with the development of rotary kilns, which could be run continuously, instead of vertical kilns, which had to be cooled, emptied, and reloaded for each batch of cement. Thomas Edison became involved in the cement industry through his involvement with iron mining. Ore processing at an iron mine owned by one of Edison's companies produced large amounts of waste sand from which magnetite ore had been separated. Edison sold the sand to cement producers until, in 1899, envisioning thousands of miles of concrete roads and cement buildings,

Cement Rock Member of the Jacksonburg Formation, impure limestone used for the production of portland cement, along I-78. —Photo by Don Monteverde, N.J. Geological Survey

Edison cement quarry in 1935. —Photo courtesy of N.J. Geological Survey

he entered the cement business. By 1902, he had set up kilns at New Village twice the size of any seen before. The immediate result was an oversupply of cement, rendering the operation barely profitable at best until 1922, the year construction of Yankee Stadium began. Edison sold 45,000 barrels of cement for the stadium.

Limestone for portland cement is no longer quarried in New Jersey, but a half dozen closed quarries still remain. Some are immense, with sheer, 100-foot cliffs dropping straight to deep water. The quarries are all on private land and posted. The better place to see the Jacksonburg Formation is near the village of Hope, off I-80 in Warren County.

Royal Green Marble Quarry

Among the most striking of New Jersey's building stones is green serpentine, quarried at Hoboken and just north of Phillipsburg. The Phillipsburg quarries, primarily the Royal Green Marble Quarry along the Delaware River bluffs, were by far the larger producers. Most of the serpentine was either crushed for talcum powder or cut and polished as verde antique marble for interior use. The serpentine occurs in the Franklin Marble of Proterozoic age.

Kittatinny Dolomitic Limestones along Carpentersville Road

From colonial times on, limestone was roasted in limekilns wherever it was found. The burned lime was used for plastering walls, mortaring stonework, and liming agricultural fields. By the twentieth century, it had become cheaper and easier for farmers to buy the lime. The limekilns are no longer used but still dot the valleys in various states of disrepair. Most are small and burned lime for the farms on which they stood. Many are piles of rock identifiable as limekilns only by the chalk-white blocks of partially burned limestone. Larger kilns can be seen near a 1,000-foot-long exposure of dolomite of the Kittatinny limestones along River Road south of Carpentersville.

The United Methodist Church in Washington in Warren County was built with serpentine from quarries near Phillipsburg.
—Photo by D. Harper

Limekilns along River Road south of Carpentersville. —Photo by Don Monteverde, N.J. Geological Survey

The outcrops near the kilns are one of the few continuous exposures of the dolomitic Kittatinny limestones in the area and have a long been studied to decipher the history of the carbonate bank that fringed the North American shore of the Iapetus Ocean in the Cambrian and Ordovician Periods. Carbonate banks and reefs, like other large ecosystems, include a wide variety of microenvironments. Corals and many other organisms had not yet evolved when the Kittatinny limestones were deposited. The carbonate bank was instead built mostly by algae and photosynthetic bacteria. Still, many microenvironments of a coral reef existed on the Paleozoic bank and left traces in the rocks. With careful searching, you can find crossbedding, oolites, stromatolites, and edgewise conglomerates.

The oolites formed in a manner somewhat analogous to hailstones building up as water freezes in layers on ice held aloft by updrafts. They form in water oversaturated with calcium carbonate. As the grains are rolled about by waves, calcium carbonate builds up in layers.

Mud-cracked surfaces and iron oxide crusts show that parts of the bank were sometimes above water. Edgewise conglomerates (semiconsolidated lime mud ripped up by waves and currents, then redeposited in a jumbled mass) show that waves or currents were sometimes strong across the top of the bank.

Stromatolites, deposited by algae growing in mats in shallow water, indicate that the water was shallow and clear enough that light at the bottom was sufficient to support photosynthesis. If you are able to find cross sections of the cabbagelike stromatolites, you may be able to see that the bottoms of the fossils point upward, toward the top of the outcrop. Rather than simply being tilted to

Oolites in dolomite of the Kittatinny limestones.
—Photo by Don Monteverde, N.J. Geological Survey

Edgewise conglomerates in dolomite of the Kittatinny limestones.
—Photo by Don Monteverde, N.J. Geological Survey

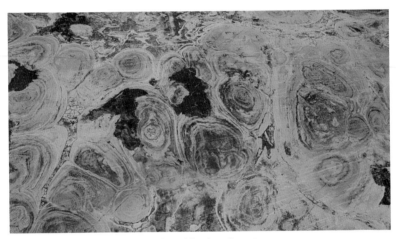

Stromatolites in dolomite of the Kittatinny limestones. —Photo by Michael Flite

its present 70 degrees from the horizontal, the sedimentary bedding here was rotated a full 110 degrees and is overturned. In deeper microenvironments, darker-colored rocks mottled with burrows were deposited where waves and currents were not constantly reworking the sediment.

Pennsylvania Border

Among New Jersey's boundaries, only the Pennsylvania boundary has been without dispute. The Pennsylvania border was set by a 1789 treaty between the two states, signed while there could be treaties between states, after the Revolutionary War but before the Constitution was ratified. The border runs down the middle of the Delaware River.

I-80
Denville—Delaware Water Gap
40 miles

West of Parsippany, I-80 crosses the Ramapo Fault, the western border fault of the Newark Basin, and climbs onto the New Jersey Highlands. Along most of the boundary, the Highlands rise steeply above the Newark Basin, but I-80 follows an abandoned river valley in its climb, and there is no obvious escarpment. In a mile and a half the route climbs 250 feet. Eastbound travelers have a view across the Watchung ridges and Newark Basin toward New York City.

It might appear as if the Highlands rose upward along the Ramapo Fault, but the Highlands are an erosional feature. They remain high because their granite and gneiss bedrock is harder and wears away more slowly than the softer sedimentary rock prevalent in the Newark Basin. The tectonic forces that opened the Newark rift basin and eventually the Atlantic Ocean during the rifting of Pangea were extensional, and the predominant effects were subsidence to the east, downdropping of the Newark Basin, and filling of the downdropped basin with sediment. Those sediments have been eroding for millions of years. By one estimate, 3 miles of sedimentary rock has been eroded from parts of the Newark Basin.

Dover Mining District and the Mt. Hope Mine

West of the Ramapo Fault, I-80 enters the Dover Mining District. For more than 250 years this area was the center of iron mining in New Jersey. When the Mt. Hope Mine closed in 1958, the Dover Mining District had produced over 26 million tons of magnetite ore, about 70 percent of the state's total. The mines closed because the underground operations were no longer profitable, not because the ore was exhausted. In one estimate, 600 million tons of recoverable ore remains in the ground.

The Mt. Hope mines exploited thirteen large, distinct ore bodies and numerous smaller lenses of ore under a bewildering array of separate mine openings and ownerships in a small area near the town of Mt. Hope. Taken together, they were the most productive of the New Jersey iron mines. The Lenni Lenape Indians brought the black rock known as succasunna to the attention of the colonists. Surface mining may have begun as early as the 1600s, and well-documented mining dates to 1710. When mining techniques improved and pumps capable of moving water from deep beneath the surface became available, deeper shafts were sunk, ore bodies were connected by tunnels, and ownership was consolidated under a single owner, the Mt. Hope Mining Company. Like all the iron mines that survived into the twentieth century, the Mt. Hope Mine became a large industrial and engineering operation.

The larger ore bodies have been described as shaped like double-edged swords, 10 to 20 feet thick, 100 to 7,000 feet wide, and sloping down into the ground at angles of 10 to 40 degrees. They followed the layering of the gneissic bedrock for the most part, but cut across structural trends in some places and were clearly emplaced after the gneiss had been metamorphosed. Their length

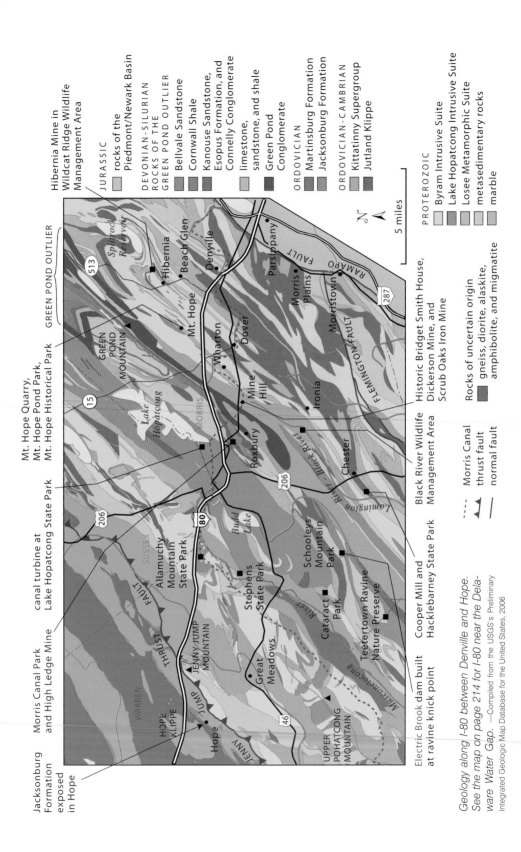

Geology along I-80 between Denville and Hope. See the map on page 214 for I-80 near the Delaware Water Gap. —Compiled from the USGS's Preliminary Integrated Geologic Map Database for the United States, 2006

JURASSIC
- rocks of the Piedmont/Newark Basin

DEVONIAN–SILURIAN ROCKS OF THE GREEN POND OUTLIER
- Bellvale Sandstone
- Cornwall Shale
- Kanouse Sandstone, Esopus Formation, and Connelly Conglomerate
- limestone, sandstone, and shale
- Green Pond Conglomerate

ORDOVICIAN
- Martinsburg Formation
- Jacksonburg Formation

ORDOVICIAN–CAMBRIAN
- Kittatinny Supergroup
- Jutland Klippe

PROTEROZOIC
- Byram Intrusive Suite
- Lake Hopatcong Intrusive Suite
- Losee Metamorphic Suite
- metasedimentary rocks
- marble

N

5 miles

Rocks of uncertain origin
- gneiss, diorite, alaskite, amphibolite, and migmatite

--- Morris Canal
◄ thrust fault
— normal fault

Jacksonburg Formation exposed in Hope

Morris Canal Park and High Ledge Mine

canal turbine at Lake Hopatcong State Park

Mt. Hope Quarry, Mt. Hope Park, Mt. Hope Historical Park

Hibernia Mine in Wildcat Ridge Wildlife Management Area

Electric Brook dam built at ravine knick point

Cooper Mill and Hacklebarney State Park

Black River Wildlife Management Area

Historic Bridget Smith House, Dickerson Mine, and Scrub Oaks Iron Mine

Miner drilling blast holes at the Scrub Oaks Iron Mine in 1941.
—Photo courtesy of N.J. Geological Survey

is unknown. The ore was followed in one case to 2,740 feet below the surface, but none of the workings reached the end of the deposits.

As is usual with ore bodies sloping more than a few degrees, the Mt. Hope magnetite was mined upward along stopes, which are underground excavations created by tunneling under the ore, then blasting the ore down from the roof of the tunnel. In the stoping method used at the Mt. Hope Mine, gravity dropped the ore blasted from the roof of the stope into a series of funnel-shaped openings to a horizontal tunnel or an incline from which it was moved to crushing and loading equipment, then to a shaft where it was hauled to the surface. After the rock was blasted down and taken away, hazardous loose rock was pried down or bolted into the roof of the stope. The next higher rock in the stope was then drilled and blasted. The blasting, ore removal, and stabilization were repeated until the stope reached the next higher stope or the top of the ore body.

The mines at Mt. Hope were on property now divided among Morris County's Mt. Hope Historical Park, Mt. Hope Pond Park, and the Mt. Hope Quarry. The parks are now peaceful woods, but the area is honeycombed with mines. Most of the entrances are collapsed or sealed, but some pits are deeper than they appear. Even the shallower openings can be dangerous. Stay on the trails in both parks.

A guide to numbered stops along the red and orange trails can usually be picked up in the parking lot of the Mt. Hope Historical Park. The woods are

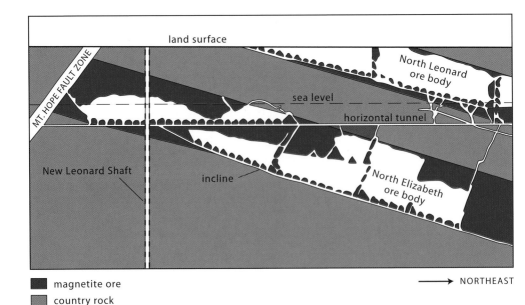

magnetite ore
country rock

⟶ NORTHEAST

Stopes in two of the thirteen major ore bodies worked at the Mt. Hope Mine. At the time the mine was working, the shallow stopes at the southwest end of the North Leonard ore body were open to the surface, 10 or 20 feet wide, and in some places over 200 feet deep.
—Modified from Sims, 1958

littered with boulders of red quartzite conglomerate of the Green Pond Formation and were brought here from Green Pond Mountain by glaciers during the ice age. Green Pond Mountain is the next ridge to the west, sometimes visible through the trees. The trails follow old roads and are littered with coal and pieces of magnetite ore. Beside the trails are pits the size of large buildings from the Teabo, Allen, and Richard Mines, spoil piles with pieces of magnetite ore, building foundations, and occasional lengths of steel cable and rusting machinery. Much of the material on the spoil piles is magnetite. Further on, the orange trail follows the abandoned bed of the Mt. Hope Mineral Railroad, which served the mines.

To reach the Mt. Hope Quarry from the parking lot at Mt. Hope Historical Park, take a short walk to a power line that brings you to the white trail then, after a short walk, to the steep, rocky blue trail leading to a spot overlooking the Mt. Hope Quarry. Before it was a quarry, this was the site of the New Leonard shaft of the Mt. Hope Mine. The New Leonard shaft was sunk in World War II and was used for raising ore until 1958. The large structure toward the center of the quarry was the headframe for the New Leonard shaft, which housed the equipment that hauled ore upward tons at a time.

The quarry is now one of the largest in New Jersey and among the ten largest in the United States. It is an important supplier of stone and asphalt and a center for the treatment and recycling of contaminated soil. Explosions are sometimes heard within the parks. They might be from testing at Picatinny Arsenal, bordering the park to the west, but are more likely quarry blasts.

Hibernia Mines

The Hibernia mines, similar to the Mt. Hope mines, began production from surface workings long before the Revolutionary War. They developed as separate mines under numerous owners, became one of New Jersey's largest producers, continued production into the twentieth century, and eventually were consolidated under a single operator. The entire group of mines exploited a single series of ore shoots at least 2 miles long and totaling 10 to 20 feet wide. Beginning in 1863, ore from the mines was shipped to the Morris Canal by the Hibernia Mine Railroad. In 1879, a 2,500-foot-long railroad tunnel was completed to allow underground loading of ore directly from mines owned by the several different companies working the deposit. By the time the mines closed in the early 1900s, the ore had been worked to 2,800 feet belowground without running out of ore. The Beach Glen Mine, along the same ore trend but across Green Pond Road, was briefly reopened in the 1920s.

Unlike the mines of the Mt. Hope area, which are hemmed in by the Mt. Hope Quarry, Picatinny Arsenal, and residential areas, the Hibernia Mines are isolated within the Wildcat Ridge Wildlife Management Area. Numerous marked and unmarked trails through the area lead past sealed or collapsed mine workings, railroad grades, wagon roads, stonework industrial structures, and a historic mining village that once had several hundred residents, a school,

Nineteenth-century iron furnace at Splitrock Reservoir near Hibernia.
—Photo by Richard Volkert, N.J. Geological Survey

a hotel, a Catholic church, and saloons. Today there is little to be seen except foundations and a large graveyard with headstones in English and Eastern European languages.

The trails can be reached from the end of Upper Hibernia Road near the village site or from a parking area on Lower Hibernia Road (Sunnyside Road on some maps). Several trails lead from parking areas at the end of Upper Hibernia Road. The trail along the closed part of Upper Hibernia Road passes through parts of the abandoned village and most of the mines. It reaches Lower Hibernia Road about a mile downhill. The mines are much safer now than they had been for decades. At the close of mining, the ore had been worked to the surface, leaving open trenches about 20 feet across, tens of feet long, and hundreds of feet down to where the mines were filled with water. The trenches and most other openings were blasted shut and filled over in 1972. Collapsed fill was replaced and most of the remaining openings were sealed in 1989. The fill, tailings piles, abandoned stone structures, and mine workings are still unstable and dangerous. Do not go near them. Pieces of magnetite ore, coal, glass, and pottery are part of this historic site and should not be collected.

From the parking area on Lower Hibernia Road just after the turnoff from Green Pond Road, the white-blazed Four Birds Trail passes a series of large stone foundations and former mining sites before reaching the Upper Hibernia Road parking area about a mile up. The Hibernia Mine Railroad tunnel is a few hundred feet from the lower parking lot. Follow the short Overlook Trail branching from the Four Birds Trail up to the old railroad grade, then along the railroad grade to the tunnel. On hot days the tunnel is evident long before you get there. Temperature in the mine is about 55 degrees year-round. In summer the chilled, dense air in the thousands of feet of workings creates a downdraft

Entrance to the Hibernia Mine Railroad tunnel. —Photo by D. Harper

that can be felt sometimes hundreds of feet from the entrance. On humid days, a mist enshrouds and further cools the entire area. In the winter, before bat populations were decimated by white nose syndrome, the warm air kept the twenty-five thousand bats hibernating in the mine from freezing.

The tunnel is closed with a grating of iron bars far enough apart for bats to go through, but too closely spaced for people. Vandalism has been a serious problem, and some people have even brought portable generators, electric saws, and torches to cut open the gates. If you find the gate open, report the condition and please do not go in.

Bridget Smith House in Mine Hill

The lives of miners until well into the twentieth century were neither secure nor well rewarded. Few longtime miners escaped injury, and there were many widows of the mines. Unlike in the coalfields of Appalachia, other livelihoods were available and few sons followed their fathers into the mines. The miners, commonly immigrants, lived in small houses with large families and few amenities. The larger mines operated company stores, and purchases were deducted from the next paycheck. In most months, the miner would owe the entire amount or more.

The Bridget Smith House at 124 Randolph Avenue in Mine Hill gives some idea of the life of a mine widow. Bridget Smith, an Irish immigrant, lived in one half of the small house with her six children. The other half was rented to another widow. The house is little changed from when it was built in 1855 and from when Bridget Smith bought it for $300 in 1879. It is the only essentially unmodified example of miner's housing from this time in northern New Jersey and is on the New Jersey and National Registers of Historic Places. It has operated with limited hours as a museum since 1998.

Green Pond Mountain and Outlier

Between Wharton and Ledgewood, I-80 crosses the Green Pond Outlier. The belt of rock is called an outlier because its relatively young Paleozoic sedimentary rocks resemble those in the Valley and Ridge Province to the west but here are completely surrounded by older rock. As in the Valley and Ridge, ridges in the Green Pond Outlier are developed on quartzite and valleys are eroded into softer rock, mostly shale and limestone. The outlier is 43 miles long, as much as 4 miles wide, and extends from Cornwall, New York, to just south of I-80 in New Jersey. Little of the Green Pond Outlier rock is visible from I-80.

Green Pond Mountain, one of the ridges of the outlier, is made of Green Pond Conglomerate and is prominently developed along NJ 15 about 1.5 miles north of its intersection with I-80. The Green Pond Conglomerate and the Shawangunk Formation at the Delaware Water Gap, 20 miles to the west along I-80, were deposited at about the same time, both shed westward from mountains raised during the Taconic Orogeny. The two formations are in many ways similar, but the Green Pond has more pieces of easily destroyed materials like shale and sandstone and larger rocks in its conglomerate beds. The coarser grain size and greater abundance of easily destroyed materials are two of many reasons that geologists concluded long ago that both formations, together with red beds and shale of the overlying formations, were derived from a highland to the east and that the Green Pond Conglomerate was deposited closer to the highland than the Shawangunk. The continuity of quartzite ridges of about this same age along much of the Appalachians indicates that the highlands ran for hundreds of miles roughly parallel to today's coastline.

The Green Pond Conglomerate was deposited closer to the source of sediment and has an abundance of easily destroyed rock fragments, including the red shale chips visible in this photo. —Photo by Don Monteverde, N.J. Geological Survey

The Shawangunk was deposited farther away and most of the rock fragments had broken down by the time the sediment came to rest. The pebbles in the Shawangunk are mostly quartz. —Photo by D. Harper

High Ledge Mine and Morris Canal Planes

The High Ledge Mine is in Morris Canal Park, a Roxbury town park near the intersection of Canal Road and Emmans Road (south of I-80, exit 28). It is representative of many small New Jersey iron mines that sat idle much of the time, opened when prices were high, and closed permanently when the Lake Superior mines came into production. The High Ledge Mine is somewhat atypical in that it briefly reopened in 1911 before being permanently abandoned in 1912. About 2,000 tons of ore was removed from two shafts and a horizontal tunnel dug a few hundred feet back into the hillside.

From the parking lot at Morris Canal Park, a short walk past a pond brings you to the bottom of one of the canal's inclined planes. The Morris Canal crossed a more rugged terrain than is usual for a canal. Where hills were too high and steep for the locks usually used to raise canal barges, the barges were hauled up inclined planes by water-powered machinery. Barges were held waiting in the pond at the park entrance until it was their turn to be floated onto a

Turbine housing and turbine for raising boats up inclined planes on the Morris Canal. The housing is at the Morris Canal Park in Roxbury Township. The turbine is at Hopatcong State Park. Water entered the turbine from underneath to lift the spinning part above the bearing surface. —Photos by D. Harper

wheeled carriage, tied down, and hauled by cable to the top of the plane then over a berm into the next higher section of canal, where they were untied and refloated. The carriages, the steel rails they ran on, and the water-powered turbine and cable-winding drum that hauled the boats up and lowered them down are long gone, but the holding pond and stonework with polished grooves left by the cable remain. Bits of anthracite coal that fell from the boats litter the ground. A look at the stonework turbine housing near the top of the plane more than repays the effort of the short climb up the hill. The iron turbine is gone from inside the housing, but similar turbines can be seen at Hopatcong State Park and, with restricted hours, at the Jim and Mary Lee Morris Canal Museum. The turbines are similar in concept to a spinning lawn sprinkler attached to a cable spool, but enormous.

To get to the High Ledge Mine, return to the bottom of the plane and follow the trail with blue markers up an abandoned road. The mine is a few hundred yards in, on the left just past a crest in the road. Do not go near the mine openings. The fences around them are sometimes in poor repair, and the shafts are slippery, deep, and usually filled with water. Waste rock with pieces of magnetite is still piled a safe distance from the mine entrances. The magnetite is easy to identify because it's black, heavy, and can be picked up with a magnet.

Ledgewood and Andover Gaps

I-80 follows a valley that carried a river southeastward across New Jersey until the Miocene Epoch. The valley, called the Ledgewood Gap here, cuts across the entire width of the Highlands and continues northward across the ridges of the Valley and Ridge Province and southward across the Watchung ridges of the Newark Basin. It has been a convenient place for roads, railways, and sections of the Morris Canal because it doesn't repeatedly climb ridges. The valley, followed by a rail line, cuts through Sparta Mountain at Andover.

Budd Lake

Budd Lake started as a glacial lake dammed between ice of the Illinoian glaciation and a ridge of Proterozoic rock to the south. When the ice melted, it left a moraine that holds back the lake today, which still drains across the Proterozoic rock through its Illinoian outlet stream. Because it has remained a lake since the Illinoian, the bottom sediments retain a record of climate through the entire Wisconsinan ice age.

Large, well-preserved fossils have contributed greatly to our understanding of the Earth and its history, but their rarity limits their usefulness in many geologic applications. Microfossils like pollen grains, spores, diatoms, and the one-celled animals known as foraminifera are often much more useful. Much of our knowledge of ice age and more recent climates is from pollen collected from peat bog and lake sediment cores. It would be unusual to find a complete tooth or bone in a 2-inch-diameter core, but pollen grains can often be recovered by the thousands. In 1968, Kathryn Harmon counted 29,662 pollen grains and spores from 66 types of plants from a 45-foot core collected in a bog along the northwest shore of Budd Lake. Profiles for five of the plant types—pines, oaks, spruce, nonarboreal pollen (not from trees) and ragweeds—are especially helpful in reconstructing past conditions. The height of the ice age is marked by spikes in spruce and nonarboreal pollen. Warmer, moister conditions beginning about 8,000 years ago are marked by a decrease in pine pollen and an increase in oak pollen. An abundance of ragweed pollen in the top few feet of sediment has been attributed to the clearing of forests for agriculture. Ragweeds are wind pollinated and produce enormous amounts of pollen.

Glacial Lake Succasunna, Cooper Mill, and Hacklebarney Gorge

Illinoian glacial deposits have been overridden by Wisconsinan glaciers through most of their extent in New Jersey but are preserved in a 3- to 8-mile-wide belt that extends between Morris Plains and the Delaware River. Unlike the much older pre-Illinoian deposits still farther to the south, which have largely been removed by erosion, the Illinoian deposits still have topographic features formed during the glaciation. Good examples can be seen in and near the Black River Wildlife Management Area, 4 miles south of I-80 exit 28. Before the Illinoian ice advance, the Black River valley drained northward. At the height of the advance, northward drainage became impossible because the Illinoian wall of ice stood across the valley. Instead, the valley ponded to form Glacial Lake Succasunna, and water spilled southward at Cooper Mill, the lowest point on the drainage divide. As is usual when a glacier ends in a lake, a delta built outward from the ice. Even though there are many similar deltas from the Wisconsinan advance, the older Glacial Lake Succasunna delta is among the clearest and most accessible. The knolls along Ironia Road west of Ironia were built at the edge of the ice sheet. The flat delta plain extends southward from the knolls for about a half mile into the Black River Wildlife Management Area and ends at a 20-foot drop down the delta front into marshes along the Black River.

The delta is littered with pebbles carried south by meltwater streams and exposed to about 150,000 years of weathering. In comparison with pebbles from Wisconsinan deposits, quartzite pebbles from the Illinoian are a little different: Illinoian Granitic pebbles have a rough surface, contrasting with the smooth surfaces of granitic pebbles in Wisconsinan deposits, and there are fewer limestone and dolomite pebbles. Limestone pebbles that have not crumbled to soil are deeply weathered.

The Wisconsinan glaciers did not come as far south in the Black River valley as the Illinoian glaciers, but they again blocked the river and, once again, created a glacial lake that drained southward at Cooper Mill into what had previously been the headwaters of a small stream. Unlike the Illinoian deposits, the Wisconsinan deposits filled the valley to an elevation higher than the outflow stream at Cooper Mill and prevented the Black River from returning to its northward course after the ice melted back. Marshlands remaining from Glacial Lake Succasunna upstream from Cooper Mill are visible from US 206 just north of Chester. The Black River, known as the Lamington River downstream from Cooper Mill, continues to spill southward into the waterfalls, gorges, and boulders of today's Hacklebarney State Park as it did in the ice age.

Cooper Mill, now part of a Morris County park, was built in 1826. Visitors can have wheat ground between 2,000-pound millstones as they watch.

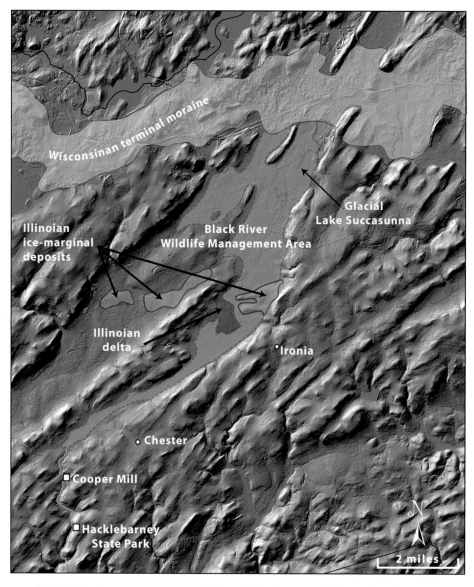

Glacial Lake Succasunna was ponded in both the Illinoian and Wisconsinan ice ages. After the Wisconsinan ice age, the northward preglacial course of the Black River remained blocked by the terminal moraine. Glacial Lake Succasunna became the present Black River marshlands through a combination of infilling by sediment, downcutting at Cooper Mill, and uplift to the north after the weight of the glaciers was lifted. —Landscape image from Ted Pallis, N.J. Geological Survey

Cooper Mill. —Photo by Richard Volkert, N.J. Geological Survey

The Black (Lamington) River flows through boulders of Proterozoic gneiss in Hackle-barney State Park. —Photo by Jane Alexander, College of Staten Island–City University of New York

The mill is at the spot where the river overflowed its previous drainage basin. This was not the first mill to be built here. There have been mills at this spot since the 1760s. The mills were here because the ice age reversal of drainage across the divide created an ideal setting for water power. Upstream the nearly flat marshland allowed a large amount of water to be ponded behind a small dam. Downstream, the steep slopes characteristic of small, headwater streams allowed water to drop far enough for water wheels and turbines to generate substantial power.

Allamuchy Mountain State Park

I-80 is within glaciated terrain through its entire passage across New Jersey, and the ice-scoured nature of the Highlands ridges is especially evident between the Green Pond Outlier and Jenny Jump Mountain. Road cuts are mantled in many places by only by a few inches of soil or none at all. Rock knolls near the highway are smoothed and streamlined by glacial scour or, on the southern, down-ice sides, steepened to small cliffs floored by talus boulders.

While boulders and glaciated outcrops of Proterozoic granite and gneiss characterize much of Allamuchy Mountain, the route from I-80 to the Deer Park Pond area of Allamuchy Mountain State Park and the trails near the pond travel around gentle hills with a few tens of feet of relief. The landscape is reminiscent of much of the northeast about 15 million years ago. From late in the Cretaceous Period until about 15 million years ago the area underwent a prolonged period of stability during which erosion reduced the landscape to low hills and broad valleys. The subdued landscape is sometimes referred to as the Schooley Peneplain. Beginning about 15 million years ago, toward the middle of the Miocene Epoch, erosion accelerated following a worldwide drop in sea level. Streams cut downward along the northeast-southwest trending belts of relatively soft sedimentary rock within the New Jersey Highlands but left surfaces on broad areas of granitic rock, commonly 5 to 8 miles wide, largely intact. Deer Park Pond lies within one of these relict uplands. The upland was scoured and sculpted in each of New Jersey's three glacial advances, but the low-relief landscapes are similar to those in Schooleys Mountain Park, a few miles south of Allamuchy Mountain State Park and south of most of the glacial activity. When downcutting began, one might have seen three-toed horses, extinct species of camels, piglike entelodonts, and saber-toothed cats. The soil would have been thicker because it was as yet unaffected by glaciation. There would have been few unweathered boulders, and wetlands would have been rare. Otherwise, the landscape was likely reminiscent of that around Deer Park Pond today.

The trails to Deer Park Pond cross ecosystems maintained to show various stages of succession. Early stages are maintained by clearing fields every year. Elsewhere there are overcrowded thickets of young birch saplings, mature birch stands with more widely spaced trees, and mixed oak-hickory-maple and hemlock-spruce forests uncleared for over seventy-five years. Along the way, fallen stone walls, cellar holes from long-gone houses, and the collapsed remnants of small iron mines and prospect pits are all that remain from the hardscrabble farming and mining of the nineteenth-century Highlands. One of these small mines, toward the north end of the Barberry Trail, is unusual in that, in addition to the waste magnetite ore and rock, there are coal, slag, scorched rock, and hundreds of shells from chowder clams. It appears that a small, and likely unsuccessful, iron furnace built here used shells from seafood houses rather than limestone for flux.

Stephens State Park

Stephens State Park is mostly within the Musconetcong River valley, and bedrock is covered almost everywhere with moraine and outwash deposits. The Morris Canal followed the valley for some distance, and the grade was low enough to use locks rather than inclined planes like the one at Morris Canal Park in Roxbury. A well-preserved lock at Saxton Falls, just north of Stephens State Park, is now a picnic area.

Much of Stephens State Park is on deposits of the Wisconsinan terminal moraine, and the park has an abundance of depositional features left by the ice. The park headquarters is in a steep-sided, postglacial channel cut through the moraine by the Musconetcong River after the ice retreated. A well-preserved nineteenth-century limekiln near the headquarters was used to burn limestone to a powder for soil improvement and plaster. Limestone lies beneath the glacial deposits, but there are no nearby exposures protruding through the moraine. The kiln was likely supplied from boulders collected from the glacial deposits.

A short walk from the headquarters across the river and up a series of wooden staircases scaling the side of the postglacial channel takes you to campgrounds on the top of the moraine. The campsites are on flat ground between bowl-shaped depressions up to 25 feet deep, kettle holes formed when buried blocks of ice left behind by the retreating glacier melted and the overlying sediment collapsed into the holes. The kettle holes are dry year-round even though they are closed depressions, not drained by any streams. A much longer hike from the park headquarters along the white-marked trail follows the moraine up the side of Schooleys Mountain and, near the upland surface at the top of the mountain, passes through an area pocked with small kettle holes. Unlike the kettle holes in the campground, these remain marshy year-round. The difference is the result of differing conditions during the ice age. At the tops of the Highlands ridges there was little water flowing south from the edge of the ice. The New Jersey glaciers were in a relatively warm climate, and the ice was at or near the freezing point. Running water melted quickly through to the bottom of the ice and from there followed a gradient that usually took it downhill along the rock beneath the glacier. Subglacial meltwater in upland areas of the Highlands most often made its way down into valleys without coming near the southern edge of the glacier. In the valleys, unlike in the uplands, large meltwater streams flowed beneath the glaciers, especially in the summer. The meltwater washed silt and clay in the glacial outwash southward from the edge of the ice, leaving sand and gravel. Kettles in the sandy sediments in the valley bottom are unable to retain water even through wet seasons because water drains downward through the sand and gravel. Moraines in the upland areas were deposited away from meltwater, and silt and clay were deposited together with the sand and gravel rather than being washed southward. The silty, clayey sediment in the upland moraines is less permeable than the valley sediments. The water does not drain as quickly downward and kettles can remain marshy even through the summer.

In an intermediate situation, depressions near the base of Allamuchy Mountain retain more water than the valley-bottom kettle holes in the campground area but less than kettle holes farther up the mountain. The depressions hold vernal ponds, wet through the springtime but dry through the summer and fall. Vernal ponds are isolated from surface water and fill with water for only a few months in late winter and spring. Vernal ponds are not restricted to glacial deposits. They are found throughout New Jersey and many are not natural. Because they are isolated from surface water, they do not have fish. Because they are dry through the summer, they do not have bullfrogs. Bullfrogs develop to maturity only where ponds remain full for several years at a stretch. Without carnivorous fish and predatory bullfrogs, vernal ponds are ideal habitat for many species of amphibians, insects, reptiles, and plants. Some amphibians breed exclusively in vernal pools and are threatened by the destruction of these largely unregulated water bodies.

Vernal pond in Stephens State Park in May (top) and in late summer (bottom; from a different perspective). —Photos by Michael Flite

Schooleys Mountain

Schooleys Mountain is a long ridge on the east side of the Musconetcong River valley. In the 1890s Schooleys Mountain was rural and, along with much of northern New Jersey, largely deforested. The Schooley surface, the flat landscape of 15 million years ago, would have been readily apparent to anyone looking across the fields. The trees have now returned and much of the surface has become suburban. The Schooley surface can be better appreciated a few miles to the north in and around the Deer Park Pond section of Allamuchy State Park.

Steep ravines cutting headward into Schooleys Mountain are clearly evident at Schooleys Mountain Park, Teetertown Ravine Nature Preserve, and Cataract Park. When erosion began to accelerate about 15 million years ago, the Schooley surface stood 100 to 300 feet above the valleys. When sea level fell, erosion lowered the valley floors so that the mountains now stand 500 to 1,000 feet above the valleys. Headward erosion in each of the streams has progressed to a knick point above which the landscape is isolated from rapid downcutting and preserves much of the original flat topography. The knick point separating the cascades of the downcut reach of the stream from the gentler upland Schooley surface is clear in each of the parks even where, in Schooleys Mountain Park, a dam has been built on Electric Brook close above the knick point.

This is not to say there have been no changes on the upland surfaces in the past 15 million years. They have continued to evolve, particularly during the

Tor in Schooleys Mountain Park.
—Photo by D. Harper

rigorous climates of the ice ages when permafrost caused soil to move slowly downhill even on gentle slopes. A tor in Schooleys Mountain Park, shown on the park trail map as Rock Outcrop, gives some idea of the amount of downwasting since the lowering of the erosional base level. Tors are pinnacles of slowly weathering rock generally thought to have begun their development underground when the surrounding rock weathered to soil. When the surrounding soil was stripped away, the tor was left standing. In this case, the tor stands on sloping land, and it is not difficult to envision soil moving downslope, slowly exposing the tor under permafrost conditions in the ice age.

Jenny Jump State Forest

Jenny Jump Mountain together with hills of Proterozoic rock to the northeast and southwest are the remains of the Jenny Jump Thrust Sheet, which was thrust westward across younger Paleozoic sedimentary rocks in the Alleghanian Orogeny. Proterozoic metamorphic rock is well exposed in road cuts where I-80 climbs up the east side of Jenny Jump Mountain between mileposts 15.6 and 15.8. Thrust faulting from the Alleghanian Orogeny is common within the New Jersey Highlands, and I-80 crosses large thrust faults at about fifteen places. In many places Proterozoic rock has been thrust atop Paleozoic sedimentary rock. In other places, relatively old sedimentary rock has been thrust atop younger sedimentary rock. The exposures of Kittatinny limestones along I-80 west of Jenny Jump, for example, are part of the Hope Klippe, where the Jenny Jump Thrust Fault pushed Kittatinny limestones atop the younger Martinsburg Formation.

Within Jenny Jump State Forest, the Summit Trail is a good place to see glacially sculpted Proterozoic bedrock. Soil is thin, and on parts of the trail there are opportunities to scramble among glacial erratics and bedrock knobs smoothed and polished by fine sand and silt at the base of the moving glacier. Glacial striations gouged by larger pieces of rock point in the direction of ice movement. At the summit, Jenny Jump Mountain overlooks Great Meadows to the southeast, several square miles of wetland remaining from Glacial Lake Pequest. The wetland was drained late in the nineteenth century and has ever

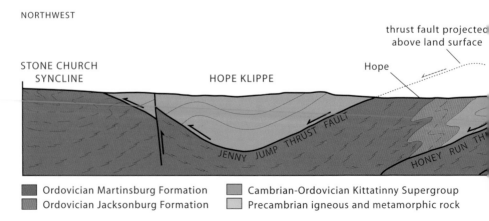

NORTHWEST

thrust fault projected above land surface

STONE CHURCH SYNCLINE

HOPE KLIPPE

Hope

JENNY JUMP THRUST FAULT

HONEY RUN TH

Ordovician Martinsburg Formation
Ordovician Jacksonburg Formation
Cambrian-Ordovician Kittatinny Supergroup
Precambrian igneous and metamorphic rock

since been the largest and most productive of New Jersey's muckland agriculture sites. Onions, carrots, and other vegetables were long major crops, and sod farming has more recently become important. Shades of Death Road, along the base of Jenny Jump Mountain, has closer views of the scenic farms and, farther north, swamps and peat bogs. Large quantities of peat were produced from the bogs until recently, and soil production and processing continues with blending of specialized mixtures for athletic fields. Pitcher's mound material for all major league and most minor league parks comes from a former peat mining company, Partac Peat Corporation, on Shades of Death Road. The mixture is a blend including some Glacial Lake Pequest sediment, some sediment from a gravel pit in Mt. Laurel in southern New Jersey, and some from other places.

Great Meadows, the lake bed of Glacial Lake Pequest, viewed from the summit of Jenny Jump Mountain. The Upper Pohatcong and Allamuchy Mountains are in the background. The level surface of these ridges is at the Schooley Peneplain level. —Photo by Ron Witte, N.J. Geological Survey

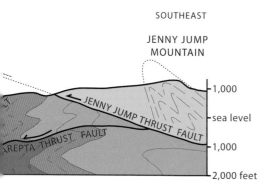

Cross section through Jenny Jump Mountain and the Hope Klippe. The arrows show the direction of movement along the Jenny Jump Thrust Fault. —Modified from Drake and Lyttle, 1985

Kittatinny Valley and Mountain

On a clear day, there is a good view across Kittatinny Valley toward Kittatinny Mountain and the Delaware Water Gap from an overlook on the eastbound side of I-80 at milepost 20.5 on the west flank of Allamuchy Mountain. The trees now block the view from the westbound overlook, but you can get a good view from the westbound lanes at a rest stop at milepost 6.3. You can see that the Kittatinny Mountain in Pennsylvania south of the Delaware Water Gap is at the same elevation as the mountain north of it. They are part of the Schooley Peneplain, a flat erosional surface that developed in early Tertiary time.

The name Kittatinny is from the Lenni Lenape Indian term for "endless mountain." Formed of quartzite of somewhat different ages along its length, it stretches from just south of the Catskills in New York to Georgia. In New York the ridge is called the Shawangunk Mountains (The Gunks of rock climbing fame). In Pennsylvania it is Blue Mountain. Farther south there are still other names. Kittatinny Valley, also with different names along its length, is even longer. Collectively known as the Great Valley, it stretches from just north of the Canadian border to Georgia.

The view of the Delaware Water Gap from the I-80 rest stop on the westbound lanes at milepost 6.3. The flat tops of the mountains on both sides of the river is the Schooley Peneplain. —Photo by D. Harper

Westward from Jenny Jump Mountain, I-80 descends into Kittatinny Valley and passes road cuts exposing the Kittatinny limestones, deposited in the Iapetus Ocean; the Jacksonburg and Martinsburg Formations, deposited as the ocean was in the last stages of closing; and the Shawangunk Formation and Bloomsburg RedBeds, shed westward from highlands raised after the ocean finally closed.

Most of the exposures of bluish white rock along I-80 in Kittatinny Valley are dolomite belonging to several formations historically grouped as the Kittatinny limestones and now grouped as the Kittatinny Supergroup. The dolomite formations total over 3,000 feet thick and were deposited through 80 million years between the early part of the Cambrian Period and the middle of the Ordovician. At this time eastern North America stood on a passive continental margin near the equator. Thick dolomite deposits built up into a carbonate bank much like those building up today on tropical passive margins of the Bahama Banks of North America and the Great Barrier Reef of Australia.

In contrast to the Kittatinny limestones, which were deposited through a long period of tectonic stability on a slowly subsiding passive continental margin, the Jacksonburg Formation was deposited through a period of change preceding the Taconic Orogeny. No ocean on Earth lasts forever, and the Iapetus Ocean had been narrowing for some time along a subduction zone on its east side. By the middle of the Ordovician Period, the Iapetus had narrowed to the extent that the carbonate bank on its western shore was first lifted upward on the forebulge of the approaching subduction zone. When the continental margin rose above sea level on the forebulge, erosion and karst development on the carbonates formed the Beekmantown Unconformity. After the uplift the margin began to be pushed downward as the oceanic trench approached, and there was a brief return to carbonate deposition, the Jacksonburg Formation. Within the Jacksonburg, the rocks record progressive deepening. The earliest deposited, lowermost beds of the formation, from when the continental margin first began to submerge, are shallow-water deposits, mostly conglomerates

Dolomite of the Kittatinny limestones along I-80. —Photo by D. Harper

of pebbles eroded from the Kittatinny limestones and shell material broken up by waves. The upper part of the formation, deposited somewhat later in deeper water, contains substantial amounts of silicate mud together with lime mud. This rock is black, shaly, and fine-grained.

The Jacksonburg Formation is much thinner than the Kittatinny limestones, between 100 and 800 feet rather than thousands of feet, and exposures

Conglomerate of the Jacksonburg Formation was deposited in shallow water. —Photo by Don Monteverde, N.J. Geological Survey

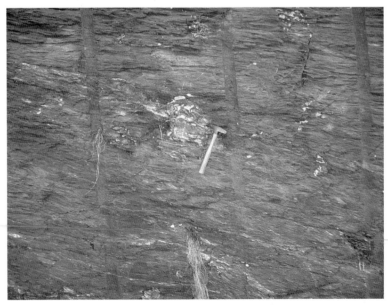

Fine-grained shaly limestone of the Jacksonburg Formation was deposited in deeper water. —Photo by Don Monteverde, N.J. Geological Survey

are correspondingly less common. The only exposures along I-80 are between mileposts 12.3 and 12.8. More accessible exposures can be seen along roads north of Hope. Shallow-water conglomerate and shell limestone, sometimes overgrown with poison ivy, crop out along Johnsonburg Road about one-half mile south of the bridge beneath I-80. The deeper-water clayey limestone is exposed a few hundred feet farther south along the road.

As the Iapetus Ocean continued to close, the margin was pushed still deeper, and the sediment changed from silty, muddy limestone to carbonate-free mud. Today the mud is slate of the Martinsburg Formation, up to about 8,000 feet thick. Both slate and shaly limestone outcrop along Johnsonburg Road, and the two can be difficult to tell apart. If weak acid is dropped on the limestone, carbon dioxide gas will bubble up as the calcium carbonate in the limestone dissolves. This will work even with warmed vinegar on a rock surface scratched to raise a bit of powder. The Martinsburg slate has no calcium carbonate and will not react.

Slate is the metamorphic equivalent of the sedimentary rock shale. While shale breaks along sedimentary bedding, slate has been metamorphosed and recrystallized to the extent that it breaks along slaty cleavage related to stresses during metamorphism. Slaty cleavage is what makes slate useful for roofing, paving stones, pool tables, and blackboards. Sheets of slate littering the bottoms of many Martinsburg slate outcrops are crossed by light brown and black

Martinsburg slate near Newton. Sedimentary bedding is vertical; slaty cleavage crosses the outcrop from upper left to lower right. —Photo by Don Monteverde, N.J. Geological Survey

bands. The bands are the remains of the sedimentary layering. Slate was quarried, until it was replaced by lighter, cheaper materials, from the Martinsburg Formation in New Jersey and, in far greater amounts, in and around Bangor, Pennsylvania. In Pennsylvania as in New Jersey, most of the slate was used for roofing. Unlike the New Jersey slate, some Pennsylvania slate was from thicker bedded shale and has none of the light brown banding. This thick slate was used for making blackboards and pool tables.

The Martinsburg Formation is exposed in several road cuts west of Hope, and there are some low, glacially scoured exposures in the woods behind the westbound rest stop at mile 6.3. Long, continuous exposures run along US 46 south of I-80, but that highway is narrow, winding, busy, and sandwiched between the Delaware River and the riverside bluffs. The cuts are extremely dangerous and should not be approached. There are safer exposures along Delaware Road in Ramseyburg (one block east of US 46) and along NJ 521 about halfway between I-80 and NJ 94.

The Martinsburg was deposited primarily by density currents in which the weight of suspended sediment caused muddy water to flow downslope along the ocean bottom. It is easy to set up a miniscule density current in a clear mud puddle. Gently stir the edge of the puddle to suspend some mud, and you will immediately see a dark current of muddy water head toward the deepest part of the puddle. At the bottom of the puddle the current will slow down, the muddy water will pool, and the mud will settle out as a layer with the coarser sediment toward the bottom and the finer sediment toward the top. The density currents were far larger and moved much faster in the ocean where the Martinsburg

Ramsey Member of the Martinsburg Formation was deposited as sediment-laden, heavy density currents flowing across the sea bottom. Where the bottom flattened, the currents decelerated and the sediment load settled out. The thicker beds are sandstone, deposited when the currents were still moving fast enough to carry sand. The thinner beds are slate formed from silt and clay deposited when the currents had slowed. —Photo by Don Monteverde, N.J. Geological Survey

Martinsburg Formation at Ramseyburg. The lighter colored beds are sandy and represent the lower parts of Bouma sequences. The darker beds were formed predominantly from silt and clay deposited higher in the sequences when density currents had slowed. The rippled bed is from the middle part of the sequence. —Photo by Michael Flite

The parts of the Bouma sequence are lettered A through E from the bottom up. In a complete sequence, the lowermost material (part A) above the scoured underlying bed is coarse sand, gravel, shells, and other large, difficult-to-move pieces of debris. Above the coarse sand and gravel is sand laid down in flat, parallel beds (part B), sand with ripples and crossbedding (part C), silt laid down in flat, parallel beds (part D), and mud without any apparent bedding (part E). Usually, though, parts of the sequence are missing.
—Modified from Bouma, 1962

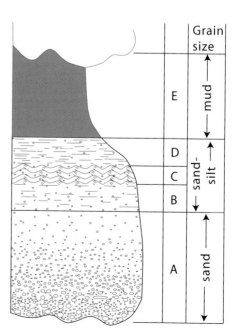

was deposited. The current often moved fast enough to scour the surfaces of beds deposited by previous density flows, picking up more sediment and more weight, and accelerating to still greater speeds. Eventually, however, the currents reached the bottom of the slope, and gravity was no longer able to keep the water moving. As the current slowed down, it was less able scour the bottom or keep sediment moving. The sediment carried by a decelerating density current is deposited in a regular sequence, the Bouma sequence described by Arnold Bouma in 1962.

Hope and Mt. Hermon

The town of Hope was founded in 1769 by the Moravians, a religious sect. The Moravians were centered in Germany, but the arrivals at Hope were from older settlements at Bethlehem and Nazareth, Pennsylvania. The town is a good place to see limestone of the Kittatinny Supergroup used as a building stone. The limestone, durable and easily shaped into blocks, was a common building stone in the nineteenth century. You can see limestone barns, houses, and bridges throughout northwestern New Jersey. Many are stunningly beautiful, but most are on private farmland or surrounded by dissimilar structures. Often they are in ruins. The simple, utilitarian limestone buildings of the Moravians were built as part of one of the oldest planned communities in the United States.

About 2 miles northwest of Hope is the crossroads town of Mt. Hermon where, in 1885, the skeleton of an extinct ice age moose, *Cervalces scotti*, was found in a shell marl pit. *Cervalces* is not a common fossil, and the Mt. Hermon

Buildings constructed from Kittatinny limestone by the Moravians at Hope in the 1770s. —Photo by D. Harper

Cervalces scotti from Mt. Hermon on display at the New Jersey State Museum in Trenton. —Photo by D. Harper

specimen is one of only two complete skeletons. The other was found in 1980 near Blairstown, only a few miles north of Mt. Hermon. Like modern deer and moose, only the males had antlers and the antlers were shed after the mating season. Antlers and, less commonly, bones have been found throughout eastern North America from Arkansas to southern Canada.

The most obvious difference between the ice age moose and the modern moose is a more deerlike face lacking the broad snout and prehensile lips of the modern moose. To some modern workers *Cervalces* is only a variety within the moose genus *Alces*. Fossils of similar animals are known from the early Pleistocene of Europe, and *Cervalces* likely migrated across the Bering land bridge. *Cervalces* died out about the same time as the melting back of the Wisconsinan glaciers and the migration of the modern moose to North America. The modern moose occupies a similar ecologic niche and may have displaced *Cervalces*.

Delaware Water Gap National Recreation Area

The Delaware Water Gap is one of many gaps through the Appalachian ridges. Water gaps host rivers. Wind gaps were cut by rivers but are now abandoned. The origin of the gaps and the now-abandoned valleys that cut straight across the upland ridges of the New Jersey Highlands has been a topic of debate for well over a century. Early workers explained the former drainage through the gaps and across the ridges as the result of superposition from a time when Coastal Plain sediments extended deep into the Appalachians. Drainage patterns across the sediments were held to have been superposed on the bedrock

View looking upstream from pedestrian bridge at Columbia through the Delaware Water Gap. Mt. Tammany, the summit area of Kittatinny Mountain (in New Jersey) is to the right. Mt. Minsi, on Blue Mountain (in Pennsylvania), is to the left. Both mountains are made of erosion-resistant quartzite of the Shawangunk Formation.
—Photo by Ron Witte, N.J. Geological Survey

as the sediments were removed by erosion. Later workers, doubting that the Coastal Plain sediments extended far inland, noted that the gradients of valleys on the Atlantic side of the Appalachians are much steeper than on the mid-continent side and suggested that the gaps might be the result of stream capture. As the steeper, higher energy Atlantic slope streams carved back into their headwaters, they intercepted other streams. Others have noted that the larger gaps are at places where the rock is folded, fractured, or faulted and therefore more easily eroded. At the Delaware Water Gap, for example, the Shawangunk Formation dips more steeply on New Jersey's north side of the gap (50 degrees at Mt. Tammany), than on Pennsylvania's south side (25 degrees at Mt. Minsi). The brittle conglomerate of the Shawangunk Formation likely was fractured and could be eroded relatively quickly at the gap where it was twisted from 25 degrees to 50 degrees. Still other researchers have stressed the role that glaciers, the ponding and overflow of glacial lakes, and the downcutting by meltwater streams may have played in the development of the gaps. Headward erosion by Atlantic basin streams, stream capture, incision of streams along fractured or faulted rock, and glaciation were probably all significant.

At Delaware Water Gap National Recreationa Area, you can visit the National Park Service nature center and walk along the riverbank trail. For those in good physical condition or those wishing to tire out the kids before a long drive, the short but vigorous climb up Mt. Tammany, 400 feet vertically to the top of the cliff overlooking the Delaware River, may be appropriate.

The Mt. Tammany climb follows the red-marked trail and includes short scrambles over bedrock ledges and boulder fields. Surprisingly, at the beginning of the trail where you might expect a cliff face of the light-colored quartzite of the Shawangunk Formation, there are red beds interlayered with the quartzite. The red beds are part of the Bloomsburg Red Beds, overlying the Shawangunk. The contact between the Shawangunk and the Bloomsburg is transitional, not abrupt, and is defined as at the lowermost red bed. The Bloomsburg crops out along the trail because the bedding, instead of being a simple tilted layer as it appears from the highway, has been folded into a paired anticline and syncline: the Cherry Valley Anticline and Dunnfield Creek Syncline. The red beds of the Bloomsburg curve downward along the trough of the syncline between white Shawangunk quartzite to the east and west. As the trail heads farther up, it crosses into progressively older rocks with fewer red layers. Where the summit overlooks the Delaware River and Kittatinny Valley, there are no red beds. The trail is on the Shawangunk Formation.

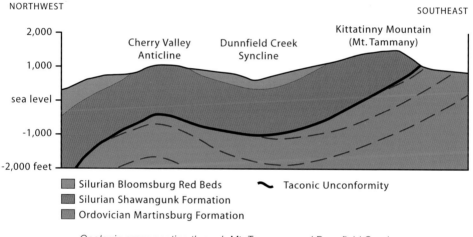

Geologic cross section through Mt. Tammany and Dunnfield Creek, on the north side of the Delaware Water Gap. —Modified from Epstein, 2001

A less challenging and equally beautiful trail follows Dunnfield Creek up the trough of the Dunnfield Creek Syncline. The relatively soft Bloomsburg Red Beds have eroded from the trough of the syncline to create the valley of Dunnfield Creek, which heads near Sunfish Pond 5 miles northeast of the water gap. The Dunnfield Creek hike follows the Appalachian Trail for a half mile, then branches to the right through a hemlock-shaded wonderland of ferns, moss-covered rocks, pools, and waterfalls across brick red rocks. Those short of time or wanting to keep their feet dry may want to turn back where the trail reaches one of several fords across Dunnfield Creek. Those who continue for the 5 miles along the trough of the syncline toward Sunfish Pond will cross onto the Shawangunk quartzite about 2.5 miles into the climb and be rewarded at their arrival at Sunfish Pond, one of the more scenic of the many glacial lakes in New Jersey.

View across the Delaware Water Gap to the dipping Shawangunk quartzite of Mt. Tammany. —Photo by D. Harper

Plunge pool over Shawangunk quartzite along Dunnfield Creek. —Photo by Ron Witte, N.J. Geological Survey

In addition to the fairly large Cherry Valley–Dunnfield Creek anticline-syncline pair, a number of smaller folds, too small to show on geologic maps and cross sections, are beautifully exposed in the Bloomsburg Red Beds along River Road (Old Mine Road) near its intersection with I-80 at exit 1.

The Shawangunk Formation and Bloomsburg Red Beds were deposited primarily in braided rivers. Occasional layers with marine or brackish-water fossils (eurypterid fragments in the Shawangunk, trails left by ancestral horseshoe crabs and the bony plates of primitive ostracoderm fish in the Bloomsburg) show that the area was at the edge of a shallow sea, which covered much of the midcontinent at this time. The Shawangunk Formation, with its rapid transitions between sandy quartzite and quartzite conglomerate, appears to have been deposited by streams with steep gradients and rapid fluctuations in flow. At that time, before the evolution of large land plants in the Devonian Period, sudden rises in stream flow would have been accentuated by the barren landscape. The Bloomsburg Red Beds are siltier and have fewer conglomerates, and the pebbles in the conglomerates are generally smaller. They are interpreted as being deposited in the waning stages of the Taconic Orogeny when the highlands to the east had been lowered by erosion and the gradient to the sea was gentler. The red color is from iron and has been interpreted as showing that erosion had uncovered the iron-rich rocks, exposing them to oxygen.

New Jersey 23
Riverdale—New York Border
40 miles

The section of NJ 23 between Riverdale and the New York border passes over the Proterozoic rock of the New Jersey Highlands before entering the Valley and Ridge Province near Sussex. Many parks in this region of New Jersey are accessible from NJ 23 and are discussed here.

Sheared Rock along the
Ramapo Fault Zone at Riverdale

At low water along the Pequannock River, exposures of black, sheared, and crumpled rock come into view within streambed boulder gravel below and for a short distance upstream from the Hamburg Turnpike bridge just east of the railroad crossing (east of I-287). A great deal is known about the geology of New Jersey, but some questions may never be fully answered. The origin of this rock is one of those difficult-to-answer questions. The rock is clearly different from other rocks in the area and has attracted local attention over the years. At some unknown time, prospect holes were dug in the unusual black rock in a nearby wooded area. As the holes are only a few feet deep, the prospectors apparently found nothing but black rock and stopped digging.

Older geologic maps show the rock as a sliver of the Martinsburg Formation of the Ordovician Period, but with a question mark. This was reasonable. The Martinsburg Formation is widespread farther west in New Jersey, and a slate

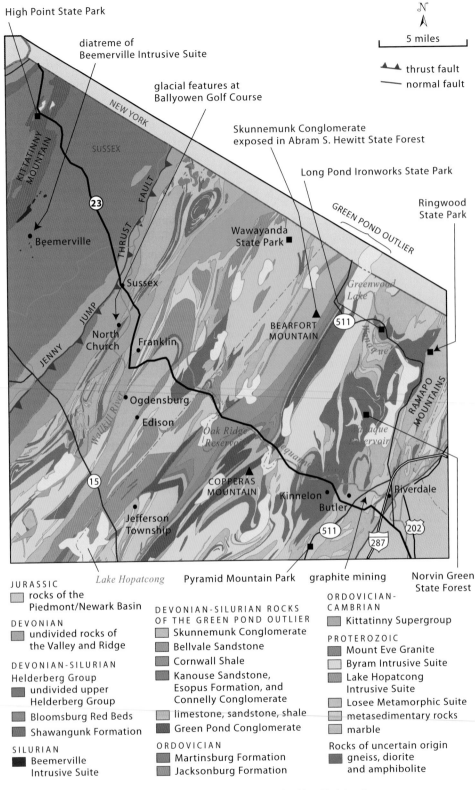

Geology along NJ 23 between Riverdale and the New York border.
—Compiled from the USGS's Preliminary Integrated Geologic Map Database for the United States, 2006

High Point State Park

diatreme of
Beemerville Intrusive Suite

glacial features at
Ballyowen Golf Course

Skunnemunk Conglomerate
exposed in Abram S. Hewitt State Forest

Long Pond Ironworks State Park

Ringwood
State Park

NEW YORK

SUSSEX

KITTATINNY MOUNTAIN

THRUST FAULT

GREEN POND OUTLIER

23

Beemerville

JUMP

JENNY

Sussex

Wawayanda
State Park

*Greenwood
Lake*

North
Church

Franklin

BEARFORT
MOUNTAIN

511

Wanaque

RAMAPO MOUNTAINS

Wallkill River

Ogdensburg

Edison

*Oak Ridge
Reservoir*

Pequannock

*Wanaque
Reservoir*

15

COPPERAS
MOUNTAIN

Kinnelon

Butler

Riverdale

Jefferson
Township

202

287

511

Lake Hopatcong

Pyramid Mountain Park

graphite mining

Norvin Green
State Forest

5 miles

▲▲ thrust fault
— normal fault

JURASSIC
rocks of the
Piedmont/Newark Basin

DEVONIAN
undivided rocks of
the Valley and Ridge

DEVONIAN-SILURIAN
Helderberg Group
undivided upper
Helderberg Group

Bloomsburg Red Beds

Shawangunk Formation

SILURIAN
Beemerville
Intrusive Suite

DEVONIAN-SILURIAN ROCKS
OF THE GREEN POND OUTLIER
Skunnemunk Conglomerate

Bellvale Sandstone

Cornwall Shale

Kanouse Sandstone,
Esopus Formation, and
Connelly Conglomerate

limestone, sandstone, shale

Green Pond Conglomerate

ORDOVICIAN
Martinsburg Formation

Jacksonburg Formation

ORDOVICIAN-
CAMBRIAN
Kittatinny Supergroup

PROTEROZOIC
Mount Eve Granite

Byram Intrusive Suite

Lake Hopatcong
Intrusive Suite

Losee Metamorphic Suite

metasedimentary rocks

marble

Rocks of uncertain origin
gneiss, diorite
and amphibolite

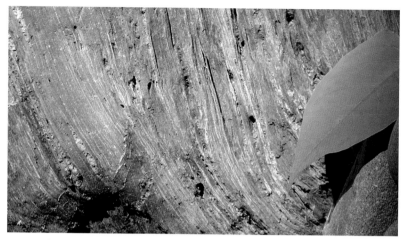

Intensely sheared rock, probably equivalent to rocks of the Jutland Klippe, along the Ramapo Fault in Riverdale. —Photo by D. Harper

of similar age and type in the New York City area was metamorphosed to mica schist in the Taconic Orogeny. The mud that gave rise to the slate and mica schist was more than likely deposited across the entire area between Kittatinny Mountain and New York City. Most has been removed from the Highlands by a combination of faulting and erosion, but it would not be surprising to find a sliver of Martinsburg that survived.

On closer examination of the rocks, however, they were found to have more in common with rocks of the Jutland Klippe found along I-78. The Jutland rocks are older than the Martinsburg Formation. They formed from mud deposited seaward of the carbonate bank of the Kittatinny limestones of the Cambrian and Ordovician Periods. Recent geologic maps show the rocks as equivalent to the Jutland rocks, but this relationship has not been confirmed. No fossils have been found in the rocks at Riverdale, and there are no stratigraphic relationships or radiometric dates to determine their age. Whatever their origin, the rocks provide a good example of shearing and crumpling along the Ramapo Fault.

Graphite and Lead Mine Road

About 1.5 miles up NJ 23 west of I-287, there is a turnoff onto Lead Mine Road, which has nothing to do with the metal lead. The name is from black lead, an old name for graphite. Graphite, like diamond, is a mineral form of pure carbon. It is best known for its use as the "lead" in pencils but also is used for crucibles, brushes in electric motors, lubricants, and batteries and to slow chain reactions in nuclear power plants. Graphite mining began in New Jersey in the 1840s, initially for stove polish, and continued sporadically until 1931. Mines were opened at fourteen places, including Bloomingdale, Annandale, Boonton, Mendham, Peapack-Gladstone, Pottersville, High Bridge, and Fairmount, but the deposits, even by standards of the time, were small. The mines suffered initially from competition from larger, richer deposits in Pennsylvania, the Adirondacks, and Sri Lanka, then succumbed to artificial graphite made from coal or as a blast furnace by-product.

Natural graphite can originate from magmatic fluids, metamorphic fluids, volcanic gases, breakdown of carbonate minerals, or organic material in sediment. The New Jersey graphite is likely from organic material in sediments. It was mined from metamorphic rocks that started out as shallow-water marine sand and mud. Algal mats were common in shallow marine environments at this time in geologic history and may have produced the carbon. Like all organic carbon and unlike most inorganic carbon, the New Jersey graphite is slightly depleted in the isotope carbon 13 relative to carbon 12.

Pyramid Mountain Park, Tripod Rock, and Montville Serpentinite

Pyramid Mountain Park, south of Butler along County Road 511, is best known as home to Tripod Rock, a gneissic glacial erratic weighing several tons. The rock is balanced where it was lowered onto three smaller rocks by the melting Wisconsinan ice. It seems improbable that the rock would have come to rest here by chance, but all the large rocks embedded in the ice came to rest on the land surface when the ice melted and it is not surprising that some might

Tripod Rock at Pyramid Mountain Park. —Photo by D. Harper

end up in improbable arrangements. The rock has been acclaimed as spiritual energy vortex and as an Indian ceremonial site aligned with solstice stones on the spring equinox. Every year a crowd gathers for the sundown event.

Tripod Rock is the best known of thousands of erratics in the park. Bear Rock, nearby on a loop trail to Tripod Rock, is impossible to miss. While Tripod Rock is not unusually large for a glacial erratic, Bear Rock is immense—about 20 feet high, 20 feet wide, and 35 feet long, one of the largest erratics in New Jersey.

Across County Route 511, in the eastern section of the park, the "Limestone Quarry" shown on park maps is one of the few areas of marble in the eastern part of the Highlands. Marble is fairly common in the western section of the Highlands, away from the large volumes of sediment being eroded from the Losee magmatic arc. The marble at Montville was quarried in the 1800s for flux for the iron furnaces of Boonton and for agricultural lime. It was well-known at the time for its wide variety of minerals, especially its gem-quality serpentine. More recently it has become known for its diopside, which fluoresces blue under ultraviolet light. In the early days of quarrying, before the value of the translucent, green to gold serpentine was recognized, it was thrown aside as waste. The serpentine started out as pockets or layers of mud within the limestone, was metamorphosed under high temperature and moderate pressure to pyroxene, then was altered hydrothermally to serpentine under lower pressures and temperatures. The alteration began at the outside of the crystals and worked its way inward. All stages of the alteration, from unaltered pyroxene, though serpentine with a core of pyroxene, to masses completely changed to serpentine can be found in the quarry.

Serpentine from the limestone quarry in Pyramid Mountain Park. The "limestone" is actually marble. The green mineral is serpentine. The gray mineral is calcite. —Photo by John Dooley, N.J. Geological Survey

Norvin Green State Forest and
the Ringwood Mining District

The Highlands area north of Riverdale is known as the Ramapo Mountains, home to the Ringwood Mining District. The Ringwood mines were among the first New Jersey magnetite mines in production and among the last to shut down. Mining was first attempted in 1685, but the first successful mining was not until 1710. At the time of the Revolutionary War, the Ringwood mines were still operating far short of capacity but were nonetheless able to contribute to the war effort. Iron mining continued as an important local industry until the Depression forced most of the workings to close in 1931. The mines were refurbished in World War II and again readied for work in the Korean War, but there was little or no ore mined at either time.

Mining at Ringwood, as at New Jersey's other magnetite districts, began with surface digging. The deposits, however, slope steeply to the southeast and quickly passed below the range of surface workings. Eventually the subsurface workings at the mine reached a depth of just over half a mile.

Unfortunately, in an outcome unusual for New Jersey mines, the abandoned shafts were used for several years through the 1960s and into the 1970s to dispose of waste, including paint residues from a nearby automobile plant. The area became a Superfund cleanup site, and health issues among local residents continue to be attributed to the waste. Clearly these are not the mines to visit as a tourist. Within the Ringwood Mining District, the better choices are the Roomy Mine and the Blue Mine in Norvin Green State Forest. Norvin Green is one of the less crowded of New Jersey's public lands and has much to offer besides the mines: challenging trails, waterfalls, ponds, and an unobstructed view in four directions from Wyanokie High Point that more than repays the climb. The Roomy Mine, worked between 1840 and 1857, is one of the few mines you can enter in relative safety. During the bat hibernation season it is closed. At other times a short crawl through a 2-foot-high passageway brings you to a 60-foot-long adit high enough to stand in. The Roomy Mine is not named for its size, but for Benjamin Roome, a surveyor. The Blue Mine, together with numerous nearby mines and ironworks, was opened in the 1760s by the German iron-master Peter Hasenclever in the 1760s. It was named for its dark blue ore. The tunnels, last mined in 1905, appear to still be intact, but the mine was dug at an angle down into the hillside and has filled with water to the entrance. Close by the entrance is a large concrete pad used as a base for steam-operated mining machinery. Tailings piles with magnetite ore remain around both mines and at small, caved-in mines and prospect pits along the trails.

Long Pond Ironworks State Park

Together with the iron mines come the furnaces at which the ore is changed from rock to pig iron and cast iron and the forges at which heated pig iron is hammered into less brittle wrought iron. The Long Pond works were powered by the Wanaque River and were an important supplier to the Continental Army in the Revolution and the Union Army in the Civil War. By the 1870s, ironworking had become centered near the coalfields and navigable waterways of Pennsylvania, and in 1882 the Long Pond works shut down.

The Long Pond Historic District includes the ruins of iron furnaces, charging areas from which the furnaces were fed, a casting house, icehouses, and waterwheels. The furnaces from 1766 and the Civil War era are being stabilized and restored. Even in their current state of disrepair, the works present a fascinating display of historic technologies and the vast improvements through this time of rapid technological innovation.

Pequannock Valley

For about 8 miles, from Butler through Kinnelon and through the Newark watershed as far west as Oak Ridge Reservoir, NJ 23 follows the Pequannock River as it passes by igneous rocks metamorphosed to gneiss during the Ottawan Orogeny. Many kinds of igneous and metamorphic rocks can be seen in freshly blasted cliffs behind shopping centers along the highway: pink and white granite, granite pegmatite, black amphibolite, and a variety of gneisses. You can see the same rocks in their more natural, weathered state in any number of parks in the area.

West of the shopping centers, the valley is predominantly within gray diorite gneiss for several miles. West of the diorite gneiss, NJ 23 passes mostly pink granite gneiss within 3 miles of the Newark watershed. (Stopping within the watershed property without a permit is forbidden, and the route is heavily patrolled.) Even though the diorite gneiss and granite gneiss are close by one another and visually similar except in color, they were formed under completely different geologic conditions and at different times during the Proterozoic Eon. The diorite gneiss started as magma above subducting oceanic crust along the Losee magmatic arc, an arc of islands related to the subduction that eventually led to a collision between continents in the Ottawan Orogeny. A radiometric date based on uranium and lead in zircons shows that the rock had cooled and begun to crystallize by 1,248 million years ago.

The metasedimentary rocks in the eastern Highlands were derived mostly from rapidly eroding mountainous islands of the volcanic arc and formed from immature sediment, in which even some easily weathered minerals had not broken down. Metasedimentary rocks in the western Highlands were derived mostly from lower-lying areas of the interior of North America. Sediments were more mature, richer in quartz, and deposited slowly enough that pure calcium carbonate dissolved in seawater precipitated undiluted in some places as the limestone that was later metamorphosed to the Franklin Marble.

The granite is richer in quartz and is pink from microcline, a potassium-rich feldspar. It is part of the 1,185 million-year-old Byram Intrusive Suite, almost 100 million years younger than the Losee rocks. At this time the Losee arc, formerly offshore, had welded firmly to North America, and arc-related rocks were no longer forming in the New Jersey Highlands. The most likely explanation for the influx of heat that melted rock to produce the Byram Intrusive Suite is delamination of a slab of rock from the lowermost crust. The delaminated slab sank downward, allowing hotter mantle material to rise upward and melt the overlying rock.

This rusty-weathering metasedimentary gneiss along NJ 23 formed from graywacke, an impure sandstone. Elsewhere in the New Jersey Highlands, similar rock hosted graphite mines in the nineteenth century. Most of the black flakes in the rock here are biotite mica, but graphite can be found as well. —Photo by D. Harper

Layered metavolcanic gneiss along NJ 23. The darker layers are predominently amphibole; the lighter layers are predominantly quartz and feldspar. —Photo by D. Harper

Pink granite of the Byram Intrusive Suite along NJ 23.
— Photo by D. Harper

—Photo by Richard Volkert, N.J. Geological Survey

Green Pond Outlier

Between the Charlotteburg Reservoir and the Oak Ridge Reservoir, NJ 23 crosses the Green Pond Outlier, further discussed in the I-80 road guide in this chapter. A rest stop overlooking the Charlotteburg Reservoir straddles the thrust fault contact between Proterozoic rock to the east and the Green Pond Conglomerate of Silurian age to the west. The contact is covered, but its location can be judged within a few feet based on a change from blocky outcroppings of quartzite to a gentler surface developed on the gneiss. A short walk to the west, if you're careful of the traffic on this busy road, brings you to an anticline-syncline pair well-known to virtually all geologists and most undergraduate geology students in New Jersey.

While the Valley and Ridge area of New Jersey has only one prominent, ridge-forming quartzite conglomerate, the Silurian Shawangunk Formation, the Green Pond Outlier has two: the Silurian Green Pond Conglomerate shed

Copperas Mountain looking south from a rest area along NJ 23. The contact between Proterozoic rocks below and the Green Pond Conglomerate is at the change, visible when the leaves are down, from blocky-weathering quartzite to the smoother slope of the Proterozoic gneiss. —Photo by Don Monteverde, N.J. Geological Survey

Anticline-syncline pair in the Green Pond Conglomerate along NJ 23 at Newfoundland. —Photo by Michael Flite

westward from highlands raised during the Taconic Orogeny, and the Devonian Skunnemunk Conglomerate, shed westward from highlands raised in the Acadian Orogeny. Thick sandstone and conglomerate equivalent to the Skunnemunk underlie wide areas of Pennsylvania and New York. Likely sandstone and conglomerate at one time covered much of the area between the Green Pond Outlier and the Pennsylvania exposures but have been removed by erosion. The Skunnemunk Conglomerate is not exposed along NJ 23 because it lies within the trough of a syncline that plunges to the north and has been eroded from the southern part of the outlier. The hard rock forms the ridge of Bearfort Mountain to the north. High, barren outcrops of the conglomerate at the crest of Bearfort Mountain in Hewitt State Forest overlook Greenwood Lake to the east and more heavily wooded ridges of Proterozoic gneiss to the east and west.

Skunnemunk Conglomerate.
—Photo by Richard Volkert, N.J. Geological Survey

Franklin Mining District

The Franklin Mine at Franklin and the Sterling Hill Mine at Ogdensburg are the most important mines of the Franklin Mining District. The mines, only a few miles apart, were home to one of the world's richest zinc deposits and for many years one of the world's most profitable mining districts. The mines are in Middle Proterozoic Franklin Marble. More different minerals come from here than any other place on Earth, and the area is known as the Fluorescent Mineral Capital of the World. Hundreds of museums worldwide have fluorescent mineral displays, and virtually all of them include rocks from these mines. Displays at two museums right at the mines are among the best. The Franklin Mineral Museum, in an engine house that supplied power to the mines at Franklin, has arguably the most spectacular display of fluorescent minerals from the district, a mine replica, and mineral collecting in waste rock at the Buckwheat Mine Dump. The Buckwheat rocks are periodically turned with earth-moving equipment so that good specimens of the ore can always be collected. Occasional night-time hunts for fluorescent minerals are a special treat. The Sterling Hill Mining Museum has tours through mine tunnels where you can see fluorescent rocks in place. Visitors are free to collect a hand-sized piece from reserves left at the time the mine closed. Exhibits in the mine buildings showcase mining, ore minerals, and fluorescent minerals from the Franklin district and beyond.

The fluorescence of Franklin minerals is most spectacular under shortwave ultraviolet light, which has an energy of about 5 electron volts. The ultraviolet light kicks electrons from a ground state to a high-energy, excited state. The high-energy state is unstable, and the electrons immediately begin losing energy to return to the ground state. Some energy is given up as heat, and some by quenching of energy by neighboring atoms. In the fluorescent minerals, much of the energy not lost to heat or quenching is given off as light when an electron loses energy.

The fluorescence of the Franklin ores was discovered accidentally in the early 1900s when sparks from primitive electrical equipment in the mines caused the rocks to glow. Sparking machines were quickly built, and fluorescence was soon being used to follow ore zones and monitor the quality of mill concentrates. Later, fluorescence was used to judge whether or not exploratory

Ore from the Sterling Hill Mine under natural light (left) and the same specimen under shortwave ultraviolet light (right). The green-glowing mineral is willemite (zinc silicate). The red mineral is calcite (calcium carbonate). The black, nonfluorescent mineral is franklinite (zinc oxide). —Photo courtesy Sterling Hill Mining Museum

drill holes passed close to the ore body. If the hole was close to the ore, calcite in rock cores retrieved from the holes would glow red. Calcite farther from the ore had no fluorescence. Still later, fluorescence was used to monitor mine tailings in streams.

The glaciers scoured the bedrock here about 18,000 years ago, removing all the soil and exposing the ore, which must have been noticed by the local Indians. There is tenuous evidence that the Indians led Dutch prospectors to Franklin in the 1600s, and that the Dutch, mistaking the red mineral zincite (zinc oxide) for copper ore, made doomed attempts to smelt it for copper. Successful iron mining began in the area about 1772, but the zinc ores were not as easily mastered. The Franklin ores were mined in the 1770s by Lord Stirling. As the Dutch according to legend did before, Lord Stirling tried to smelt copper from the zinc ore and achieved only frustration. Zinc was not identified in the rock until the early 1800s. In 1810 zincite from Franklin became the first new mineral described from North America.

Through much of the nineteenth century, ambiguous deeds, overlapping claims, and legal shenanigans did more than the difficult ore to hold back profitable mining. Ownership of both the Franklin and Sterling Hill deposits had been consolidated by Samuel Fowler in the early 1800s. Almost immediately after he sold the property in 1836, however, splitting up of properties and mining rights began. Separate rights could exist on a single piece of land for zinc ore, iron ore, franklinite (a specific zinc mineral), limestone, and surface use. Poorly written documents and inappropriate splitting of rights to minerals intimately intermingled in the ore were an invitation to confusion, inefficiency, legal manipulation, exploitation, and fraud. Finally, in 1897, the deposits were again consolidated under a single owner, the New Jersey Zinc Company. From then until the mines closed, both the Franklin and Sterling Hill mines were owned and managed by New Jersey Zinc.

In comparison with the nineteenth century, mining in Franklin District in the twentieth century was well organized and efficient and provided regular employment to residents of Franklin and Ogdensburg. Like any mineral deposit, however, the Franklin District ore was nonrenewable. The Franklin

Mine was completely worked out by the mid-1950s and closed forever. The Sterling Hill Mine shut down in 1986, hampered by a combination of tax issues, corporate takeovers, low zinc prices, and the high cost of mining the deep levels the mine had reached. Enough ore remains below the ground for another ten years of mining, but the easily worked reserves are gone.

Edison Mines

In addition to the zinc mines, a few iron mines are included in the Franklin Mining District. The largest were the Edison Mines on Sparta Mountain, probably Thomas Edison's most expensive failure. Edison developed methods for grinding magnetite ore into sand-sized particles, magnetically separating the magnetite from the waste sand, then compressing the iron-rich concentrate into pellets for easy shipping. Millions of dollars were spent on the mines and on crushing and pelletizing machinery. At the peak of operations about five hundred people were working at the site. The technology was successful, but the Edison Mines could not compete with easily mined and easily shipped iron ore from newly opened mines on the shores of Lake Superior. In 1900, only a few years after the process was developed, the mines shut down.

North Church Delta

From Franklin, a short drive west on County Route 651 brings you to North Church, atop the North Church delta. As the ice age glaciers melted from New Jersey, they left distinct recessional moraines where the ice stabilized for periods of tens to hundreds of years. The North Church delta was built into Glacial Lake North Church while the ice stood at one of the recessional moraines, the Augusta Moraine. The North Church delta consists of a hummocky back side, deposited directly in contact with the ice, and a flat delta plain built into the lake to the south. The Ballyowen Golf Course, built on the hummocky knob

Kettle holes in the North Church delta before development of the Ballyowen Golf Course. The glacial features were made part of the layout of the course. —Photo by D. Harper

and kettle portion of the deposit, resembles Scottish upland golf courses similarly laid out on hummocky glacial terrains.

Kittatinny Valley

About a mile east of Sussex, NJ 23 passes over a cluster of thrust faults marking the border between the Highlands and the Valley and Ridge Provinces. The Kittatinny Valley has eroded into the soft shale of the Martinsburg Formation of Ordovician age.

Beemerville Intrusive Suite

In the Kittatinny Valley east of Sunrise Mountain are rocks of the Beemerville Intrusive Suite, a group of igneous rocks dating from the Taconic Orogeny. The best known outcrops of Beemerville rock are on Rutan Hill, a small hill on private land just south of the intersection of Neilson Road and County Route 519. Dikes of related rock cross through much of northwestern New Jersey, intruding gneiss and other Highland rocks.

Rutan Hill is a diatreme, a pipelike volcanic neck created by an upward explosion of magma propelled, somewhat like the explosion of a very large pressure cooker, by steam, carbon dioxide, and other volcanic gases. The volcanic rock of the hill is loaded with large and small fragments of the granite, gneiss, dolomitic limestone, and slate the diatreme shattered through as it exploded to the surface. The volcano was buried by sand and gravel of the Shawangunk Formation soon after it erupted, then disinterred and worn down to its roots during the erosion of Kittatinny Valley.

Crest of Rutan Hill. Outcrops of volcanic rock are visible below the large tree.
—Photo by Michael Flite

Lava at Rutan Hill with fragments of shattered country rock through which it exploded.
—Photo by D. Harper

Dike from the Beemer-ville Intrusive Suite cutting Proterozoic gneiss near McAfee north of Franklin.
—Photo by D. Harper

High Point State Park

High Point, 1,803 feet above sea level, is the highest point in New Jersey. The tower, built between 1928 and 1930 to honor all war veterans, adds another 200 feet. From the top of the tower, you can see much of northwestern New Jersey, parts of New York to the north, and Pennsylvania across the Delaware River to the west. You can also see the ridge of Kittatinny Mountain running miles to the northeast and southwest. From Kittatinny Valley, the ridge looks like a single

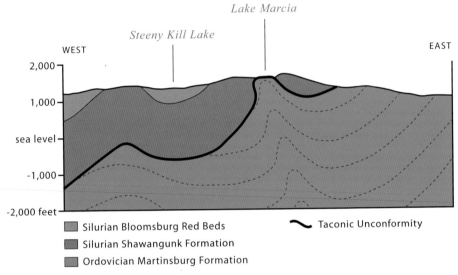

Geologic cross section through folds near High Point. —Modified from Monteverde, 2004

High Point from Lake Marcia. —Photo by D. Harper

wall, an unbroken ledge of quartzite tilted to the west. From the air you can see that the ridge is kinked into anticlines and synclines. The most easily seen folds are just north of the Delaware Water Gap and near High Point. Lake Marcia is at the crest of a breached anticline, where erosion of the sharply bent, fractured quartzite of the Shawangunk Formation has exposed the softer slate of the Martinsburg Formation below. Steeny Kill Lake is in the trough of an adjacent syncline, where the more easily eroded Bloomsburg Red Beds have worn down. The High Point monument is on the nose of the anticline, where erosion has not worn through the quartzite. The north-facing window of the monument, looking down the nose of the anticline, overlooks a single ridge of quartzite. The south-facing window overlooks a double-crested ridge, one crest on each side of the valley created by erosion of the softer, underlying Martinsburg slate.

The quartzite of Silurian age was deposited on an eroded surface of the Martinsburg Formation of Ordovician age. The erosion occurred as the land rose during the Taconic Orogeny. The contact between the two formations is called the Taconic Unconformity.

Magnetite and the New Jersey–New York Border

Probably the most hotly contested of New Jersey's boundaries was the land border with New York. The original charters of New York and New Jersey were unclear and contradictory, and there were overlapping land claims between the holders of huge land grants, traditional in New York, and small farmers moving northward from New Jersey. Armed conflict was a possibility until a compromise survey was completed in 1772. The line was intended to be straight, from the confluence of the Delaware and Neversink Rivers near Port Jervis to the Hudson River at 41 degrees north latitude. Instead of being based on true north from the North Star, however, known even in 1772 as the best way to conduct a survey, the line was surveyed using a compass, an especially poor choice in the magnetite-rich areas of the New Jersey Highlands. The line is far from straight. At Greenwood Lake, the border is south of the true line by 2,541 feet. The line was resurveyed properly by New Jersey in 1872, and it was recommended that the properly surveyed line be accepted as the boundary. Naturally, New York objected, and it was decided to leave the border as it was established in 1772.

Old Mine Road

39 miles

Old Mine Road follows the Delaware River from the Delaware Water Gap northward through a glaciated valley floored with Silurian and Devonian rocks, most in state or national parkland. A well-entrenched legend holds that Indians led Dutch explorers to a copper deposit at Pahaquarry, and the Dutch built the Old Mine Road in the 1650s to haul ore to ships bound from Esopus, New York, to smelters in Europe. There is a small, lean deposit of copper ore at Pahaquarry, and there is a long history of mining attempts. It is unlikely, though, that the Dutch built the Old Mine Road. Road building through 104 miles of wilderness

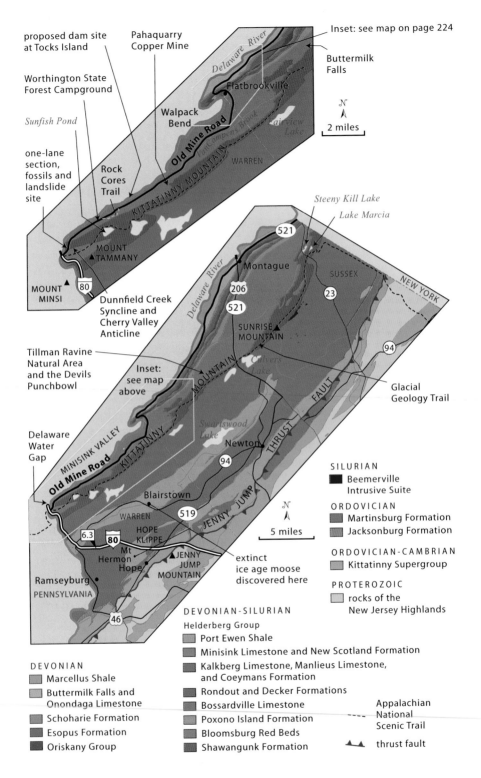

proposed dam site at Tocks Island

Pahaquarry Copper Mine

Worthington State Forest Campground

Sunfish Pond

one-lane section, fossils and landslide site

Rock Cores Trail

Walpack Bend

Old Mine Road

Flatbrookville

Delaware River

Flat Brook

Fairview Lake

WARREN

KITTATINNY MOUNTAIN

Inset: see map on page 224

Buttermilk Falls

N

2 miles

Steeny Kill Lake

Lake Marcia

521

Montague

SUSSEX

NEW YORK

MOUNT TAMMANY

Delaware River

206

521

SUNRISE MOUNTAIN

Culvers Lake

MOUNTAIN

THRUST

FAULT

23

94

Glacial Geology Trail

MOUNT MINSI

80

Dunnfield Creek Syncline and Cherry Valley Anticline

Tillman Ravine Natural Area and the Devils Punchbowl

Inset: see map above

Swartswood Lake

Newton

94

KITTATINNY

Delaware Water Gap

MINISINK VALLEY

Old Mine Road

Blairstown

519

JENNY JUMP

N

5 miles

WARREN

HOPE KLIPPE

Mt Hermon

Hope

JENNY JUMP MOUNTAIN

extinct ice age moose discovered here

6.3

80

Ramseyburg

PENNSYLVANIA

46

DEVONIAN

- Marcellus Shale
- Buttermilk Falls and Onondaga Limestone
- Schoharie Formation
- Esopus Formation
- Oriskany Group

DEVONIAN-SILURIAN

Helderberg Group

- Port Ewen Shale
- Minisink Limestone and New Scotland Formation
- Kalkberg Limestone, Manlieus Limestone, and Coeymans Formation
- Rondout and Decker Formations
- Bossardville Limestone
- Poxono Island Formation
- Bloomsburg Red Beds
- Shawangunk Formation

SILURIAN

- Beemerville Intrusive Suite

ORDOVICIAN

- Martinsburg Formation
- Jacksonburg Formation

ORDOVICIAN-CAMBRIAN

- Kittatinny Supergroup

PROTEROZOIC

- rocks of the New Jersey Highlands

- - - Appalachian National Scenic Trail

▲▲ thrust fault

Geology along Old Mine Road between the Delaware Water Gap and the New York border.
—Compiled from the USGS's Preliminary Integrated Geologic Map Database for the United States, 2006

would have been a major project in the 1600s and would have been recorded. No records exist. Moreover, the Indians and Dutch had hostile relations following massacres by the Dutch in the 1640s. It is unlikely that road building and mining would have been attempted or gone uncontested. Also, the ore is low-grade, and there was no shortage of high-grade copper ore in Europe. Finally, the oldest documented road to Pahaquarry is shown connecting to a ferry about 1 mile downstream on a 1790 map. Older maps exist, and none show roads near Pahaquarry on the New Jersey side of the river.

In its 43 miles from the Delaware Water Gap to the New York border, the Old Mine Road passes stratigraphically upward from sedimentary rock of the Shawangunk Formation and Bloomsburg Red Beds, composed of sand, gravel, and mud shed westward from highlands raised in the Taconic Orogeny, through thirteen relatively thin formations deposited at the eastern edge of a shallow, shifting interior seaway, and onto the Marcellus Shale, the earliest formation related to the approaching Acadian island arc. Deposition of these deepwater muds was premonitory to the welding of the island arc onto North America during the Acadian Orogeny.

The Delaware Valley upstream from the Delaware Water Gap is known as the Minisink Valley. According to tradition the name is from the Minsi Indian (a tribe of Lenni Lenapi) for "mountain people of land from which water is gone." Reportedly the tribe believed that the valley once held a large lake that burst out through the water gap. European settlement began in the 1720s, and the valley was contested between Indians and the colonists until the Revolutionary War. It is unlikely that many Indians were living in the New Jersey part of the valley after the French and Indian War of the mid-1750s. There was a larger Indian presence farther north in New York and Pennsylvania. On July 22, 1779, a force of Mohawks and loyalists defeated colonial insurgents in the Battle of Minisink Ford, along the river between Pennsylvania and New York.

Settlement continued after the war, and the area prospered into the mid-1800s. Just upstream from the Delaware Water Gap the village of Brotzman-ville stood in part on a stream terrace now used for the Worthington State Forest Campground. The village had a post office, several houses, a sawmill, a gristmill, a school, a quarry, and a limekiln. The mills were powered by small streams on the slopes of Kittatinny Mountain. The limestone for the kiln would have been picked from glacial materials as there is no limestone bedrock in the immediate vicinity. Like much of the rural northeast, the Minisink Valley went into decline after the 1850s.

Three-Minute Light

Immediately north of the Delaware Water Gap on Old Mine Road is a traffic light that stays red or green for a full three minutes. Be patient. The light controls traffic along a half-mile stretch of single-lane road. The road had two lanes before the 1980s but had to be closed several times after slides from above covered the road with rocks, or slides from below carried away sections of pavement. The rocks slide because fractures that slope down toward the road, and below the road toward an abandoned rail line, have been exposed by road cuts along the hillside. When rock at the base of the slope was dug out, the rock

Bedrock fractures slope toward Old Mine Road, presenting a rockfall hazard. —Photo by D. Harper

above the fractures was left unsupported and began sliding and toppling downward. After a 1980s rockslide carried the southbound lane downward onto the abandoned rail line, the National Park Service decided that it was unwise to rebuild a two-lane road. Rather than build out onto the unstable slope below or excavate farther into the unstable slope above, the road was converted to a single lane.

Fish Fossils

Fossils of the primitive, jawless ostracoderm fish *Vernonaspis* and *Americaspis* have been found in a low outcrop of the Bloomsburg Red Beds along the one-lane section of Old Mine Road. Ostracoderms lived during the Ordovician and Devonian Periods. Unlike many other jawless creatures, the ostracoderms did not rely on cilia to move food toward their mouths. Instead, they used suction from a muscular pharynx to pull in small, slow-moving prey. Their name is from the Latin *ostracon* (shell) and the Greek *derm* (skin), after the shell-like plates armoring the fronts and sides of the fish. When the fish died, the plates were scattered by waves, currents, and scavengers. The fossils are fingerprint-like impressions left when the scattered plates dissolved.

Tocks Island Dam Site and the Rock Cores Trail

The Delaware River, which originates along the New York–Pennsylvania state line at the confluence of its East and West Branches and forms state boundaries all the way to Delaware Bay, has been described as the only major free-flowing river east of the Mississippi. This is not from lack of dams on tributary streams, dam proposals for the main stem, or adequate dam sites. A great many dams have been proposed, but the proposals were seldom seen as equally beneficial to states on both banks of the river and were repeatedly blocked by the seemingly disadvantaged state. Much of the water for New York City comes from reservoirs on tributaries to the Delaware, and other tributaries have been dammed for hydroelectric power and flood control. The Rock Cores Trail overlooks Tocks Island, the site of the most recent dam proposed for the main stem of the Delaware.

Geologic conditions for building a dam are not ideal at Tocks Island. Conditions are more favorable at Walpack Bend, about 10 miles upstream, where a dam could be anchored in rock along its entire length. Planning for a water supply dam at Walpack Bend was well along when, on August 12, 1955, Hurricane Connie dumped up to 12.5 inches of rain in the Delaware watershed. On August 18, Hurricane Diane dumped an additional 11 inches. Floods claimed one hundred lives, cost millions in property damage, caused a widespread call for flood control, and placed the Delaware within the Corps of Engineers flood control mandate. A 1957 Corps of Engineers study found that a reservoir at Tocks Island was feasible and would have double the storage capacity of a Walpack Bend reservoir while adding only 50 to 60 percent to the cost. From that time, Tocks Island became the preferred site.

Difficult conditions in both the rock and the overlying glacial deposits caused repeated delays, budget shortfalls, and cost overruns. In the bedrock, stability of a cut standing more than 300 feet high above the spillway was a major concern. An adit was driven into the hillside to investigate the rock, and 36-inch-diameter core holes were drilled. Geologists were lowered down the holes to make field notes and install stress-measuring instruments. The findings were not encouraging. Just as at the three-minute light, there are numerous slope-parallel fractures. Some were continuous across the entire slope above the dam and open enough to allow groundwater flow. It was predicted that the entire mass of rock above the spillway would slide downhill if supporting rock at the base were excavated.

The glacial deposits, more than 200 feet of sand and mud, presented different problems. Neither the sand nor the mud was well suited for the foundation. The clean, permeable sand would allow underflow and undermining. The mud had little strength and was prone to liquefaction. Some cores through the mud, in fact, liquefied while being removed from the coring equipment.

While the geologic conditions were far from ideal, it was generally agreed that a safe dam could be built. An experimental quarry was to be opened to evaluate ways to stabilize rock above the spillway. Seepage through the sand and gravel was to be controlled by grouting, installation of drains, and placement of impermeable barriers. The unstable silt and clay were to be excavated from some areas, and the dam was to be further stabilized by widening its base from less than 1,000 feet to over 3,000 feet.

From $90 million in 1962, the estimated cost of the dam rose to $400 million by 1975 and was still climbing. Soaring costs and budget shortfalls were clearly important in the demise of the project, as were questionable cost-benefit ratios in the initial plan, incomplete evaluation of eutrophication, questionable recreation benefits, and infrastructure needs that had not been addressed. Perhaps equally important in leading to strong grassroots opposition were public relations disasters in land acquisition, mismanagement of the acquired land, and changing public attitudes toward large dams through this stage in the development of the environmental movement. No single issue stands out as the one that killed the Tocks Island Dam, but the project had become politically untenable before the scheduled 1975 groundbreaking. It was formally deauthorized in 1992.

Little remains at Tocks Island to identify it as the subject of one of the formative events of the environmental movement. The adit constructed to investigate rock conditions at the spillway is about 30 feet above the roadway, securely

These 36-inch-diameter cores were drilled to investigate bedrock conditions at the proposed Tocks Island dam site. —Photo by D. Harper

gated to allow access to bats but deny it to humans. The sound of water falling from the bedding plane faults can be heard from the entrance. A couple of the 36-inch-diameter rock cores lie on the hillside near the northern end of the Rock Cores Trail. Many more are on the hillside a few hundred feet directly up the slope from those along the trail. The cores are broken mostly along bedding planes, and the breaks show well-preserved mud cracks, ripple marks, and fossil burrows.

Pahaquarry Copper Mine

The earliest mining at Pahaquarry, probably in the 1750s, must have been inspired by the bright green and blue copper minerals malachite and chryso-colla. These are secondary minerals created by the weathering of chalcocite, the primary ore. They are only present in negligible amounts, mostly near the surface and along fractures. Chalcocite, by contrast, is dull gray and would not have attracted attention. Interest in mining by the 1750s is known from deeds, wills, and the notation "Mine Brook" on a map. It appears that two or possibly four adits were dug and ore was crushed at a stamp mill powered by Mine Brook, but the mining was abandoned without any ore being shipped.

The next serious interest in the deposit was in the mid-nineteenth century when speculation was sparked by an expanding brass industry and an increased need for copper sheathing for the hulls of ships. A mining lease was signed in 1829, but assay results were disappointing and there was little or no digging. In 1847, the old adits were cleaned out and about ten new openings made. Ore was shipped by wagon to Flemington, where one of the owners operated a mine

Adit at the Pahaquarry Copper Mine. —Photo by D. Harper

and smelter. The operation was not profitable, and the mine shut down within a year. Again in 1861, the mine opened and closed within a year.

Profitable mining at Pahaquarry is difficult because the ore is lean and because the chalcocite is disseminated through the rock instead of being concentrated in veins. Much of the chalcocite was lost during separation from the host sandstone even when the ore was ground to a powder. The mines were reopened in 1901, and at least three different concentrating processes, each using different equipment, were tried between 1901 and 1913. Each failed. In 1913, with a total production of three refined copper ingots worth about $15 each, the mine and equipment were sold in a bankruptcy proceeding.

From the Coppermine parking area, trails lead past the former locations of a tramway and at least seventeen shafts and tunnels. Most are caved in and barely recognizable. One well-preserved adit is gated. At the top of the trails are strip mines and tailings piles. The trail to the strip mine passes outstanding outcrops of sandstone in the Bloomsburg Red Beds. The rock is covered by fine, parallel grooves carved by sand and stones embedded at the base of the ice age glaciers. Many sandstone outcrops had these grooves at the end of the ice age, but the markings weathered with the passage of time and are mostly hard to see. The exposures along this trail were preserved beneath soil until early in the twentieth century when they were uncovered by miners.

Glacier Features along Kittatinny Mountain

Well-known overlooks face eastward from the ridge crest of Kittatinny Mountain at Fairview Lake and Sunrise Mountain. Both are along the Appalachian Trail but only short walks from parking areas. The overlooks are above steep, bouldery talus on the east slope of the ridge and look east across Kittatinny Valley to the granite and gneiss ridges of the New Jersey Highlands. The valley is floored by the Paleozoic Kittatinny dolomitic limestone formations and Martinsburg slate. Underfoot at the overlooks, the quartzite of the Shawangunk Formation was formed from sand washed westward from highlands raised in the Taconic Orogeny. The sand was deposited in braided stream, delta, and beach environments on the east shore of a wide, shallow inland sea west of the rising mountains. Even though the rock has been metamorphosed to quartzite, much of the layering and crossbedding typical of beaches, braided streams, and sandy deltas is still visible.

Long after the rock was cemented to quartzite, the ice age glaciers carved it into streamlined roche moutonnée shapes and added polish, chattermarks, and gouges. Most of the glacial features are from a time when the ice was thick, and the streamlining and scouring show that the ice was moving directly south across the ridge. As the ice thinned, topography had more of an effect and the ice was cast into a lobe flowing southwestward down Kittatinny Valley. Ice banked against Kittatinny ridge even flowed, briefly, southwestward across the ridge and toward the Delaware River. In the brief time ice was moving across the ridge, a small boulder of nepheline syenite from a distinctive, small intrusion at Beemerville, east of the ridge, was picked up and carried across the crest of the ridge. It now sits along the Glacial Geology Trail, protected from collectors by a steel cage. The trail is in Stokes State Forest off Sunrise Mountain Road.

Nepheline syenite boulder along Glacial Geology Trail, secure from collectors.
—Photo by Sondra Flite

Glacial polish, chattermarks, and crescentic fractures on quartzite on the trail to Sunrise Mountain. The ice moved from left to right across the outcrop. The crescentic fractures are longer cracks in the rock, and their horns point in the direction the ice was moving. Chattermarks are smaller, with some rock removed, and their horns point in the direction the ice was coming from.
—Photo by D. Harper

The short, easy trail to the Fairview Lake overlook follows a roadway that led to a development of summer homes condemned for parkland as part of the Tocks Island Dam project. Fairview Lake, at the edge of Kittatinny Valley below the overlook, began its existence as a glacial lake trapped south of the ice in an area of thick glacial till and drumlins. In its retreat from the terminal moraine, the ice did not melt back at a constant rate. It retreated episodically, leaving several lines of glacial deposits where the ice stood for periods of a few tens of years up to a few hundreds of years. Fairview Lake was impounded by one of these small moraine and outwash deposits.

The trail to the Sunrise Mountain overlook is steeper than the road to the Fairview Lake overlook and has carefully placed rock steps. Rock outcroppings along the trail provide good examples of crossbedding in quartzite and glacial polishing, crescentic fractures, and chattermarks. At the top, stunted, twisted trees attest to the severity of life on the dry, windswept ridge.

Ravines, Waterfalls, and Glacial Meltwater

Tillman Ravine, Vancampens Brook, and Dunnfield Creek are only the best known of the many scenic creeks along the flanks of Kittatinny Mountain and Walpack Ridge. Buttermilk Falls is the best known of the many waterfalls. Some creeks are postglacial; others, including Tillman Ravine and Vancampens Brook, date from the retreating glaciers and have remained in the channels cut by glacial meltwater. The Devils Punchbowl along Tillman Ravine and smaller potholes along Vancampens Brook remain from the short times when meltwater ran down the creeks. Boulders and gravel spinning in eddies in the torrential meltwater flows drilled the potholes down into the rock.

A more dramatic illustration of the power of glacial meltwater, now unfortunately hidden by trees much of the year, is offered by boulder conglomerates along Walpack-Flatbrook Road just north of Flatbrookville. The boulders are from meltwater streams and are cemented together by calcium carbonate dissolved from limestone in the conglomerates. The calcium carbonate was precipitated when the water either evaporated or lost carbon dioxide to the atmosphere and became less acidic. The conglomerates have attracted the attention of geologists since the mid-1800s. At that time, the science was split between catastrophists, who believed that the Earth had been shaped by a series of sudden, violent events beyond our understanding, and uniformitarians, who believed that the same processes we now see operating have been operating as we now see them through the entire span of geologic time. Henry Rogers, like most North American geologists of the time, was a catastrophist. In his 1840 *Descriptions of the Geology of the State of New Jersey*, Rogers attributed many landscapes and surface deposits to the most recent catastrophe, an immense flood that he believed swept into the state from the west, then down the Delaware Valley and across the Coastal Plain, cutting away tens of feet of clay and greensand and spreading gravel across the Coastal Plain. He cites the bouldery gravel at Flatbrookville as "evidence of the short duration and violence of the action by which the miscellaneous debris from the adjacent rocks was hurled together." The gravel was only one of numerous features across New Jersey that Rogers used to illustrate the effects of the flood. It is now well-known that

Buttermilk Falls flows over the Bloomsburg Red Beds of Silurian age.
—Photo by Emma Rainforth, Ramapo College of New Jersey

Ice age gravel cemented to rock by calcium carbonate, Walpack-Flatbrook Road.
—Photo by D. Harper

meltwater from even small areas of glacial drainage can easily move large rocks, and the cemented gravels are confidently ascribed to meltwater flowing between the ice and the valley wall.

Walpack Bend

At Walpack Bend, the Delaware River does a hairpin turn, flowing about 1 mile northward before turning again and resuming its southward flow. At the bend, the river crosses the first ridge of the Valley and Ridge Province west of Kittatinny Mountain, known as Godfrey Ridge in Pennsylvania and Walpack Ridge in New Jersey. Walpack Ridge, standing about 400 feet above the river, is substantial but easy to overlook in comparison to the nearby Kittatinny Mountain with its 900 feet of relief. The bend in the river coincides with a 2,800-foot-long offset in the crest of Walpack Ridge due to folding. Weakening of the rocks along the fold axes may account for the river crossing the ridge at this location and for the two sharp bends.

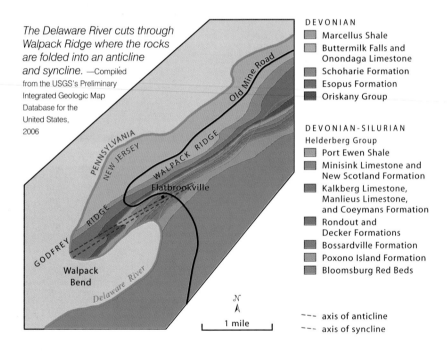

The Delaware River cuts through Walpack Ridge where the rocks are folded into an anticline and syncline. —Compiled from the USGS's Preliminary Integrated Geologic Map Database for the United States, 2006

DEVONIAN
- Marcellus Shale
- Buttermilk Falls and Onondaga Limestone
- Schoharie Formation
- Esopus Formation
- Oriskany Group

DEVONIAN-SILURIAN
Helderberg Group
- Port Ewen Shale
- Minisink Limestone and New Scotland Formation
- Kalkberg Limestone, Manlieus Limestone, and Coeymans Formation
- Rondout and Decker Formations
- Bossardville Formation
- Poxono Island Formation
- Bloomsburg Red Beds

--- axis of anticline
--- axis of syncline

Silurian and Devonian Rocks of North of Walpack Bend

In contrast to the Bloomsburg Red Beds and Shawangunk Formation along the river south of Walpack Bend, the formations exposed north of the bend are thin, measured in tens of feet to a few hundred feet rather than from hundreds to thousands of feet. By the time the thinner formations were being deposited, the Taconic Orogeny was over. Compression of the crust was no longer raising mountains to the east, and large volumes of sediment were no longer being shed westward. The mountains had worn down, and New Jersey stood near the eastern shore of a shallow sea covering the interior of the continent, similar in many respect to Hudson Bay but much warmer. Small changes in sea level or small uplifts or subsidences of the land led to sudden, widespread changes in the area covered by water and the types of sediment being deposited. This gave rise to thin formations, which can nonetheless be mapped across thousands of square miles. Fifteen separate formations with a combined thickness of about 1,000 feet have been mapped through this area. Several are less than 50 feet thick.

Many formations are richly fossiliferous or preserve unusual sedimentary structures. Most of the fossils and structures are in parkland where collecting is prohibited or on private property where collecting without permission can be treated as thievery. Three of the more intriguing features are *Zoophycos* trace fossils, most abundant in the Esopus Formation; thick mud-cracked limestone in the Bossardville Formation; and patch reefs of the Coeymans Formation.

Zoophycos is the name given to marks left by the feeding pattern of an organism, probably a worm, that lived below the sediment surface and fed by ingesting mud rich in organic materials. The animal stayed within a presumably tasty layer in which there was an abundance of organic material and followed a regular, efficient feeding pattern, which covered the entire surface. The result resembles a rooster tail and gave an early name, cauda galli grit (*caudagalli* is Latin for "rooster tail") to the Esopus Formation. *Zoophycos* lived in relatively deep, oxygen-poor water that allowed organic detritus to build up on the bottom and be buried.

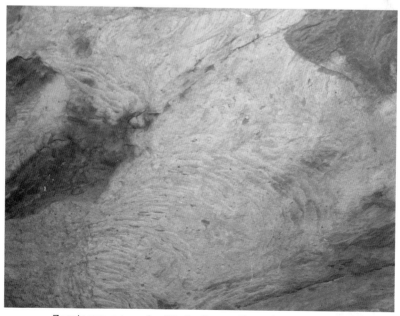

Zoophycos, a trace fossil in the Esopus Formation at Bevans Rock Shelter near Bevans in Sandyston Township. —Photo by D. Harper

The tops of the desiccation columns in the Bossardville Formation. Rather than being surface mud cracks as you would see in a dried puddle, the cracks in the Bossardville penetrate several feet deep. The columnar aspect is visible toward the bottom of the photo. The columns were initially relatively regular polygons but were compressed into oblong shapes during deformation of the rock. —Photo by Don Monteverde, N.J. Geological Survey

Limestone from the flank of a patch reef in the Coeymans Formation. The small, circular, beadlike fossils are stem segments from crinoids, related to modern sea lilies. The fragments were washed by waves and currents from higher on the reef. The cabbagelike fossil is a stromatoporoid and likely grew where it fossilized. —Photo by Don Monteverde, N.J. Geological Survey

The thick mud cracks in the Bossardville Formation show that the inland sea was not consistently deep across northwestern New Jersey. The mud cracks formed only when the sea withdrew and the bottom was exposed to the atmosphere.

The patch reefs in the Coeymans Formation are mounds of limestone several hundred feet across and 50 or so feet thick. They started in shallow, wave-tossed waters where calcium-secreting organisms, mostly the long-extinct stromatoporoids, stabilized the loose lime sand and lime mud of the seafloor, then built upward almost to the water surface. It is unclear what modern animals, if any, stromatoporoids are related to. Some scientists think they are related to sponges. Stromatoporoids, not corals, were the primary reef builders in the Silurian Period.

At first the patches look simply like masses of cemented fossils, but careful mapping has revealed well-organized environments similar to those in modern reefs. Reef flanks were covered by debris washed from shallower water. Solidly cemented limestone built around the margins directly exposed to strong waves. Carbonate sand, mud, and pellets accumulated in the protected interior of the reef. Carbonate mudstone built up on flats exposed above high tides. In one of the reefs, researchers even found differences between sediments on the upwind and downwind sides of the reef.

The westernmost and youngest of the formations is the Marcellus Shale, a black shale rich in organic materials that, west of New Jersey, is being exploited for its natural gas. In New Jersey the shale is far too thin and close to the surface for gas production. The Marcellus was deposited on a relatively deep, oxygen-poor sea bottom when the Earth's crust was beginning to bend downward in advance of the Acadian island arc.

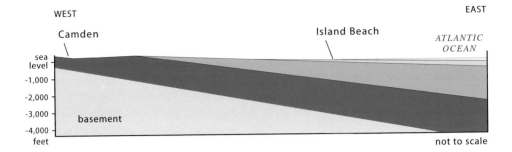

TIME		FORMATION	LITHOLOGY
QUATERNARY HOLOCENE		beach deposits	sand, gravel
		estuarine deposits	silt, mud, peat
		surficial deposits	
TERTIARY		Pensauken Formation	sand, clayey silt
		Bridgeton Formation	sand, clayey silt
	OUTER COASTAL PLAIN	unnamed unit at Cape May	sand with interbeds of thin to thick clay
		Cohansey Formation	sand, some clayey silt
		Kirkwood Formation	sand, gravel, clayey silt
		Shark River Formation	clayey silt, fine quartz sand, glauconitic sand
		Manasquan Formation	clayey silt, fine quartz sand, glauconitic sand
		Vincentown Formation	sand, clayey silt, glauconitic sand, calcarenite
		Hornerstown Formation	glauconitic sand
CRETACEOUS	INNER COASTAL PLAIN	Tinton Formation	sand, glauconitic sand
		Red Bank Formation	sand, clayey silt, some glauconitic sand
		Navesink Formation	glauconite sand
		Mount Laurel Formation	sand
		Wenonah Formation	silty sand, some glauconite
		Marshalltown Formation	clayey silt, glauconite sand
		Englishtown Formation	sand, clayey silt
		Woodbury Formation	clayey silt
		Merchantville Formation	clayey silt, glauconitic sand
		Cheesequake Formation	clay, clayey silt
		Magothy Formation	sand, clayey silt
		Raritan Formation	sand, clayey silt
		Potomac Formation	gravel, sand, silt, clay

Most of the formations in the Coastal Plain are made of some combination of unconsolidated sand, silt, or clay. —Modified from Owens and others, 1998

COASTAL PLAIN
Pinelands, Beaches, and Marshes

New Jersey's Coastal Plain is commonly subdivided into the Inner Coastal Plain, where sandy and clayey, semiconsolidated formations of Cretaceous age are exposed, and the Outer Coastal Plain, veneered by unconsolidated Tertiary-age sands of the Pinelands. The fertile soils of the Inner Coastal Plain earn New Jersey the Garden State nickname. The nutrient-poor soils of the Pinelands support little agriculture except for cranberries and blueberries in lowland bogs. There is no hard rock exposed in the Coastal Plain—it is buried beneath thousands of feet of sediments. The constant washing of waves along the Jersey Shore has created entire islands of sand that shift with each passing storm.

SEDIMENTATION ON THE COASTAL PLAIN

After the Atlantic Ocean opened up in Jurassic time, sediments eroded from the Appalachian Mountains began to accumulate on the coast and continental shelf. Rivers carried sand, silt, and clay seaward, depositing it in deltas, beaches, estuaries, and shallow lakes. One might expect a simple layer cake of sediment to build up as crust subsided and rivers delivered sediment, but the reality of sedimentation on the subsiding continental margin was much more complex.

As the new crust of the Jurassic-age rift basins cooled and subsided, the sea encroached landward. Marine and shoreline sediment was initially deposited only in areas now offshore but eventually came to be deposited as far west as the base of the present-day Watchungs and Sourland Mountain. The oldest sediments now onshore are mostly sand deposited in Cretaceous time in rivers and deltas as the sea advanced, with intermittent stops and retreats, landward. For much of the time after the landward advance of the sea onto the Coastal Plain, sea level was higher than it is now, and most of the thick wedge of sediment underlying the Coastal Plain was deposited offshore.

As might be expected, the water was deeper over the more seaward part of the continental shelf. Going from the shoreline seaward, sand and gravel commonly gave way to silty sand, clayey silt, and then glauconitic sand and silt. In general, sand and gravel were deposited in shallow water toward the inner part of the continental shelf. The silty sand, clayey silt, silty clay, and glauconitic sand and silt represent progressively deeper water. Glauconite is a greenish mineral that forms slowly from clay and tiny flakes of mica and clay in oxygen-poor marine environments like the digestive tracts of bottom-dwelling creatures. On much of the shelf, the clay and mica were buried without becoming glauconite. The glauconitic formations represent only the times of deepest water or slowest sedimentation.

Superimposed on the generally shallow to deep progression from onshore to offshore, sediments on the continental shelf record seven cycles of sea level rise and fall, four in Late Cretaceous time and three in Cenozoic time. Rises in sea level were sudden, with deepwater glauconite directly overlying shallow-water sand and gravel. Falls in sea level were more gradual, and formations often have gradational boundaries from glauconite through silty sand, sandy silt, and sand as the water grew progressively shallower. Erosion along the northwestern Coastal Plain has exposed the landward portions of the formations deposited in these cycles, and the sediment types from glauconite to sand are well represented. To the east, the water remained deep through the duration of some cycles, and the shallower-water sediments are entirely missing.

Superimposed on the cycles of sea level rise and fall are variations in the amount of sediment being carried to the Coastal Plain. Some of the changes were from the shifting of rivers that caused more or less material to be brought to particular sections of the continental shelf. Others are related to changes in climate that increased or decreased erosion. Cycles from times of rapid sedimentation are thick. Cycles from times of slower sedimentation—sediment starved times—are thinner, with more shell material and glauconite. The Vincentown Formation, from one of these sediment-starved times, is mostly sand but has layers of broken up shells (lime sand) completely without sediment carried from land.

Vincentown lime sand has been lithified to a soft limestone by calcium carbonate dissolved from the shells and reprecipitated as a cement. Most of the fossils are bryozoan colonies. Each of the small holes housed an individual bryozoan. The colonies built up by sprouting new animals from a single founding bryozoan. —N.J. Geological Survey specimen; photo by D. Harper

Between 15 and 10 million years ago, an ice cap grew on Antarctica and caused a major, worldwide drop in sea level. As the sea receded eastward, it left behind the Cohansey Formation, an assemblage of beach and nearshore deposits best known for the sands that blanket the Pinelands.

From about 10 million years ago to the present, water has remained locked up in Antarctica. The ocean never again advanced far across the Coastal Plain. Initially after the sea level dropped, rivers headed southward straight across the bedrock of northern New Jersey, then continued southward down a gentle seaward slope, the Beacon Hill Plain, left by the receding ocean. The plain was flat even in comparison with today's Coastal Plain. Gravel from rivers crossing the plain, the Beacon Hill gravel, may once have covered much of southern New Jersey, but erosion has removed all but a few remnants capping the highest hills, usually 50 to 100 feet above the surrounding countryside. The Clarksburg Hills, Mt. Pleasant Hills, and Woodmansie upland are all remnants of this river plain. Although sometimes mapped separately, the Beacon Hill gravel is usually considered the upper part of the Cohansey Formation.

With the drop in sea level, New Jersey entered the next phase of its development, the gradual lowering of the land surface by erosion of both the bedrock to the north and the unconsolidated sediments of the Coastal Plain. As the streams cut downward, the Coastal Plain formations underlying the Cohansey came into view along the western edge of the Coastal Plain. By about 8 million years ago, erosion had uncovered the Potomac, Raritan, and Magothy Formations, a belt of easily eroded sands along the inner edge of the Coastal Plain, and a parallel belt of less easily eroded, semiconsolidated silty clay, clay,

Sand, like that in this freshly cleaned exposure at Sand Hills along US 1 in South Brunswick, can preserve sedimentary structures, such as crossbedding, for millions of years but is easily eroded by running water. —Photo by D. Harper

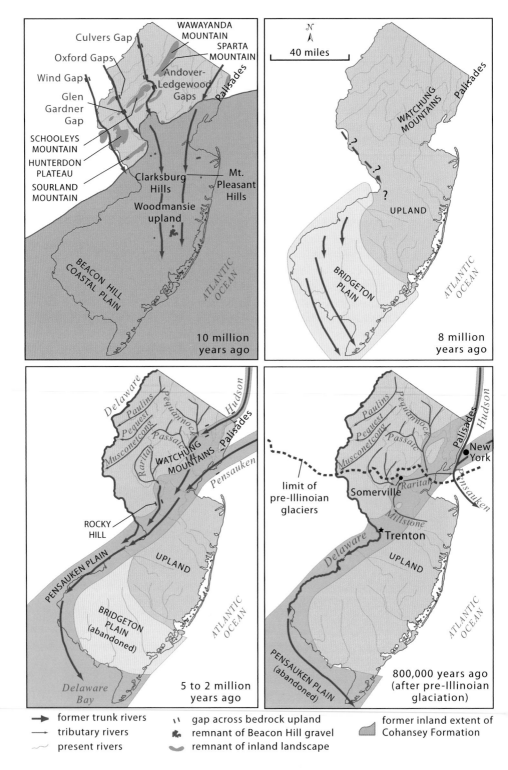

The development of plains and uplands on New Jersey's Coastal Plain from 10 million years ago to 800,000 years ago. —Modified from Stanford, 2005; Stanford, 2009

and glauconitic formations a few miles to the east. The rivers abandoned their paths straight south across the Coastal Plain and, similar to the Delaware River today, became entrenched along the easily eroded sands between the bedrock west of the Coastal Plain and the semiconsolidated formations to the east. They ran parallel to the shoreline for several tens of miles before turning southeast toward the ocean.

The earliest predecessor to the Delaware River, the Bridgeton, turned seaward south of Camden and beveled off the Coastal Plain formations to a flat, seaward-sloping surface across a 50-mile-wide swath from Camden southward past Delaware Bay. This surface, the Bridgeton Plain, has since been dissected by the Delaware, Cohansey, Maurice, and Great Egg Harbor Rivers, but substantial areas of the flat upland remain. Reflecting the gradient of the Bridgeton River, the upland drops from 150 feet above present sea level near Lindenwold to 120 feet near Hammonton and 50 feet on the upland side of a wave-cut scarp at the edge of the Absecon marshes at Pleasantville.

Even though the Bridgeton Plain extends across the Pinelands, much of the land, even as far east as the vineyards near Cologne, is farmland. The river sediments of the Bridgeton Formation, which cover the pure quartz sand of the Cohansey Formation, give rise to more productive soil than the nutrient-poor quartz sand typical of the Pinelands. Further, the flat topography of the Bridgeton Plain is easily tilled. The Bridgeton Plain around Bridgeton, Millville, and Vineland is one of the richest agricultural areas of New Jersey, widely known for its vegetables, orchards, blueberries, and vineyards.

River gravel of the Bridgeton Formation overlies sandy beach deposits of the Cohansey Formation in a gravel pit in Cumberland County. —Photo by Otto S. Zapecza, N.J. Geological Survey

From 5 to 2 million years ago, another predecessor of the Delaware River dominated the landscape. The Pensauken River, a much larger river than today's Delaware, flowed westward along the Long Island Sound lowland and across central New Jersey from Perth Amboy to Trenton, and from there closely paralleled the present Delaware. Both the Delaware and Hudson Rivers were tributaries. The valleys of both the Pensauken and Delaware Rivers extend southwestward to about 40 miles southwest of Camden, then turn southeastward toward the Atlantic. The Pensauken River eroded an 8- to 10-mile-wide swath of land several tens of feet below the Bridgeton Plain. The river initially eroded its valley when sea level was low. At a later time of higher sea level, the floor of the river built upward with the deposition of 100 feet of sand and gravel, the Pensauken Formation, forming the Pensauken Plain. The surface was built to about 50 feet below the Bridgeton Plain. Along the Delaware Valley south of Trenton, most of the Pensauken Plain has been removed by erosion. North of Trenton the former valley between Perth Amboy and Trenton is no longer occupied by a major river, so the Pensauken Plain has seen much less erosion than the Delaware Valley. The plain has been lowered to some degree by erosion but is in good part preserved. Similar to the Bridgeton Plain, the Pensauken Plain drops in elevation downriver. The plain is 150 feet above sea level at South Amboy, 120 feet near Hightstown, 100 feet near Trenton, and about 90 feet near Camden.

The modern Delaware River dates from the pre-Illinoian ice age when the headwaters of the Pensauken River abandoned their valley across central New Jersey for a course straight eastward from the New York City area to the Atlantic. Similar to the Pensauken, the downriver reaches of the Delaware have responded to lowered sea levels by cutting downward and to higher sea levels by building the floodplain upward. When sea level was lowest at the height of the Wisconsinan ice age, the Delaware channel was about 150 feet below present sea level south of Cape May, 120 feet below sea level southeast of Millville, and about 90 feet below sea level at the Delaware Memorial Bridge. In upriver reaches to the north, by contrast, the volume of sand and gravel washing downriver from glaciers was greater than the river could carry, so instead of cutting downward, the floodplain built upward. At Trenton glacial outwash built the floodplain to an elevation of about 50 feet.

After the ice age, the pattern of cutting and filling reversed. With sea level rise, the channel along the lower reaches was mostly filled with up to 150 feet of postglacial river and estuary sediment. Without dredging and other human interference, the river would continue to build up its channel in response to sea level rise. Upriver from Camden, the sediment load decreased after glaciers melted from the drainage basin, and the river was able to cut down into the outwash built up when the river was overloaded. At Trenton the river has cut completely through the glacial outwash to bedrock just above sea level.

Coastal Plain Hills

One of the distinctive features of the New Jersey Coastal Plain is a widely spaced scattering of small ridges and conical hills usually 50 to 100 feet above the surrounding countryside. Sand Hills, Mt. Holly, and Mt. Laurel are relatively close to the New Jersey Turnpike, but there are similar hills in the Pinelands. Apple Pie Hill and the Forked River Mountains are the best known. Most of the hills are capped with gravel or ironstone, and the resistant caps have commonly been given as the reason the hills have not succumbed to erosion. Mt. Holly and Mt. Laurel are capped by ironstone. Apple Pie Hill and the Forked River Mountains are capped by gravel. In a different interpretation of Coastal Plain downcutting, Scott Stanford of the New Jersey Geological Survey suggests the resistant caps influenced the locations of the hills but do not protect them from erosion. In this interpretation, the resistant materials deflected streams away from where the hills now stand in the early stages of downcutting, but after the streams became deeply incised in the sandy Coastal Plain formations, much of the valley widening was the result of sapping by springs rather than by overland flow along streams. Precipitation falling on upland areas soaks into the sand instead of flowing overland and only becomes effective at erosion where it reemerges, commonly from a spring at the top of an impermeable clay layer. The resistant caps are undermined rather than eroded from above and offer little protection to the hills.

The small hills of the Coastal Plain have not completely eroded away because the effectiveness of springs in eroding the hills decreases as the area of upland decreases. If there is a large area of upland, a great deal of water soaks into the ground, and the large springs are able to sap away quickly at the valley walls. When the uplands have been reduced to small hills or ridges, the flow rate to springs decreases to negligible, and erosion slows to almost nothing.

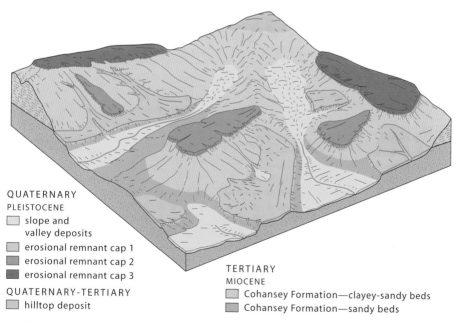

QUATERNARY
PLEISTOCENE
☐ slope and valley deposits
☐ erosional remnant cap 1
☐ erosional remnant cap 2
☐ erosional remnant cap 3
QUATERNARY-TERTIARY
☐ hilltop deposit

TERTIARY
MIOCENE
☐ Cohansey Formation—clayey-sandy beds
☐ Cohansey Formation—sandy beds

As springs sap away at upland areas, small hills capped by more resistant beds of different ages remain, forming the hills of the Coastal Plain. —Modified from Newell and others, 2000

THE JERSEY SHORE

Barrier islands line the Atlantic Coast of New Jersey from Sandy Hook to Cape May. They are ridges of sand that parallel the mainland but are separated from it by bays and tidal marshes. From a geologic standpoint, the barrier islands are temporary features. They migrate inland as sea level rises and out as sea level falls. Large storms can breach islands, changing landscapes. Despite the lack of solid ground, many resort towns have been built on barrier islands, including Atlantic City. Nothing draws a vacationer like a sandy beach.

Beaches have been compared to rivers of sand propelled by coastal waves and currents. Unlike the water in a river, however, sand on a beach often reverses direction when wind and waves change. In New Jersey, summertime sand movement is most often to the north in response to waves from the southeast. In wintertime, waves from the northeast are the most effective sand movers, and average movement is to the south. On most southern New Jersey beaches, waves from the northeast move the greatest amount of sand, and sand movement is on average south. To the north, along the Monmouth County shore, the beaches are sheltered by Long Island from fully developed waves from the northeast, and waves from the southeast move more sand in most years. Net sand transport is to the north. Depending on the beach and the year, somewhere between 200,000 and 300,000 cubic yards of sand can be expected to move northward or southward in a year. This is equivalent to thirty fully loaded sand trucks moving up the beach each day.

Beach at Sandy Hook with the New York skyline in the distance. —National Park Service photo

A beach may lose sand one year and gain sand the next. Long-term trends are difficult to discern. Just as with weather, in which a series of hot summers may be a random fluctuation or the result of global warming, a few summers of beach erosion may be a random event or signal the start of an erosional trend. Without careful records, there is no way to tell the difference. Beach profiles showing the width and shape of the beach through many years are needed. Over the past twenty-two years, profiles of one hundred beaches from Raritan Bay to Delaware Bay have been surveyed twice yearly by the Beach Profile Network of Richard Stockton College. Profiling on land is straightforward. Profiling seaward is less comfortable, and many older profiles end at low tide. They do not track sand from the time winter storms move it offshore until the storms die down and the sand returns to the beach. The Stockton profiles, by contrast, are measured past the offshore bars even if the water is cold and rough. They track sand through the entire annual cycle. One of the most reassuring findings of the Beach Profile Network is that sand pumped onto beaches at great expense in beach nourishment projects has stayed on the beaches for years rather than washing away in a few months, as some predicted.

The coastline is constantly changing, but changes in the beaches and off-shore bars were of little concern except to sailors even through the mid-1800s. There were few permanent structures other than lighthouses. With the increasing construction of large beachfront hotels and resorts in the decades after the Civil War, however, the instablility of beaches increasingly became an economic issue for land dwellers. Through the middle of the twentieth century, groins, seawalls, and jetties were the favored means of dealing with inconvenient shoreline changes. These physical, constructed features are known as hard stabilization. After construction of a railroad, now replaced by a road, along Sandy

A beach nourishment project in action. —U.S. Army Corps of Engineers photo

Hook, protection against the formation of inlets that periodically breached the base of Sandy Hook became important. In 1898 a massive, 15-foot-high seawall was completed along 3 miles of the shorefront at Sea Bright. The seawall has become notorious as an extreme example of hard stabilization and the New Jerseyfied beach. While the wall at least temporarily halted westward migration of the shoreline, there was until recently little or no beach seaward of the wall even at low tide. Further, inland flooding and sand overwash were problems after even moderate storms, erosion of the clays and salt marsh sediments at the foundation of the wall was a constant threat, and the cost of repairs to the wall was, over the years, substantially more than the value of the houses it was protecting. A 1984 storm, for example, caused $84 million in damages to the wall. In 2012, Hurricane Sandy breached this wall as well as others along the Atlantic Coast.

Whereas at Sea Bright stabilization of the beachfront was attempted using a wall of rock, groins were used along much of the remaining Jersey Shore. Groins are walls of rock or steel pilings built from the beach straight into the water. Sand being carried along the beach by waves is stopped at the groin and causes the beach to build outward. Unfortunately for the next person down the beach, the groin stops the sand but doesn't stop the waves. Without sand coming from the updrift side of the groin, the downdrift beach erodes. The downdrift beachfront owner must either install a groin in self-defense or demand that taxpayers do so. Without a doubt, many beachfront buildings would have been destroyed without the protection of seawalls, groins, and jetties. Well-designed groins can

Historical photo looking south at the seawall at Sea Bright. —Library of Congress photo; unknown date

be useful where there is an abundance of sand, and there are unquestionably situations where groins are called for.

After the disastrous Ash Wednesday storm of March 6 to 8, 1962, demonstrated the ineffectiveness of many hard stabilization projects, they came increasingly into disfavor in comparison with soft approaches. The hard stabilization had offered little protection against a really large storm, and the costs, including many borne by taxpayers, were enormous. Soft approaches include physical measures, like the encouragement of dune growth with plantings and sand retaining fences, and administrative measures, like zoning against building in vulnerable areas and prohibitions against walking on dunes. Along the intensively developed beaches of New Jersey, soft approaches also came to include beach nourishment and beach replenishment, in which sand is pumped, barged, or trucked to the beach and then leveled and left to be redistributed by the waves.

Beach nourishment is expensive, and after the initial sand placement, beaches need smaller nourishments every few years. Nourishments have, however, greatly improved the health of New Jersey's beaches and the dunes protecting shoreline communities. The nourishments also contribute to the tourism that is one of New Jersey's most important economic mainstays. At Sea Bright, several attempts at beach nourishment along the seawall were not successful. The sand washed seaward or was carried northward onto Sandy Hook soon after it was put down. Finally, with an immense beach replenishment between 1996 and 2000, the beaches built 500 feet seaward. Until Hurricane Sandy in 2012, New Jersey had not been hit directly by any hurricanes or unusually severe northeast storms, so the sand either stayed on the beaches where it was placed or moved northward to nourish the beaches of Sandy Hook.

As most Jersey Shore residents are fully aware, a lot of sand did not stay put during Hurricane Sandy. At 8:00 p.m. on October 29, 2012, Hurricane Sandy made landfall near Atlantic City but affected the entire mid-Atlantic Coast. The storm, which had the widest gale diameter ever observed, hit during the highest high tide of the month, causing a record storm surge. The water level at the Sandy Hook tide gauge was 3 feet higher than the previous record. The storm

The barrier island at Mantoloking was breached during Hurricane Sandy. The Mantoloking Bridge at left was damaged. This image was taken October 31, 2012, several days before crews used bulldozers to close the breach with sand.
—NOAA satellite photo

surge also smashed the record at the tide gauge at the Battery in New York. The storm surge flowed over the barrier islands of New Jersey, from Sandy Hook to Cape May, breaching several. Oceanfront houses were damaged or destroyed, sand was deposited on the roads, and many bayside homes were flooded.

In the month following Hurricane Sandy, beach profiles measured by the Beach Profile Network of Richard Stockton College showed that many beaches were 30 to 40 feet narrower after the storm. The measurements also confirmed what many people had noticed: communities that had enhanced their beaches faired considerably better than communities that had not. Beach houses were spared where high, wide dunes protected them from the storm surge. Some folks argue that the cost of beach nourishment projects is small compared to the cost of damages, and also small compared to the tourism revenue that the Jersey Shore generates.

With sea levels rising, however, it may be increasingly difficult and expensive to protect New Jersey's beaches from storms. Tide gauges at Sandy Hook and Atlantic City both show sea level rising about 3.8 millimeters per year, but neither is well placed to measure regional sea level change. Sea level changes measured by tide gauges are the sum of land elevation change and water elevation change. Atlantic City is subsiding slowly because water is being pumped from aquifers hundreds of feet below the surface. The Sandy Hook tide gauge sits on recently deposited sediment that may still be compacting. The Battery in New York City may provide a more realistic estimate for sea level rise along the mid-Atlantic. A tide gauge at the Battery is on solid rock and shows sea level rising at 2.7 millimeters per year, roughly a foot per century.

Beachcombing

In addition to the remains of sea life and various man-made items, beachcombers on New Jersey's beaches may find unusual minerals and fossils. Heavy mineral concentrations are common on beaches worldwide, but the minerals vary from place to place. In New Jersey, black patches on the beaches, sometimes mistaken for contamination, are about half ilmenite with smaller amounts of zircon, monazite, rutile, garnet, and a few other minerals. On many Atlantic Coast beaches, similar-looking black patches are mostly magnetite and, unlike the black sand on New Jersey beaches, can be picked up with a magnet. Ilmenite was mined from dredge ponds near Lakehurst from 1962 to 1982. The ilmenite, which is titanium dioxide, comes from layers in beach sand deposited millions of years ago when the shoreline passed through Lakehurst. The ilmenite was not mined for titanium metal but was instead refined to a pure white titanium dioxide powder to replace lead in interior paint.

Fossils, broadly defined as any evidence of past life, are constantly washing up on the beach. Most of the fossils are carried landward, similar to sand being carried to the beach from offshore bars, by the upward and shoreward movement of water beneath wave crests. Most of the large bones are no doubt destroyed in the surf, scooped up and discarded with the sea wrack when the beaches are cleaned, or taken home and displayed as "whale bones."

While some fossils are carried onshore from shallow depths, a great many more lie below the wave base and are destined to remain offshore unless the

View looking west at Seaside Heights on May 21, 2009 (top) and November 5, 2012 (bottom), a week after Hurricane Sandy. The red arrow points to a building that was moved about a block inland from its original location. The yellow arrow in each image points to the same feature. The storm surge destroyed the boardwalk and washed sand from the beach onto the roads. Note that a bulldozer has already plowed the sand on some streets.
—U.S. Geological Survey

growth of glaciers in an ice age again lowers sea level. Fossils are recovered on occasion by clam dredgers from miles offshore on the continental shelf, but fossils are far from the most valuable or attention-grabbing things pulled up with the clams. Relics from shipwrecks can be more valuable, and unexploded munitions from two world wars and decades of military target practice grab one's attention faster. As with beach finds, large bones will usually be attributed to whales, and clammers will usually throw them back. Skulls and teeth are more likely to be collected. Teeth from mastodons living on land uncovered by the lowering of sea level at the height of the Wisconsinan ice age have been brought back from as far offshore as the edge of the continental shelf. The Barney's Dock walrus, part of a skull with both tusks intact, was dredged up 24 miles east of Little Egg Inlet. It lived more recently than the mastodons dredged from the continental shelf. It is the same species as today's walrus and must have lived at a time when the water had risen from its lowermost ice age elevation but was still frigid enough for walruses. The walrus is on display at the Rutgers Geology Museum.

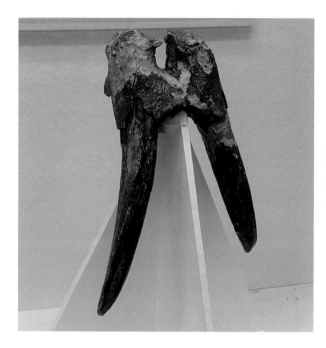

Barney's Dock walrus in the Rutgers Geology Museum.
—Photo by D. Harper

Shells on many New Jersey beaches include some that are blackened as though they had been buried in swamp muck or some other oxygen-poor sediment for many years. Many are from creatures that would not normally be found on beaches or in open ocean waters. In particular, hundreds of thousands of blackened oyster shells are washed up every year. The oysters being washed up, *Crassostrea virginica*, are estuary dwellers and do not live seaward of the beach. The oysters likely grew in coastal lagoons similar to Barnegat Bay when the beaches and barrier islands were to the east of where they are now, and the shells were buried in estuarine mud. The beach has migrated westward and the mud is now offshore and being eroded by waves. The blackened oyster shells are being washed loose and carried shoreward onto the beach.

The shells cannot be dated using carbon 14 because it depends on carbon isotopes in the atmosphere. The carbon in the calcium carbonate and organic matter in the shells is from seawater, and the carbon 14 levels cannot be compared with those in the atmosphere. Instead of using carbon 14, shells from beaches in Maryland and Virginia have been dated using amino acid racemization, a dating method based on chemical changes in amino acids after the death of an organism. Many shells are several thousand years old. Some are over 40,000 years old.

Tidal Marshes

Tidal marshes, also called salt marshes, form behind barrier islands and along the shores of estuaries such as Delaware Bay. They are within reach of the tides, so the water is salty, but freshwater streams also flow into many of them. The miles of tidal marshes behind New Jersey's barrier islands can be difficult to fully appreciate from the Garden State Parkway, the main road down the coast. Even along the numerous Cape May roads crossing the marshes, stopping to see the marshes close up can be difficult. There are numerous boardwalks across tidal marshes at parks and nature centers from Sandy Hook to Cape May, but few trails lead directly on foot into the marshes. This protects shoes as well as the marsh. The Wetlands Institute at Stone Harbor is one of the few nature centers where students not worried about their shoes are invited right onto the surface of the marsh to feel it shake when they jump and to dig the toes of their shoes into the surface to see the black anaerobic mud and smell the hydrogen sulfide.

In comparison with the tidal marshes of urban northeastern New Jersey and along the Delaware River tributaries, the broad expanses of marsh behind southern New Jersey's barrier islands and around Delaware Bay have fared reasonably well. The marshes have a long history of human use, and most of it is not seen in a negative light. Salt hay harvesting, mostly for animal feed, for example, is a sustainable practice, which began early in the colonial period and has continued, on a much reduced scale, to the present. Diking of salt marshes for freshwater farming was widespread in the marshes of Delaware Bay from the time of colonial settlement by the Swedes and Dutch in the mid-1600s. The practice was destructive of salt marsh but a proud part of marshland cultural heritage. The diked fields were used well into the twentieth century. Dam removals are allowing some of the fields to revert to salt marsh.

Tidal marsh in Barnegat Bay. —Photo by Zedreh Allen-Lafayette, N.J. Geological Survey

Two of the practices most destructive of the marshes have been stopped. First, salt marsh ditching and salt pond drainage for mosquito control were widespread in the 1930s and early 1940s. The ditching didn't control the mosquitoes but did cause the marshland waters to become fresh enough to allow freshwater shrubs and trees to invade large areas formerly in tidal marsh. The ditching and draining were stopped in the face of public outcry. The ditches still cross the marshes, but fortunately salt water and salt marsh cordgrass have returned to most of the marshes.

Second, residential developments built in the marshlands in the 1960s had intertwined roadways and canals so that each resident had a garage for the car and a slip for the boat. Aside from being completely destructive of valuable wetlands, the practice was not legal. English Common Law carried into New Jersey usage holds that all lands washed by the tides are common property. "Lands washed by the tides" sounds fairly straightforward, but in practice the boundary of the common property is difficult to draw. Tides vary through the month and from year to year, and the inland sides of tidal marshes may not be "washed by the tides" even though they are at or below high tide. The extent of public lands had long been poorly delineated and the common law provision was widely disregarded until the marshland developments and other such incursions caused public outcry. The outcry stopped the developments and led to an emergency program to identify legally defensible ways to identify state-owned wetlands and complete maps showing where they were.

Canals were dug for development of marshland along the north side of this property on Long Beach Island, but construction was halted before roads and houses were built. —Landscape image from Ted Pallis, N.J. Geological Survey

New Jersey's bays and tidal marshes are, on a geologic time scale, temporary features. Without sea level change, they would fill with sediment and be
gone within a few tens of thousands of years. Most of the sand coming into
New Jersey's coastal wetlands is carried along beaches by waves and currents,
then swept through inlets by landward flow during flood tides. In addition to
the sand, silt and clay are carried inland by tidal currents and seaward into
the marshes by streams. Rivers from the Pinelands carry little sediment, however, so most of it comes from the sea. While much of the sand carried inland
remains in deltas and sand sheets close behind the barrier islands, some of the
sand and most of the finer sediment is repeatedly deposited and resuspended
until it settles out or is filtered out by mussels and other filter feeders in the
quiet waters and dense vegetation of tidal marshes. As the sand and mud accumulate, the marshes build upward and outward into the bays. Because there
is little way for sediment to be carried above water, the marshes build to a flat
expanse at the high tide level. Outward growth of a marsh into the adjoining
bay is controlled by a balance between sea level rise and the rate at which sand,
silt, clay, and peat build onto the marsh. If sea level is rising faster than the
marsh can build up or if the marsh becomes exposed to larger waves, the area
of marsh can be expected to shrink. If sediment is being built onto the marsh
faster than rising sea level submerges the marsh, the marsh expands and will
eventually build entirely across the bay.

Deltas form on both sides of inlets through barrier islands. During flood
tides, sand is swept throuh the inlet and deposited. Sand is also carried seaward
from inlets by ebb tides, but this sand is more quickly dispersed by ocean waves.
Ebb tide deltas are, therefore, seldom as dramatic as flood tide deltas, which can

*Flood tide delta
built by sand
swept landward
through Barnegat
Inlet by flood
tides.* —Landscape
image from Ted Pallis,
N.J. Geological Survey

last long after the inlet the sand came through is gone. The Intracoastal Waterway, a system of canals and channels along the Atlantic Coast, takes semicircular detours around lenses of sediment on the landward sides of barrier islands at Ship Bottom, Seaside Heights, Monmouth Beach, and a few other places. Some of these are likely flood tide deltas from long-gone inlets.

In addition to the sand carried into bays behind barrrier islands by flood tides, much is carried landward by waves washing across the tops of the islands. The islands stand, in most places, about 10 feet above high tide and block waves during all but the most intense hurricanes and northeast storms. When the islands are breached, a storm can leave a blanket of sand stretching hundreds of feet back into the bays and marshes. The 1962 Ash Wednesday storm caused devastation along the entire length of the New Jersey shoreline but nowhere more dramatically than at Harvey Cedars. Before the storm, the barrier island was lined with houses. After the storm few were left.

Sediment layers from cores collected in marshes behind the barrier islands at Brigantine and Whale Beach in southern New Jersey have been dated using three methods: carbon 14, pollen changes associated with colonial settlement, and lead and copper increases from the industrial revolution. The cores include sand layers consistent with the 1962 Ash Wednesday storm and historically recorded storms in 1950, 1944, 1938, and 1821. There are more sand layers deeper in the cores, left by storms that hit the beach before European colonists were keeping records. Hurricane Sandy of 2012 surely left a layer of sand that includes bits of boards, broken glass, pieces of furniture, bottles, plastic, and plaster.

THE PINELANDS

The Pinelands, commonly known as the Pine Barrens, is an ecologically unique area set aside in 1979 as the Pinelands National Reserve. The reserve encompasses 1.1 million acres and includes parts of seven counties in southern New Jersey. It is the largest semiwild area between Boston, Massachusetts, and Richmond, Virginia. At the time the reserve was established, the Pinelands were sparsely settled but in the path of advancing suburbanization. There was little commercial activity beyond blueberry and cranberry growing, but a jetport four times larger than Newark, LaGuardia, and JFK combined and a new city for over 250,000 people had been proposed. The Pinelands is especially vulnerable to environmental degradation because its sandy soil offers little protection to groundwater. The reserve was established in good part as the result of citizen concern over inappropriate development. The New Jersey Pinelands Commission is implementing a regional plan to protect the ecological and cultural resources of the Pinelands. The commission has identified growth centers and environmentally sensitive areas and is directing growth by such means as transferrable development rights.

The Pinelands owes its existence to sea level fluctuations some 15 to 10 million years ago in the middle and late Miocene Period. Sea level fluctuated worldwide as Antarctic glaciers grew and shrank before stabilizing as a continental ice sheet. In New Jersey, shorelines and back-barrier lagoons passed eastward and westward across the Coastal Plain several times, each time leaving layers of clean sand deposited on beaches, deltas, and wave-swept coastal environments, interbedded with clayey layers deposited in back-barrier lagoons. The entire thickness of sand and clay, up to 350 feet thick, make up the Cohansey Formation. The clean sand became the nutrient-poor soil of the Pinelands, covering over 1 million acres—more than 20 percent of New Jersey's land area. The clay, with few surface exposures, is less well-known than the sand. It is covered over in most places by windblown sand or sand slumped from upslope but has importance to the Pinelands. Commercially the clay was dug at a number of places for brick and pottery. Ecologically it controls the movement of water below the land surface. Little water flows across the sandy soil of the Pinelands because it moves into and through the sand. There is little erosion by overland flow. Water flows down through the sand until it reaches a layer of clay. It then flows laterally and emerges as springs. Erosion is focused where the springs sap away at the overlying sand. In addition to localizing erosion, the springs are where iron-laden water comes to the surface, depositing the bog iron important to the history of the Pinelands.

The name Pinelands identifies the upland pitch pine forests representative of the area but does no justice to its many other environments. The pitch pines have evolved to thrive in the dry sandy soil and depend on fires. They can sprout branches directly through scorched bark, and their cones open to allow seed germination only after being heated by fire.

Pinelands forest in winter. Through much of the Pinelands a thick understory of huckleberry, blueberry, laurels, and ferns would be leafed out in the summer. —Photo by D. Harper

Oak and mixed oak-pine forests become dominant where fires are less frequent or quickly extinguished. Leaf litter and pine needles build up beneath the pines, creating an acidic mix ideal for the germination of oak seedlings. Without fire, the pinecones do not open. At Batsto Village in Wharton State Forest, fires have been controlled for many decades, and the predominant trees are oaks. A short walk out from the village on trails along Batsto Lake brings one into pine and mixed oak-pine forests.

At the other extreme dwarf pine forests cover dry, windy uplands that burn, on average, once every ten years, about twice the usual frequency of Pinelands fires. The dwarf pines grow along with similarly dwarfed blackjack oaks in four areas of pine plains, mostly in remote areas. The species of trees in the pine plains grow to full height elsewhere in the Pinelands, and the exact reason for their diminutive stature in the plains is not fully known. The pines are known to be genetically distinct, but which factors among the frequent fires, low water tables, high winds, and soil deficient in nutrients even by Pinelands standards are most important has proven difficult to determine.

Today the Pinelands are sparsely settled, but this has not always been so. Beginning in the 1700s and through the mid-1800s, the area was well suited to industry. The upland forests provided wood and charcoal for a surprising range of small industries. Sawmills, paper mills, iron furnaces, boat works, and glassworks were established along valleys where the streams could be harnessed for water power. Ocean-going ships put in at Tuckerton for barrels of the acidic Pinelands water, which would stay fresh through multiyear voyages, and to vie for cranberries, as good as limes for preventing scurvy. In the days before large-scale commercial

Dwarf pines near County Route 539 in Stafford Forge Wildlife Management Area. The fully grown trees are about 4 feet tall. —Photo by D. Harper

production, the demand for the berries was greater than the supply. Distilleries processing pine tar to turpentine were set up anywhere there was a minimal amount of water for cooling and access for wagons or boats.

Beginning in colonial times, trees from the upland pine forests were exploited for lumber, firewood, and charcoal with little regard for the environment. Even by the mid-1700s, there were fruitless calls for more responsible forest management. Fires were commonly set by charcoalers who would then buy the scarred trees, useless for anything but charcoaling, at a discount price. By the 1840s, scarcity of wood was becoming problematic, and the bog iron industry became obsolete by 1850.

Glass and paper continued to be manufactured for a time, and charcoaling continued into the twentieth century. By the 1860s, however, steam was replacing water power and railroads replacing coastal shipping in small boats. Large factories with access to deepwater ports and coal made much of the Pinelands industry obsolete. Boat works remain important along the coast, and glassworks remained important in the larger towns of Millville, Glassboro, and Vineland, through the mid-twentieth century. Towns in the interior of the Pinelands, though, were abandoned, and the forests returned. Today the primary economic activities are cranberry growing and tourism.

Much of the Pinelands was purchased by Joseph Wharton of Philadelphia in 1876. Wharton had in mind to establish a series of reservoirs and canals to direct the Pinelands water westward to replace Philadelphia's notoriously poor drinking water. The project was stymied when, in the 1870s, New Jersey passed laws preventing the export of water, and the ban was upheld by the courts as

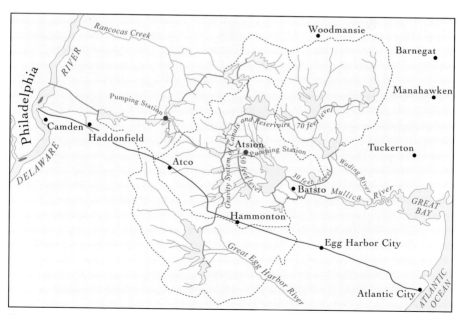

Dams, reservoirs, and canals in Joseph Wharton's plan to redirect Pinelands water to Philadelphia and Camden in the 1870s. Drainage basins shown with dashed lines. —Modified from Smith, 1891

not interfering with interstate commerce. Instead of a water supply watershed, the property became the Wharton family's summer retreat until it was purchased for parkland in 1954.

Cedar and Hardwood Swamps

Wetter areas of the Pinelands with well-oxygenated water host cedar swamps. Where the water is more sluggish and thus contains less oxygen, hardwood swamps are dominated by trees more tolerant of stagnant water, mostly sweetgum and red maple with less abundant hollies and swamp white oaks. The hardwood swamps are similar in many ways to the hardwood swamps of northern New Jersey and not unique to the Pinelands.

Cedar swamps are among the most picturesque and best-loved of New Jersey's forests and are by no means restricted to the Pinelands. In addition to being picturesque, the cedars are among the most sought-after trees for timber. The wood is strong, light, easily bent when steamed, water-resistant, and so resistant to rot that cedar shingles can last up to two hundred years. As early as the mid-1700s the demand for cedar for boats, barrels, fenceposts, and the ribs and planking for boats was so great that many thought the species would soon be cut to extinction. Benjamin Franklin, for one, advocated planting red cedars in upland areas to replace the disappearing Atlantic white cedars. The trees, though, are resilient and fast growing, and the swamps can be cut two or three times per century. Further, many cedar swamps were found to stand on thick peat bogs in which logs are perfectly preserved.

Hardwood swamp in Estell Manor County Park, across the parking lot and a short hike through the woods from the ruins of the Estell Manor glassworks. —Photo by D. Harper

For many years cedar mining was a common practice in logged-out swamps and even in coastal salt marshes where the salt-intolerant cedars had long since succumbed to postglacial sea level rise. By all accounts, cedar mining was not an easy task. Logs were found by probing the bogs with iron rods to find large logs worth digging out. When a log was found, the miner, working in a flooded pit, would dig and saw at tangles of buried branches and smaller logs until the desired log broke loose and floated to the surface.

Cedar swamp. —Photo by D. Harper

RAISING OR MINING BURIED CEDAR TIMBER.

Cedar mining. —Lithograph from Cook, 1857

Some of the larger cedar swamps have been converted to cranberry bogs. A number of these commercial bogs can be seen along County Route 563 south of Chatsworth and are the focus of cranberry festivals during the fall harvest. Many other cutover swamps have returned to cedars, and trails in most of the Pinelands parks and forests pass close by cedar swamps or cross over them on boardwalks.

Bog Iron Formation

Bog iron precipitates out of water at springs. The iron comes from the decomposition of iron minerals in the Coastal Plain sediments and remains dissolved until the water comes into an oxygen-rich environment. Some of the iron may precipitate because it goes from a chemically reduced state to an oxidized state and becomes insoluble, but little iron would be deposited without the help of bacteria. If you pick up one of the rust-covered twigs in a stream or marsh, the red iron oxide will fall away, leaving only a thin, slightly slimy bacterial film. The bacteria obtain some of their energy from the energy-releasing chemical reaction that creates the red precipitate. The bacteria use the energy to combine water and carbon dioxide into carbohydrates. Without the bacteria, the deposition of bog iron would be far slower and the deposits far smaller. In the summertime, the staining can be dramatic, covering the stream bank, bottom gravel, and twigs under the water, and even forming an iridescent film on the water surface. In the cold of winter the bacteria are less active, and the red commonly disappears.

Despite the dramatic coloration, the actual amount of iron being precipitated is usually tiny. There are reports of miners harvesting newly deposited iron every decade or so, but this is rare. At most places, it would take centuries

Iron oxide (bog iron) precipitation at springs on the Manasquan floodplain in Allaire State Park. —Photo by D. Harper

to build up a substantial iron deposit. Even after 150 years, little bog iron has built up at former mining locations in the Pinelands.

Where does the iron in the water come from? Clearly the iron was carried upward by groundwater flowing from springs and deposited at or near the surface, but where below the ground did the hundreds of thousands of tons of iron that allowed the iron industry to thrive for over one hundred years come from? For some of the deposits around the margins of the Pinelands the answer seems clear. At Tinton Falls and Allaire, the groundwater flows through glauconitic formations, which can be seen along the stream banks. Glauconite is an iron-rich silicate that weathers to less iron-rich clays, releasing the iron to the subsurface environment. Pyrite is another common iron-bearing mineral that can break down in the subsurface and contribute to iron in groundwater. The largest of the bog iron deposits, however, were from Batsto upriver past Atsion and along the Wading River northward past Martha. Iron-bearing minerals other than the bog ore are conspicuously absent in both areas.

The source of the iron along the Batsto and Wading Rivers is best explained by deeply circulating groundwater. Very little of the water that falls as rain on the Pinelands flows overland to streams. Instead it sinks into the sand, flows underground, and reaches streams by way of springs, often directly below the streambed. Some of the water circulates only a short distance and comes to the surface along the headwaters of the Pinelands rivers. This water picks up little iron, and there are few bog iron deposits along these headwater streams. Water that travels farther through the sediment has more time to accumulate iron from the small amounts present in the Cohansey Formation. At the surface the Cohansey is leached to an ashy gray, but only a few inches down, visible in many Pinelands road cuts, the sand is colored light orange by traces of iron oxide. Some of the water circulates still deeper, deep enough to pick up iron from pyrite and iron-rich clay in the Kirkwood Formation. The water that has traveled the greatest distances through the subsurface is richer in iron. It comes to the surface along the lower reaches of the rivers but upstream from coastal marshes. Upward flow is blocked beneath the marshes by impermeable estuarine sediment. The largest bog iron deposits are thus localized, as at Batsto and along the Wading River, below headwater streams and upstream from tidal marshlands.

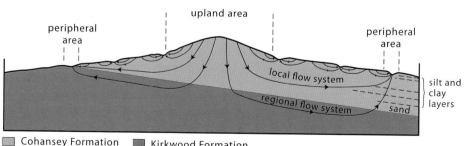

Water seeps into the sandy soils of the Pinelands and then flows laterally when it encounters more impermeable clay formations. —Modified from Rhodehamel, 1970

Revolutionary War cannonballs made from bog iron mined at Batsto for the Continental Army. —Photo by D. Harper; cannonballs from Terry L. Schmidt

New Jersey bog iron was first worked in 1674 in Tinton Falls. Iron production at Batsto was not begun until 1766, almost a century later. With its large bog iron reserves, abundant wood for stocking the furnaces, and seashells for flux from seafood houses and Indian middens, Batsto quickly became an important supplier of iron. Its importance increased further in the Revolutionary War when imports were cut off by a British blockade. The bogs, furnaces, and forges were essential to the war effort, and the workers were exempted from military service. New Jersey schoolchildren are routinely told of the cannonballs produced at Batsto, but the cannonballs were less important than nails, chains, cooking kettles, salt drying pans, wagon wheel rims, and other camp hardware without which the cannonballs would have been useless. After the war, New Jersey's bog iron continued to gain importance until about 1790. Production included pig iron, firebacks, and miles of cast-iron water pipe for New York City.

The bog iron mined in the Pinelands and elsewhere in southern New Jersey varied from place to place. In some places it was earthy and easily dug, a few inches to a couple of feet thick, and over 50 percent iron by weight. Often the deposits were filled with stumps, tree trunks, and branches replaced by iron oxide in perfect detail, even to having the bark become ore. In other places iron-cemented sandstone, called ironstone, was broken up and separated into ore and sand by water-powered stamp mills and by women hired as ore pounders at wages comparable to those of men.

As of 1830, there were fourteen iron furnaces in southern New Jersey. By 1840 the industry was in decline, and by 1850, after about 175 years of production, the bog iron industry was obsolete. The ore had been largely worked out, and the wood for charcoal production had become scarce. Even if there had been plenty of ore and wood, the industry would not have been competitive with the furnaces of northern New Jersey and Pennsylvania. By the 1850s, the iron industry had moved on to large coal-fired furnaces, magnetite ore, limestone rock (instead of seashells) for flux, steam-powered machinery for generating volumes of blast air inconceivable with water power, and easy access to canals and railroads. A typical charcoal-fired bog iron furnace could produce only 2 tons of iron per day.

Glassmaking

Because of the purity of the quartz sand of the Cohansey Formation, the Outer Coastal Plain was particularly well suited for glassmaking and the mining of silica sand needed for making silica gel, cosmetics, and abrasives. The sand has been carried through streams, rivers, and surf so many times that everything other than quartz and a small percentage of similarly durable heavy minerals has been reduced to silt or clay and washed away. Similar to the sand on today's beaches, the sand of the Cohansey Formation originated to the north and was carried southward along the beaches by longshore drift. Much of the sand was undoubtedly eroded from already fairly pure Coastal Plain formations and still further purified before deposition in the Cohansey Formation. Many glassworks and silica sand pits were far south on the Coastal Plain because the sand there has been carried farther along the beaches and become cleaner.

The first successful glassworks in the colonies was established in Alloway, New Jersey, by Caspar Wistar in 1789. By the time glassmaking lost its economic importance to southern New Jersey, glass had been made at over two hundred glassworks in over fifty towns. At the beginning of the twentieth century, child

Ruins of Estell Manor glassworks at Estell Manor County Park. —Photo by D. Harper

laborers worked alongside union workers in dangerous fire-prone conditions. The Owens-Illinois Glass Company still manufactures closures for glass and metal containers in Glassboro, and silica sand is still dug from pits in southern Cumberland County, but commercial glassmaking is gone from New Jersey. A number of artists still produce works in glass, and there are daily glassblowing demonstrations at the Museum of American Glass at Millville. The Heritage Glass Museum in Glassboro is open with limited hours. Little else remains of the historic glassworks. Other than the Estell Manor glassworks, preserved as ruins, the buildings were wooden and most burned down.

ROAD GUIDES TO THE COASTAL PLAIN

New Jersey Turnpike
Garden State Parkway—Delaware River
91 miles

Wisconsinan Terminal Moraine

Just south of the Garden State Parkway interchange, the Turnpike climbs up the back side of the terminal moraine built up by the Wisconsinan glaciers at their southernmost advance. A water tower east of the Turnpike marks the top of the moraine. The tower was placed here to take advantage of the elevation. Water towers are built to regulate pressure in water systems more than to store water and must be at higher elevations than the piping in the systems.

When the ice between Springfield and Perth Amboy was building up the terminal moraine, most of the meltwater was channeled through a valley now occupied by US 22 and onto an outwash plain after which Scotch Plains and the Plainfields take their names. Little water crossed the moraine between Scotch Plains and Perth Amboy, and silt and clay were not sorted out of the glacial till. Well-developed knob and kettle topography once existed along parts of this moraine but was largely obliterated during suburbanization. The kettle holes in the silty deposits did not drain downward and remained wet and marshy year-round.

Air above the ice age glaciers was dense and heavy because of the cold, and much of the time winds blew downward and southward from the ice. These katabatic winds were strongest immediately south of the ice and left an abundance of sand-blasted pebbles, called ventifacts, from the moraine southward past the Plainfields, New Brunswick, and as far south as Princeton. Quartzite pebbles are common in this area, and the soil was not stabilized, as it is today, by thick vegetation. Many pebbles have been sandblasted into shapes that can easily be attributed to windblown sand but almost impossible to imagine as the

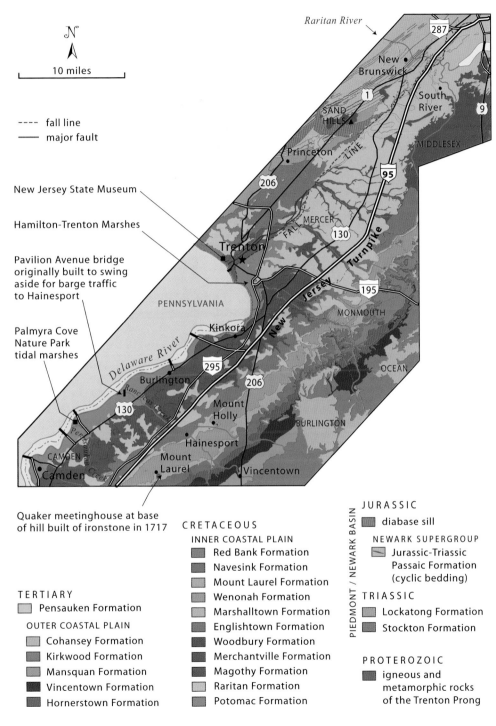

N

10 miles

- - - - fall line
———— major fault

Raritan River

New Brunswick

South River

287

9

1

SAND HILLS▲

MIDDLESEX

Princeton

206

95

New Jersey State Museum

Hamilton-Trenton Marshes

Pavilion Avenue bridge
originally built to swing
aside for barge traffic
to Hainesport

Palmyra Cove
Nature Park
tidal marshes

FALL LINE

MERCER

130

195

New Jersey Turnpike

Trenton

★

PENNSYLVANIA

MONMOUTH

Kinkora

Delaware River

295

206

Burlington

130

Mount Holly

BURLINGTON

OCEAN

Rancocas Creek

Hainesport

Mount Laurel

Vincentown

Pensauken Creek

CAMDEN

Camden

Quaker meetinghouse at base
of hill built of ironstone in 1717

CRETACEOUS

INNER COASTAL PLAIN
Red Bank Formation
Navesink Formation
Mount Laurel Formation
Wenonah Formation
Marshalltown Formation
Englishtown Formation
Woodbury Formation
Merchantville Formation
Magothy Formation
Raritan Formation
Potomac Formation

JURASSIC
diabase sill

NEWARK SUPERGROUP
Jurassic-Triassic
Passaic Formation
(cyclic bedding)

TRIASSIC
Lockatong Formation
Stockton Formation

PROTEROZOIC
igneous and
metamorphic rocks
of the Trenton Prong

PIEDMONT / NEWARK BASIN

TERTIARY
Pensauken Formation

OUTER COASTAL PLAIN
Cohansey Formation
Kirkwood Formation
Mansquan Formation
Vincentown Formation
Hornerstown Formation

*Geology along the New Jersey Turnpike between the Garden State Parkway and Mt.
Laurel.* —Compiled from the USGS's Preliminary Integrated Geologic Map Database for the United States, 2006

This ventifact from New Bruns-wick is known as a dreikanter, from German referring to the three faces.
—Photo by D. Harper

result of rolling and tumbling along a streambed. Ventifacts are also common in the gravels of southern New Jersey but may date from times other than the ice ages. Ventifacts can be shaped in a matter of months and are known from deserts, high plateaus, beaches, and floodplains.

Pensauken River Valley

From Elizabeth to the Delaware Memorial Bridge, the New Jersey Turnpike follows the valley of the former Pensauken River, a major river that drained the Long Island Sound lowland and possibly much of southern New England through much of the Pliocene Epoch until the pre-Illinoian glaciation. Early in the history of the river during a time of low sea level, the river cut a deep, wide valley along the inner edge of the Coastal Plain. Sea level did not stay persistently low, however, and subsequent higher sea level caused the river to switch from deepening its valley to filling it. Unable to move the sediment load from upstream across the now flatter gradient to the ocean, the Pensauken River built up a floodplain of sand and gravel close to 150 feet thick above the deepest parts of the downcut valley. The formations of New Jersey's Inner Coastal Plain clay belts, mined from South River northward and from Trenton southward, are continuous beneath the sand and gravel in this area but too deeply buried to be mined.

Sand Hills

The Sand Hills stand at an elevation of about 200 feet on US 1 a few miles south of New Brunswick and provide long views across low-lying areas to the north and south. The crest of the hills, marked by a water tower, is a good place to contemplate the amount of sediment eroded from New Jersey's Coastal Plain in the 10 million or so years since the establishment of permanent glaciers on Antarctica. Sea level dropped in the world's oceans and exposed sediments, such as New Jersey's Coastal Plain, to erosion. When the seas receded, they left a flat, southeastward-sloping plain about 100 feet above the top of the Sand Hills.

Rancocas Creek

Rancocas Creek is a fairly typical freshwater tidal creek, somewhat larger and more picturesque than many along the Turnpike. Like most of the creeks along the Turnpike south of Burlington, its valley was flooded by rising sea level at the end of the ice age. It is hard to imagine today that the creek was at one time a barge route to Hainesport, 8 miles inland from the Delaware River. The Pavilion Avenue bridge near the mouth of the creek had only about 4 feet of clearance and was built to swing aside to let the barges pass. The bridge can still be swung, but only if special equipment is brought in. The permanent equipment was removed for lack of barge traffic in 1910.

Ironstone Cap of Mt. Laurel

Mt. Laurel is capped with ironstone, which is sand cemented by iron oxide. Ironstone is common throughout the Coastal Plain. Sand cemented by silica is less widespread, but fairly common in the southwestern Coastal Plain. In the absence of other building stone, the ironstone and to a lesser extent the silica-cemented sand were used for construction. The stone has proven durable, and you can see hundreds of ironstone buildings and walls across the Coastal Plain. Many other buildings have ironstone foundations and cellar walls, which cannot be seen.

Ironstone construction is, perhaps, most common in the Rumson area of Monmouth County, but ironstone was used wherever it was solid enough to be quarried and shaped. Much of the ironstone cap that once covered Mt. Laurel is gone. Large pieces can still be found on the summit, but much of the cap was quarried. The Quaker meetinghouse at the base of the hill, built with this stone

The Mt. Laurel Quaker meetinghouse, at the base of Mt. Laurel, was constructed with ironstone quarried from the Mt. Laurel caprock. —Photo by D. Harper

in 1717, enlarged in 1760, and reconfigured in 1798, demonstrates its durability. Stone from the 1717 section of the building was reused in 1798. There has been little weathering or breakage of the stone after almost three hundred years.

Palmyra Cove Nature Park

Palmyra Cove Nature Park, accessible from NJ 73, is similar to many parks along the lower Delaware River in that tidal marshes occupy the lower-lying section of the park and a range of upland habitats has been created on land filled with sand dredged from navigation channels. Trails to the marshland cove at the south end of the park are in stark contrast to the industrial landscape across the river. Palmyra Cove affords an interesting contrast to the marshes upriver at Trenton. At both places, the tide range has increased because dredging of a navigation channel up to 40 feet deep and 400 feet wide in the 1930s allowed more water to surge up and down the river in each tidal cycle. High tide became higher and low tide became lower. Tidal marshes, given enough time and sediment, build to a flat surface at the high tide level. Substantial amounts of sediment wash into the marshes at Trenton, and much of the marsh has already built up to the higher high tide level. Palmyra Cove is isolated from sediment sources and remains a low marsh, flooded during all but the lowest tides.

The Delaware River tidal marshes are freshwater almost to the Delaware Memorial Bridge despite being tidal. It is not necessary, and would be unwise, to taste the water to determine its saltiness. One need not even know whether the plants and shells from the river are marine or freshwater species. It is sufficient to examine a few clamshells at low tide. River water is usually less saturated with calcium carbonate and more effective at dissolving the shells of clams. Freshwater clams have adapted to this by evolving thick shells and a thick, protective coating of a black, organic material known as periostracum. Where the periostracum has worn away, the shells are usually deeply pitted. Pitting on shells in marine environments is more often the result of predation or colonization by the boring sponge *Cliona* and unrelated to the wearing away of the periostracum.

This freshwater clam from Palmyra Cove Nature Park is pitted where its protective coating, the periostracum, has worn away and exposed the shell to water undersaturated with calcium carbonate.
—Photo by D. Harper

Pennsauken Creek's Contribution to Baseball

From the beginning of baseball, it has been the umpire's job to remove gloss from new baseballs so that pitchers could get a better grip. Until the 1930s, they used tobacco juice, dirt from the baselines, or whatever else came to hand. Now, in both major leagues and most minor league games, umpires use Lena Blackburne's Rubbing Mud, dug from a secret place on Pennsauken Creek. The mud was brought to baseball by Lena Blackburne, a coach with the Philadelphia Athletics. After hearing too many gripes about the tobacco juice, Blackburne scooped up a handful of Pennsauken Creek mud, tried it on a baseball, and found that it worked better than tobacco juice.

Greensand Marl and Dinosaurs

The New Jersey Turnpike follows the trend of the greensand marl belt of New Jersey's Coastal Plain. Towns and geographic features in the marl belt were given names like Marlton, Marlboro, and Marl Creek. In turn, geologic formations, the Marshalltown marl and the Manasquan marl were named after places where marl was dug. Marl usually refers to a mixture of clay and calcium carbonate, commonly shell fragments. In mid-Atlantic usage, however, greensand marl refers to a sandy or clayey mix of the light green to black mineral glauconite with quartz sand, silt, mica flakes, pieces of shell, and calcium phosphate nodules. Glauconite is a low-temperature, low-pressure form of mica that forms very slowly by a chemical reaction between clay or mica at the ocean floor and chemicals in the seawater. The chemical reaction that forms glauconite goes forward only in oxygen-poor environments, and the grains grow only while they are in oxygen-poor digestive tracts, decaying feces, or below the surface of sediment rich in organic matter. Because the chemical reaction is extremely slow, glauconite is common only where sedimentation is very slow. On the New Jersey Coastal Plain, this was usually in deep water far seaward on the continental shelf.

Potassium in the glauconite, together with lime, clay, and calcium phosphate usually found together with the glauconite in greensand deposits, made the material an effective soil conditioner. It was being used by the early 1700s to enrich the sandy soil of southern New Jersey. Early on, small quantities were dug by hand and transported by horse cart. By the 1860s, glauconite mining was a substantial industry in southern New Jersey. Up to a million tons were used annually, dug by steam shovels or washed from pit faces by hydraulic sluices. From the pits, it was loaded onto barges and trains for wide distribution.

By 1900, the greensand industry had largely shut down. Nitrate fertilizers were being produced in enormous quantities from atmospheric nitrogen, and large phosphate deposits were being mined in the Gulf States. Farmers were using artificial fertilizers, which yielded nitrogen, phosphorus, and potassium far more easily than the greensand. Glauconite continues to be used as a specialty gardening product, but the days of large-scale production for soil improvement are over.

About 1920, well after the use of greensand marl as a soil conditioner had been superseded by artificial fertilizers, glauconite was found to be useful as an

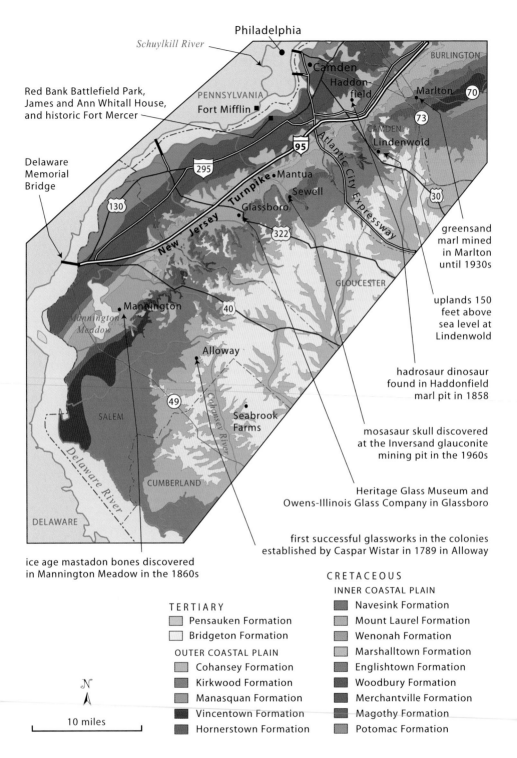

Philadelphia

Schuylkill River

BURLINGTON

Camden

Haddon-
field

Red Bank Battlefield Park,
James and Ann Whitall House,
and historic Fort Mercer

PENNSYLVANIA

Fort Mifflin

Marlton

70

73

CAMDEN

Lindenwold

95

Atlantic City Expressway

Delaware
Memorial
Bridge

295

Turnpike

Mantua

Sewell

130

New Jersey

Glassboro

322

30

greensand
marl mined
in Marlton
until 1930s

GLOUCESTER

uplands 150
feet above
sea level at
Lindenwold

Mannington

40

Mannington Meadow

Alloway

hadrosaur dinosaur
found in Haddonfield
marl pit in 1858

49

SALEM

Seabrook
Farms

Cohansey River

mosasaur skull discovered
at the Inversand glauconite
mining pit in the 1960s

Delaware River

CUMBERLAND

Heritage Glass Museum and
Owens-Illinois Glass Company in Glassboro

DELAWARE

first successful glassworks in the colonies
established by Caspar Wistar in 1789 in Alloway

ice age mastadon bones discovered
in Mannington Meadow in the 1860s

CRETACEOUS

INNER COASTAL PLAIN

Navesink Formation

TERTIARY

Pensauken Formation

Bridgeton Formation

OUTER COASTAL PLAIN

Cohansey Formation

Kirkwood Formation

Manasquan Formation

Vincentown Formation

Hornerstown Formation

Mount Laurel Formation

Wenonah Formation

Marshalltown Formation

Englishtown Formation

Woodbury Formation

Merchantville Formation

Magothy Formation

Potomac Formation

N

10 miles

Geology along the Turnpike between Marlton and the Delaware Memorial Bridge.
—Compiled from the USGS's Preliminary Integrated Geologic Map Database for the United States, 2006

ion-exchange medium for treating hard water. In ion exchange an atom loosely bound to the ion-exchange medium is traded for an atom dissolved in water. In this case, the glauconite gave up sodium in exchange for calcium, which causes the hardness and leads to scaling in boilers and pipes. Glauconite is not a particularly effective ion-exchange medium in comparison with artificial plastic-based compounds, but because it is cheap and because the sandy nature of New Jersey's greensand makes it suitable for water treatment, glauconite has continued to be used for large-scale industrial and municipal water treatment. For many years, the only glauconite mining operation in the United States has been the Inversand Pit in Sewell, Gloucester County. However, the continuing development of inexpensive, effective artificial ion-exchange materials may soon bring the end of glauconite mining.

Historically, New Jersey's marl pits have been regarded as the birthplace of North American vertebrate paleontology. Until the vast accumulations of dinosaur bones in Colorado and Wyoming were discovered in 1877, the Cretaceous reptiles of North America were known primarily from the bones of turtles, mosasaurs, and seagoing crocodile-like reptiles from the marl pits. Bones and teeth of land-dwelling dinosaurs are found from time to time, but the hadrosaur found in Haddonfield in 1858 is still the only reasonably complete dinosaur skeleton ever found in New Jersey. As in any field, there was cooperation and competition among researchers. In one incident Arnold Guyot of

Mosasaur skull found at the Inversand glauconite mining pit in the 1960s, Sewell, Mantua Township, Gloucester County. The photo was taken at a fossil preparation lab of the New Jersey State Museum. The opening toward the back of the lower jaw is not a broken bone. It is a hinge that allowed this fierce predator to open its mouth wider than a fixed jaw could to allow larger and more agile prey to be caught. —Photo by D. Harper

Princeton had arranged to meet a marl digger at a train station to buy a fossil. Othniel Charles Marsh of Yale, a well-to-do competing paleontologist, chartered an express train and got to the station first with a higher offer. Guyot arrived to an empty station.

It was also in New Jersey that the infamous "bone wars" between Marsh and Edward Drinker Cope of the University of Pennsylvania began. By 1866, Cope had established a network among marl diggers and would periodically travel through the marl belt to purchase new specimens. Soon after Cope graciously allowed Marsh to accompany him on one of these trips, it became apparent that Marsh had established his own relationships with the diggers and was buying many of the best fossils. Animosity between the two only increased with time, and by the time dinosaur hunting moved westward to Colorado, Utah, and Wyoming, there were physical confrontations between crews working for the two researchers and armed guards were posted at digging sites.

Haddonfield—Home of New Jersey's State Dinosaur

While New Jersey has few collecting sites where hundreds of fossils can be collected without effort, it has produced numerous fossils of historic importance and continues to produce fossils of scientific value. Outstanding among the historically important fossils, the late Cretaceous Haddonfield dinosaur, *Hadrosaurus foulkii*, was excavated in 1858. Earlier that year, William Parker Foulke brought some unusually large fossil bones to Joseph Leidy, then one of the foremost anatomists in the United States. Dinosaurs had been proposed as a group of animals only a few years before in England by Richard Owen, but Leidy knew of them from lectures at Philadelphia's Academy of Natural Sciences. He and Foulke returned to the Haddonfield marl pit where the bones had been found and recovered a few additional bones and teeth. Together with the earlier finds the Haddonfield specimen was confirmed to be a dinosaur. In fact, even though only a quarter of the bones were found, it was at that time the most complete dinosaur skeleton ever found. Most of the bones were vertebrae, but the pelvis and enough limb bones were found to completely change the understanding of dinosaurs. Leidy saw that the arm bones were much shorter than the leg bones and the pelvis was shaped for an animal that stood on two feet, not all four as in all previous dinosaur reconstructions. Very soon after the 1858 discovery, anatomists noticed similarities between the skeletons of dinosaurs and those of birds. In the 1860s Thomas Huxley, in part based on the Haddonfield fossil, became the first to argue that birds evolved from dinosaurs.

In 1868, Benjamin Waterhouse Hawkins at the Philadelphia Academy mounted casts of the bones in life position, filling in the missing bones. This was the first time a dinosaur skeleton had ever been mounted for museum display. The creature was about 25 feet long, probably weighed 7 to 8 tons, and stood about 10 feet tall. Its blunt teeth confirm that the hadrosaur was a vegetarian evolved to chew twigs and tough-stemmed leaves. Unfortunately, as is common with vertebrate fossils, none of the skull other than a few teeth was found. This is not surprising. The head is often the first part to fall from a rotting corpse and roll away or be destroyed. Skulls are missing from many vertebrate fossils.

Statue of hadrosaur, the official New Jersey state dinosaur, in the Haddonfield town center. The dinosaur was scaled down so as not to overwhelm its surroundings. —Photo by D. Harper

This Haddonfield dinosaur restoration at the New Jersey State Museum exhibit, prepared in the 1930s, has become something of an artifact. In today's reconstructions, the posture is more nearly horizontal and the skull is less ducklike. —Photo by D. Harper

Hadrosaurus foulkii, Latin for "Foulke's bulky lizard," became the official state dinosaur of New Jersey in 1991 after years of hard work by a teacher, Joyce Berry, and her fourth-grade classes at Strawbridge Elementary School in Haddon Township. The site of the discovery is commemorated by a plaque. A stained glass window and floor decoration in Trenton's State House Annex, a bronze sculpture in Haddonfield (suitably scaled down so as not to overwhelm the downtown neighborhood), and numerous other reconstructions reflect the fossil's status as an official New Jersey symbol, a truly unique representative of the state's prehistoric past, and one of the most historically important fossils ever found. The original bones are at the Philadelphia's Academy of Natural Sciences. The hadrosaur is still the most complete dinosaur fossil from eastern North America, but bits and pieces confirm that the dinosaurs of eastern North America were much like those living at the time in the western states, where numerous complete skeletons have been collected. The bones of hadrosaurs are among the most common dinosaur remains found in marine deposits, suggesting that these animals lived in and around coastal environments.

Red Bank Battlefield Park, Fort Mercer, and the James and Ann Whitall House

Fort Mercer, one of two Revolutionary War forts built to protect the Delaware River approach to Philadelphia, was built on Red Bank. Fort Mifflin was in Pennsylvania on the other bank of the river. On October 22, 1777, a Hessian force sent to take the fort was defeated by a far smaller rebel contingent. Ann Whitall, a Quaker, reportedly remained at her spinning wheel through the entire battle, carrying it to the basement only after cannon fire destroyed sections of the stone walls around her. When the battle was over, she treated the wounded, rebels and Hessians alike. The name Red Bank likely refers to red sand or clay of the Potomac Formation, much of which is colored red or yellow by small amounts of iron from the oxygen-rich depositional environment. Any exposures once in the park are now grassed over.

Across the Delaware, the Schuylkill River now has a deep shipping channel and is easily spotted from Red Bank. The name Schuylkill, Dutch for "hidden river," hints at a different past. Anyone who has seen the movie African Queen will remember Humphrey Bogart and Catherine Hepburn descending miles of open river only to end up dragging their boat through leech-infested marshland to within feet of one of the African Great Lakes. That was not a Hollywood fantasy; it was a delta. Sand and mud repeatedly blocked the river channel, forcing the water to spread upward and outward into ever smaller distributaries. Similarly, the Schuylkill built a marshland delta into the wider, slower-moving Delaware River, keeping it hidden from the river side. The delta extended across much of South Philadelphia, which was marshland until it was drained and filled in the nineteenth century.

Mannington Mastodon

One does not usually think of New Jersey as home to free-roaming elephants, but teeth and bones of mammoths and mastodons have been found in the sands and gravels of southern New Jersey, in the ice age peat deposits of northern New Jersey, and in fishing dredges miles offshore. Mastodons are the most common of the elephants, and most of the complete fossils are from peat bogs. Several are on display in museums and are among the best loved of the fossils. The peat bog elephants are of all ages and commonly uninjured, consistent with being drowned after getting mired in the peat.

The mastodon at the Rutgers Geology Museum is unusual in being from the southern New Jersey muck of Mannington Meadow rather than northern New Jersey peat. It is a large specimen; the lower jaw alone weighs 120 pounds. The tusks were found in the 1860s by a farmer digging muck to spread on sandy soil elsewhere on his farm. They soon disintegrated, as do many fossils after they are dug out of muck or peat. The next owner of the farm, Joseph Hackett, came across the rest of the bones while digging muck in 1869. People came from miles to see the bones, inspiring Mr. Hackett to cart them around through the following fall and winter to be seen at fairs and public places for ten cents. Reportedly he made over $1,000. In 1872, George Cook, state geologist, purchased the bones for $300 from a special fund. The bones were preserved in linseed oil or paraffin to keep them from disintegrating, and for years Cook tried to find funding to have the bones mounted for display in his Rutgers Geology Museum. They were not assembled until 1892, three years after Cook's death. The missing or decomposed bones were fashioned from wood.

New Jersey–Delaware Boundary and the Delaware Memorial Bridge

The Delaware boundary has long been the subject of dispute. Normally when two states are divided by a river, the boundary follows the center of the river or the shipping channel, or snakes among islands. This ensures rights for those on both banks. The Delaware boundary was set in 1682 by a grant to William Penn from the Duke of York and is unusual in that it follows a circle and specifically includes the entire Delaware River. The 12-mile circle is centered on the Wilmington courthouse. The section of river within the circle runs from Logan Township downriver to Elsinboro Township. New Jersey has attempted to redefine this section of its boundary in a more conventional manner, but the entire Delaware River within the circle, as upheld by the U.S. Supreme Court in 1934, remains Delaware territory. The entire the Delaware Memorial Bridge is thus in Delaware.

While the boundary has been settled, contentious issues continue to arise. For many years, for example, New Jersey clammers within the 12-mile circle had to operate under Delaware law. The issue became moot when the fisheries became subject to federal regulation. More recently, questions of fairness came up again when Delaware refused to issue permits for the construction of loading facilities at a natural gas shipping facility planned for the New Jersey side of the river.

In another peculiar aspect of the boundary, there are two small parcels of Delaware land on the New Jersey side of the river. Based on English Common Law, land that builds up or erodes naturally along a river accrues or is lost to the owner of the riverbank. Thus sediment deposition on the New Jersey banks adds to New Jersey, and erosion takes away from New Jersey. Adding land by filling, on the other hand, does not change the location of boundaries. Filled land in the Delaware River remains Delaware territory even if the fill is built outward from New Jersey. One of the Delaware parcels east of the river is the tip of Artificial Island, created by filling during construction of the Salem Nuclear Power Plant.

Garden State Parkway
Woodbridge—Cape May
133 miles

About a mile north of the exit to the New Jersey Turnpike, the Garden State Parkway crosses from Newark Basin rocks, which were deposited during the rifting of the supercontinent Pangea, onto Coastal Plain sand and clay formations, which were deposited at the edge of the widening Atlantic Ocean. In contrast to the Newark Basin sedimentary rocks, which are predominantly river and lake sediments, the Coastal Plain formations are predominantly coastal and marine.

Dinosaur Tracks at Woodbridge

For many years, until the discovery of dinosaur tracks in Maryland and Virginia in the early 2000s, the only Cretaceous dinosaur footprints from east of the Mississippi were from a New Jersey clay pit. (Triassic prints have been collected by the thousands.) The Cretaceous dinosaur footprints are from the Hampton

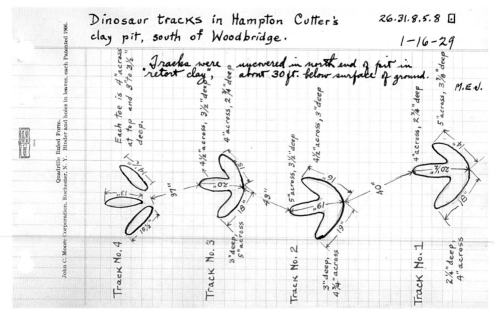

Field notes on the Woodbridge dinosaur trackway by Meredith Johnson, assistant state geologist, 1929. —From N.J. Geological Survey Permanent Notes collection

Cutter Clay Works, where Woodbridge Mall now stands. Tracks were found several times, likely all from the same bed, a firm clay layer covered over by sand soon after the tracks were made. Tracks were found at three separate times in 1929 and 1930. Four of the tracks from one set were cast in plaster, carefully wrapped, and removed for display at the New Jersey State Museum. Three of the tracks and all of the plaster casts have disappeared. The only remaining track is at the Rutgers Geology Museum.

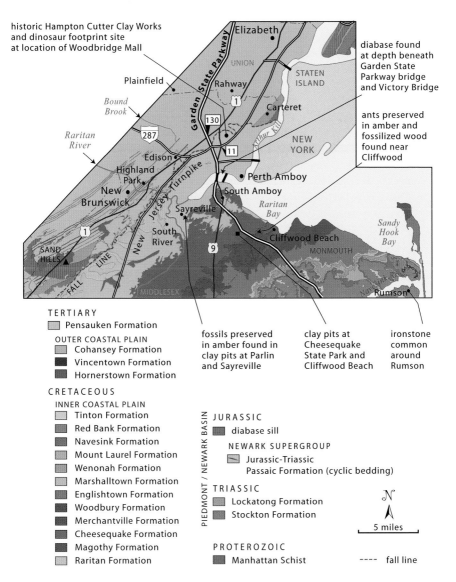

Geology along the Garden State Parkway between Woodbridge and the Navesink River.
—Compiled from the USGS's Preliminary Integrated Geologic Map Database for the United States, 2006

Terminal Moraine

The Parkway crosses onto the Wisconsinan terminal moraine, a ridge built by the glaciers at their southern maximum, at milepost 131.2, just south of the Amtrak railroad bridge. The moraine reaches an elevation of about 140 feet beneath the Parkway but is only poorly visible from the road. It is better seen along the Turnpike and in the area around Short Hills, the Plainfields, Metuchen, and Edison. Short Hills, now just a town, first referred to the entire arc of the terminal moraine, deposited beneath the lobate front of the glacier from Short Hills to Perth Amboy. The hills are difficult to see today through the trees and buildings but would have been visible for miles when houses were few and trees largely restricted to woodlots and windbreaks. They would have been much more noticeable when travel was by foot or horseback and even small hills would slow a wagon.

Raritan River

Before the Pleistocene ice age, the Raritan River ran eastward from Bound Brook toward Rahway rather than southward toward New Brunswick. Before they reached their southernmost position, the glaciers blocked the east-trending valley, forcing the Raritan southward. With the glaciers at their maximum, the ancestral Raritan drained meltwater from Budd Lake to Perth Amboy and must have been an impressive sight in summertime. Between Highland Park

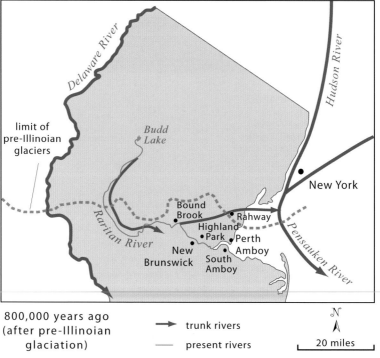

The ancestral Raritan River flowed through the Rahway area before glaciers forced it south. —Modified from Stanford, 2005; Stanford, 2009

and New Brunswick the flat top of the channelway is 1,200 feet wide and cut 40 to 60 feet below gravel deposited before or shortly after the river was forced southward. Where it passed the vicinity of today's Parkway bridge between Perth Amboy and South Amboy, the ice age river quickly eroded through the unconsolidated Coastal Plain sediments and formed swift, steep rapids across the hard diabase of the Palisades Sill. A rough idea of the spectacle can be imagined based on bedrock elevation downstream from New Brunswick. Red sandstone bedrock is exposed near sea level at New Brunswick. Diabase of the buried section of the Palisades Sill is 68 feet below sea level in borings through postglacial sediments at the Parkway bridge and 90 feet below sea level in borings at the Victory Bridge just under a half mile downstream from the Parkway.

New Jersey Clay Industry

From the early 1800s into the early twentieth century New Jersey's clay belt, stretching from Woodbridge to the Arthur Kill, southward to Sayreville, and along the Raritan Bay shore through Cheesequake and Cliffwood Beach, provided the raw material for roofing tile by the acre, ceramic pipe by the mile, and bricks by the million. Clay for over 80 million bricks was being shipped annually from Woodbridge alone by the 1850s, and in the peak years around 1900 New Jersey accounted for more than one-third of the national clay output. The Sayre and Fisher Brickyard stretched for 2 miles along the Sayreville waterfront.

Brickyard workers in kiln in 1899 on the west bank of Pennsauken Creek.
—Photo courtesy of N.J. Geological Survey

The clay formations are continuous beyond the industrial clay belt along a band crossing New Jersey from Staten Island to Delaware, but there was little production between the Raritan River and Trenton because the clays lie beneath the Pensauken Formation, a thick sand and gravel deposit left by the long-gone Pensauken River. Clay was dug from Trenton southward along the Delaware, but the amount was smaller and there were fewer brick works and tile works. Trenton and East Liverpool, Ohio, were the two preeminent pottery, porcelain fixture, and fine china manufacturing centers in the United States for over one hundred years. Much of the clay used in Trenton was dug locally, but the high-quality clays used in the best of the ceramics were brought from out of state.

Within the main clay belt, the quality and composition of the clay varies from place to place and from bed to bed. In Late Cretaceous time, New Jersey was close to the equator and to the west of a warm ocean. It had a humid, tropical climate in which the minerals feldspar and mica weathered to a white, high-quality clay known as kaolinite. Proterozoic rocks of the New Jersey Highlands and adjacent New York and Pennsylvania are rich in feldspar, mica, and quartz, and weathered mostly to kaolinite and quartz grains. Sandstones of the Newark Basin are predominantly quartz and weathered to a soil with less clay and more sand than the Proterozoic rocks.

Once weathered, the sand and clay were picked up by streams and carried to where they were deposited in meandering rivers, mangrove swamps, deltas, beaches, and offshore. Sand was deposited in higher energy environments like stream channels and beaches. Sandy clay, used mostly for brick, was deposited in the less energetic environments of floodplains, coastal lagoons, and offshore below the wave base. Silty clay was deposited in the quietest environments, some far offshore and some on land, for example, in oxbow lakes created when a meandering river changed course. The highest-quality clay, kaolinite, flocculates quickly into larger particles in freshwater. The purest kaolinite was dug from clay beds deposited in inland environments in the Cretaceous Period when the climate was warm and moist. Less desirable clay minerals, commonly illite and chlorite, are a more typical weathering product of cooler climates and flocculate more easily in salty or brackish water. New Jersey's lower-quality brick and terra-cotta clays were dug from clay deposited in nearshore and offshore environments and from post-Cretaceous times when the climate was no longer tropical. Whether the clay was deposited on land or offshore, the pits are on land. If you read that a particular clay is mined from offshore deposits, it is clay that was deposited when sea level was higher.

While most of the clay was carried onto the Coastal Plain by rivers, some was mined from soil weathered from the rock it still overlies. The Raritan Fire Clay, along the banks of the Raritan River, weathered more of less in place from Newark Basin shale. In some pits, the walls showed progressively less weathering downward. Around Carteret, the Coastal Plain formations were deposited above the Palisades diabase rather than above shale. Soil preserved beneath the Coastal Plain formations passes in several feet from soft, white clay composed of completely weathered diabase, into harder subsoil in which the less easily weathered minerals of the diabase are preserved, and finally into black, unweathered diabase.

By the 1920s, the New Jersey clay industry was losing importance. While clay remained the most significant of New Jersey's mineral products in tonnage and value into the 1930s, production fell by more than 50 percent in the Depression and never recovered. By the 1950s few clay pits were still open. Clay was still abundant, but land prices and local opposition made it difficult to open new pits. Brick, roofing tile, and ceramic pipe had been replaced for many uses by lighter, cheaper, less brittle materials. There is still demand for clay, especially for landfill liners and covers, but the production of sand and gravel and crushed stone now greatly exceeds that of clay. All that remains from the Sayre and Fisher works is an enormous chimney in Sayreville's waterfront park and the millions of bricks and miles of terra-cotta piping and roofing tile still in use throughout the northeast.

Fossil Plants and Insects from Sayreville to Cliffwood

In addition to their bricks, the New Jersey Coastal Plain clays have long been known for their fossils: wood, leaves, amber, insects, and flowers. Even though the fossils were preserved mostly in deltaic and coastal environments, many are terrestrial, not marine. Some are from animals and plants preserved where they lived in deltaic and coastal wetlands. Others are from animals and plants that lived inland and were washed seaward by streams and rivers. Cliffwood is named for the fossil wood lignite, exposed in cliffs overlooking Raritan Bay. The cliffs have been stabilized to prevent erosion, and fossil wood is now only rarely seen.

Fossil leaves are common in the clays and attracted the attention of early workers. Unfortunately, even though leaves are common, they are difficult to collect, even more difficult to preserve, and seldom seen in collections. The film remaining from the leaves flakes away and the clay dries and crumbles from beneath the fossils. George Cook, the New Jersey state geologist in the mid-1800s, assembled a large collection of leaves, but they received little careful scientific study. Serious study of New Jersey's fossil leaves began in the 1880s with the production of carefully prepared, beautifully illustrated, and exhaustive monographs by Arthur Hollick of the New York Botanical Gardens and John S. Newberry of Columbia College. Newberry found that the leaves collected by Cook had, with the passage of time, become practically worthless for scientific study. A second set of monographs, illustrated with photographs rather than lithographs, was produced between 1903 and 1911 by Edward W. Berry of Johns Hopkins University. In both the 1880s and early 1900s, the authors identified numerous plants as ancestral to modern groups based in good part on leaf shape. This was in line with the accepted practice of the time. For some lineages, like the ginkgo, this has proven valid, but recent work on the internal and external microscopic structures of fossil leaves and chemical compounds preserved in the fossils suggests that many similarities between leaf shapes of fossil and modern plants are due to convergent evolution rather than direct lineal descent.

More recently, fossil insects and flowers from New Jersey clays have come to be important in understanding the history of plant life and the interplay between plants and insects early in the history of flowering plants. The insects, preserved in amber, were the first to be studied. Amber, which is fossilized tree resin, was known from Camden, Woodbury, and the Trenton area before 1816 and was reportedly so common in some Staten Island clay pits that it was burned for heat. In 1967, two ants were found in a piece of amber collected by an amateur along the Raritan Bay bluffs near Cliffwood. At the time, these were the oldest known ants. The ants are clearly workers from a social colony, but scientists from Harvard and Cornell Universities found several wasplike characteristics not seen in modern ants. This lent weight to a previously hypothesized evolution of ants from wasps. The oldest fossil bee, from about 80 million years ago, is a stingless worker from a piece of Late Cretaceous amber collected many years ago in Kinkora, Burlington County. The amber lay unstudied in the collections of the American Museum of Natural History in New York until the 1980s, when scientists polished the surface to see inside and found the bee. It was a worker bee similar to modern bees in being colonial and adapted for pollen gathering. Similar to the ants found earlier at Cliffwood, it had wasplike features. Based on this specimen, it seemed reasonable that bees evolved from predators to something like their modern form and social behavior in the 50 million years between the development of flowering plants in Early Cretaceous time and the explosion of flowering plants by Late Cretaceous time. In the 80 million years since then, bees have changed comparatively little.

In the 1990s, the importance of fossils from New Jersey clay pits increased greatly when a bed rich in amber-bearing lignite in a Parlin clay pit was brought to the attention of scientists by a group of amateurs. The amateurs lent many specimens of scientific value for study, and scientists from the American Museum of Natural History in New York, the New York Botanical Garden,

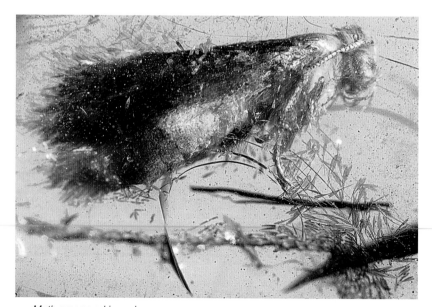

Moth preserved in amber. —Image courtesy of David Grimaldi, American Museum of Natural History

Cornell University, Johns Hopkins University, and as far away as Sweden spent countless hours cataloging and interpreting fossils entombed in the amber. As well as bees and ants, there are spiders, spiderwebs, moths, millipedes, mushrooms, feathers, and even frogs and lizards. Some insects were preserved with their parasitic mites still attached!

No account of insect evolution would be complete without consideration of the plants and flowers they are so intimately related to. By a happy coincidence, fossil flowers of the same age as the amber were found in the Crossman sand and clay pit in Sayreville a few years after the amber discovery. Flowers are temporary, delicate features and are rarely fossilized. Our understanding of the relationships among plant groups has traditionally been based in good part on the structure of flowers, and the scarcity of fossils has been a major hindrance to understanding plant evolution.

In one highly unusual bed at the Crossman pit, cellulose and other easily destroyed plant materials were reduced to nearly inert, much more easily fossilized charcoal, apparently by a Cretaceous forest fire, then buried in silty clay and preserved for 90 million years. A greater variety of Late Cretaceous fossil flowers has been found here than anywhere else in the world, and the site has become a benchmark in tracing plant evolution. The flowers and insects together in the same deposits allowed broad-based studies by workers with individual expertise in plant and insect evolution. Together they greatly increased our understanding of flowers and their pollinators 90 million years ago.

The clay pit has become a residential development, but before the construction 26 tons of the fossil-bearing clay was collected and preserved for future study.

Fossil flower about the size of a pinhead from the Crossman sand and clay pit in Sayreville. The Cretaceous flowers from Sayreville are mostly small.
—Image courtesy of William Crepet, Cornell University

Pyrite on Raritan Bay Beaches

Dig into the muddy bottom of any pond or below the surface of any tidal marsh, and you will encounter sulfurous odors and dark staining. The odors are from hydrogen sulfide (H_2S). Iron in a chemically reduced state and organic matter contribute to the dark color. Over time, the iron forms crystals of pyrite, an iron sulfide commonly known as fool's gold. A number of New Jersey's Coastal Plain formations were deposited in oxygen-depleted environments and are rich in pyrite. Before the construction of retaining walls to prevent erosion, pyrite nodules were common on some Raritan Bay beaches. Reportedly, at one time they were gathered and roasted as an iron ore. Open roasting of sulfide ores releases large amounts of hydrogen sulfide, and before strict environmental regulations were in place, it was one of the most environmentally destructive smelting methods known. Fortunately, nonsulfide iron ores are plentiful in New Jersey and not much pyrite was roasted.

Less fortunately, pyrite does not have to be roasted to produce acid. Through much of the nineteenth century it was common to spread glauconite marl onto the sandy, nutrient-poor soils of southern New Jersey as a soil conditioner. Some glauconites, known as poison marls, contained large amounts of pyrite in addition to the beneficial phosphorus, potassium, and lime. When poison marls were inadvertently applied, the soil became acidic and could be ruined for years. More recently, soil at some of New Jersey's clay pits has remained barren for decades after their abandonment because of soil acidity.

In addition, digging into pyrite-bearing sediments next to streams has caused fish kills and can turn drinking water into a weak acid. Most of the time, the acidity is low and the water will still meet drinking water standards. Because of the danger to streams and drinking water, soil must be tested before digging

Soil at an abandoned sand and clay pit. The soil has remained barren for decades because of soil acidity. —Photo by D. Harper

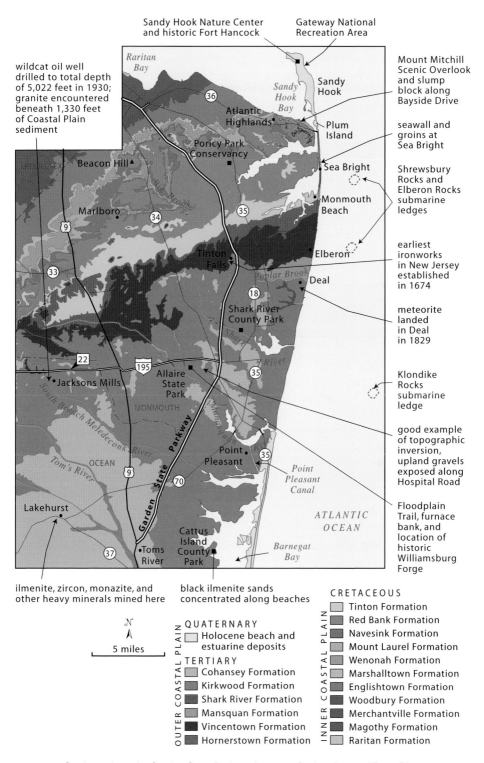

wildcat oil well drilled to total depth of 5,022 feet in 1930; granite encountered beneath 1,330 feet of Coastal Plain sediment

Sandy Hook Nature Center and historic Fort Hancock

Gateway National Recreation Area

Mount Mitchill Scenic Overlook and slump block along Bayside Drive

seawall and groins at Sea Bright

Shrewsbury Rocks and Elberon Rocks submarine ledges

earliest ironworks in New Jersey established in 1674

meteorite landed in Deal in 1829

Klondike Rocks submarine ledge

good example of topographic inversion, upland gravels exposed along Hospital Road

Floodplain Trail, furnace bank, and location of historic Williamsburg Forge

Raritan Bay

Sandy Hook Bay

Sandy Hook

Atlantic Highlands

Plum Island

Sea Bright

Monmouth Beach

Elberon

Deal

Beacon Hill

Poricy Park Conservancy

Marlboro

Tinton Falls

Poplar Brook

Shark River County Park

Shark River

Jacksons Mills

Allaire State Park

MONMOUTH

South Branch Metedeconk River

OCEAN

Tom's River

Point Pleasant

Point Pleasant Canal

ATLANTIC OCEAN

Lakehurst

Cattus Island County Park

Barnegat Bay

Toms River

ilmenite, zircon, monazite, and other heavy minerals mined here

black ilmenite sands concentrated along beaches

N

5 miles

QUATERNARY
- Holocene beach and estuarine deposits

TERTIARY
- Cohansey Formation
- Kirkwood Formation
- Shark River Formation
- Mansquan Formation
- Vincentown Formation
- Hornerstown Formation

OUTER COASTAL PLAIN

CRETACEOUS
- Tinton Formation
- Red Bank Formation
- Navesink Formation
- Mount Laurel Formation
- Wenonah Formation
- Marshalltown Formation
- Englishtown Formation
- Woodbury Formation
- Merchantville Formation
- Magothy Formation
- Raritan Formation

INNER COASTAL PLAIN

Geology along the Garden State Parkway between Raritan Bay and Toms River.
—Compiled from the USGS's Preliminary Integrated Geologic Map Database for the United States, 2006

is allowed in pyrite-rich geologic formations. If the tests show that acid may be a problem, excavation is allowed only with protective measures like limiting exposure of excavated materials to a few hours and spreading acid-neutralizing pulverized limestone.

Mt. Mitchill

At 266 feet, Mt. Mitchill is by some measures the highest coastal headland south of Maine. The Mt. Mitchill Scenic Overlook has views across the village of Atlantic Highlands toward New York City and Long Island. When you look across the New York Bight toward Long Island, you can sometimes see tilefish boats working the deep water of the Hudson Channel. The seaward slope, toward Atlantic Highlands, is overly steep and prone to slumping, probably because of undermining by waves and currents before Sandy Hook built northward between the ocean and the toe of the slope. An abundance of the mineral glauconite, which weathers to an incohesive clay, may be a contributing factor. Continuing slow downhill creep is evident from widening of cracks in foundations and separation of porches and stairways from houses, particularly after heavy rains. Larger failures in the past have been inferred at nine locations along the slope from scarps and offsets in sedimentary layering. One

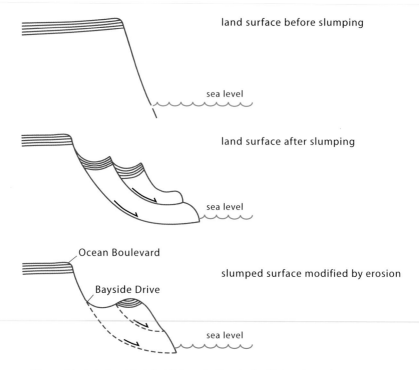

Slump block below Mt. Mitchill Scenic Overlook. Of the slump blocks along the bluff overlooking Sandy Hook Bay, this block is the most youthful in appearance and may be the one that slid in 1782. —Modified from Minard, 1974

such collapse in the spring of 1782 at Greenland Bank, an older name for Mt. Mitchill, was heard by residents. Descriptions from the time say that about 40 acres of land gave way.

The scenic overlook is at the edge of one of the larger slump blocks along the bluff. Beds matching those at the top of the slope are now about 85 feet lower and were rotated as much as 40 degrees as the block slid down the curved detachment surface. Bayside Drive, at the base of the steep slope, marks the inner edge of a 450-foot-wide downdropped block. Of the slump blocks along the slope overlooking Sandy Hook Bay, this is the most youthful in appearance and may be the one that slid in 1782.

Sandy Hook

Like any shoreline, anywhere, anytime in geologic history, the Jersey Shore is a fleeting feature. About 18,000 years ago, at the height of the most recent ice age, the shore stood near the edge of the continental shelf, about 80 miles east of where it is today. When the glaciers melted, sea level rose and the shore-line retreated, quickly at first, then more slowly through the last 2,000 or so years when most of the ice was gone. Even with the decreased sea level rise, the beaches are far from stable. Along the Monmouth County shoreline, beaches were eroding rapidly before aggressive shoreline stabilization beginning at the very end of the nineteenth century. Property records show as much as 2,000 feet of shoreline retreat since about 1650. In other places, the shoreline has receded less or even moved slightly seaward.

Sandy Hook spit is one of those places where sand eroded from beaches else-where comes to rest, or at least it did until recently. At Sandy Hook, waves and currents carried the sand eroded along the Monmouth County shore toward the tip of the hook, and the constant arrival of new sand caused the spit to build northward into deeper water. In 1764 Sandy Hook Lighthouse was built close to the tip of the hook. Since then Sandy Hook has grown more than 1 mile northward to the edge of the main shipping channel into New York Harbor. The hook is no longer growing because sand carried to the channel is dredged out as fast as it goes in.

While Sandy Hook is no longer building northward, it is still constantly changing. On the seaward side of Sandy Hook, the beaches are storm-dominated and strongly seasonal and show dramatic change from year to year. Seaward of the coastal dunes, wintertime storms tear away at the beach face, moving sand onto offshore bars. The resulting beach face is steep. Above the high tide line, winds blow the lighter quartz sand from the beaches onto the dunes, leaving behind a veneer of gravel, debris, and dark-colored heavy miner-als. Through the spring and summer, gentler waves move sand shoreward and eventually weld sandbars onto the beach face. Clean sand washing onto the beach is blown landward across the gravel and debris of the landward part of the winter beach, further contributing to the beloved wide, clean expanse of the summertime beach.

None of the Jersey Shore beaches has been stable through the historic record, but Sandy Hook is one of the easiest places to envision the changes. At times, the hook has been attached to the mainland at Atlantic Highlands, at other

On this Jersey beach in winter, winds have blown away the quartz sand, leaving a lag deposit of pebbles, shells, heavy mineral sand, and debris above high tide. —Photo by D. Harper

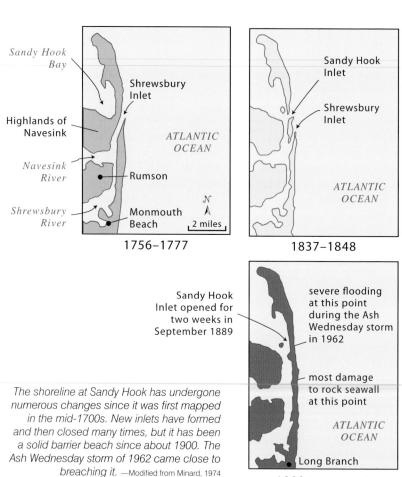

Sandy Hook Bay

Shrewsbury Inlet

Highlands of Navesink

ATLANTIC OCEAN

Navesink River

Rumson

Shrewsbury River

Monmouth Beach

N

2 miles

1756–1777

Sandy Hook Inlet

Shrewsbury Inlet

ATLANTIC OCEAN

1837–1848

Sandy Hook Inlet opened for two weeks in September 1889

severe flooding at this point during the Ash Wednesday storm in 1962

most damage to rock seawall at this point

ATLANTIC OCEAN

Long Branch

1900 to present

The shoreline at Sandy Hook has undergone numerous changes since it was first mapped in the mid-1700s. New inlets have formed and then closed many times, but it has been a solid barrier beach since about 1900. The Ash Wednesday storm of 1962 came close to breaching it. —Modified from Minard, 1974

times it has been an island separated from the mainland by inlets, and since about 1900, it has been part of a barrier beach extending from Long Branch to the tip of the hook.

Even now, despite stabilization efforts and beach nourishment, the hook changes shape from year to year. Wintertime erosion dominates at the narrow Fishing Beach, and the beach is bordered landward by an erosional scarp at the base of the dunes. At the northeastern tip of the hook, summertime buildup

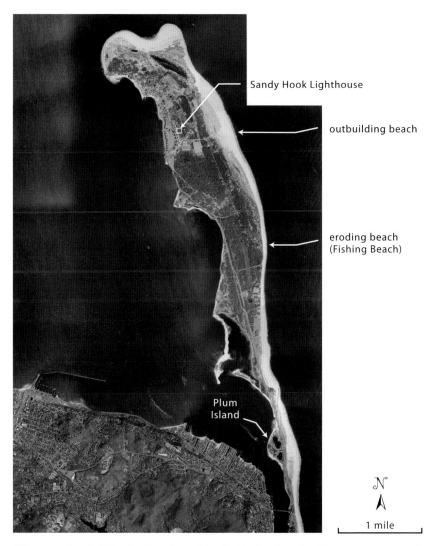

Where sand is building the beaches of Sandy Hook outward, wide expanses of sand have not yet become heavily vegetated. Where the beaches are eroding, there is only a narrow strip of beach seaward of vegetated dunes. In this photo at low tide, the eroding beach reserved for fishing is fairly wide. At high tide, there are only a few yards of beach between the water and the eroding dunes. —Landscape image from Ted Pallis, N.J. Geological Survey

predominates. Dunes and beaches are building oceanward by the addition of beach ridges a few feet high and parallel to the shoreline.

Seaward of former Fort Hancock's 9-Gun Battery, one of the trails from an observation deck leads past an elongate freshwater pond between two beach ridges. The freshwater is likely rainwater floating above seawater deeper in the sand. Another trail, heading north from the observation deck, crosses several beach ridges. The linear pattern of ridges can be difficult to discern along the trail but is clear on air photos on display at the Sandy Hook Nature Center. From the northernmost ridge it is a short walk across the beach to where sand that would have built Sandy Hook northward is now dredged from shipping lanes. This is a good place to view oceangoing freighters at an uncomfortably close distance.

In contrast to the ocean beaches, bayside beaches are not directly exposed to large wintertime storm waves and do not show the same strong seasonal changes. Even these lower-energy beaches, however, are constantly changing. Plum Island, near the southern end of Sandy Hook and now connected to land by a short causeway, is a good place to see a variety of beach processes in a small area. The west side of the island is exposed to the waves of Sandy Hook Bay and has been eroding for decades. The erosion is evident from the tangles of trees that fall into the water as the beach beneath them washes away. The sand moves northward and southward onto well-developed spits at the tips of the island, and from there across shallow water onto the bayside beaches of Sandy Hook. At low tide, the spits completely enclose small ponds north and south of the causeway.

Eroding beach on the bayward tip of Plum Island. At times the tangle of trees that have been undermined and fallen over is almost impenetrable. —Photo by D. Harper

Shrewsbury and Navesink Drowned Valley Estuaries

The Shrewsbury and Navesink Rivers, like many coastal rivers worldwide, end in drowned valley estuaries. The rivers cut deeper and widened their tributary valleys when sea level dropped during the ice ages. Their valleys flooded when the glaciers melted. Drowned valley estuaries are common, but few in New Jersey show the branching into tributaries more clearly than the Shrewsbury and Navesink.

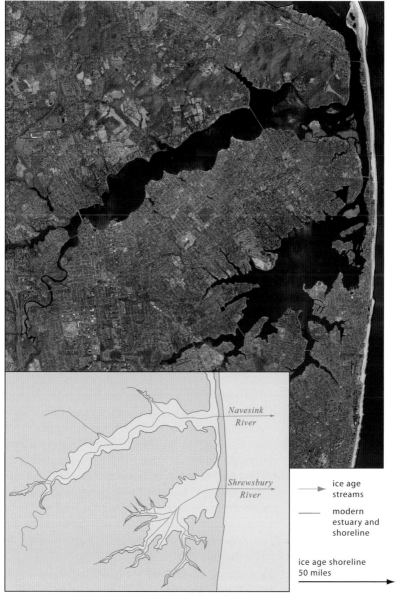

The Shrewsbury and Navesink drowned valley estuaries held rivers during the ice age. —Landscape image from Ted Pallis, N.J. Geological Survey

Fossils at Poricy Park, Big Brook, and Shark River Park

Philadelphia was the preeminent center for the study of natural sciences in North America from the mid-1700s through the mid-1800s. It is home to the Philadelphia Academy of Natural Sciences, the University of Pennsylvania, the Wagner Free Institute of Science, and other centers of learning. As most fossil collecting sites near Philadelphia were in New Jersey, North American natural history workers and Europeans comparing their fossils to those of North America became well acquainted with New Jersey fossils. The fossils were mostly from clay and marl pits that have long since grown over or been developed in this densely suburban area, or along stream banks most of which have been covered by fill, landscaped as public parks, closed to the public, or are otherwise unfit for collecting. Three sites, all well-known in the nineteenth century, are still open to the public. All three are along Monmouth County streams (Poricy Brook, Big Brook, and the Shark River). The fossils wash from stream-bank exposures and are collected from stream gravels. If you go collecting, wear heavy-soled shoes and work gloves for protection against sharp objects and broken glass, and expect to get wet and muddy. The sites are well represented on the Internet. Look them up before visiting to check conditions and accessibility. Respect the privacy of nearby residents, and follow rules as to when and where to collect, how to collect (especially, don't dig into the stream banks), and how much to take home.

The sites have different appeal. Poricy Park is the best known and most family friendly. Permits are required for groups of ten or more, and you are expected to donate finds of possible scientific value to the museum at the Poricy Park Conservancy. The nature center, along Oak Tree Road, has fossil displays to help you to identify your finds. At the collecting site on Poricy Brook, a steep bank exposes the Late Cretaceous Navesink and Red Bank Formations, about 72 million years old. Most of the face is in the Navesink Formation, a hard, silty sand peppered with greenish black grains of the mineral glauconite. The sand toward the top of the bank, stained red by iron oxide, is part of the Red Bank Formation and does not yield fossils other than sediment-filled *Callianassa* burrows, generally ascribed to burrowing, shrimplike organisms.

The fossil bank at Poricy Brook exposes a complete, though thin, cycle of sea level rise and fall. The shell layer just above the creek is at the base of the cycle from a time shortly after sea level rise. Sediment in several hundred feet of water was building up slowly enough to allow the shells to accumulate before being buried. The glauconitic sands of the steep portion of the bank are from a time of slow sedimentation when sand and mud were being carried seaward slowly enough to allow glauconite grains to grow before being buried. The red sand of the Red Bank Formation at the top of the bank was deposited in shallower water from which the clay and mica flakes were washed seaward and quartz sand was the predominant sediment.

Fossils can be seen embedded in the Navesink Formation, and washed out fossils can be picked up from gravel bars or sieved from bottom sediments with a kitchen colander or wire mesh screen. Most of the fossils are from a shell bed

The stream-cut bank at Poricy Brook in Monmouth County has been well-known for over a century. Fossils in the sandy clay are constantly but slowly washing into the brook as the bank erodes. Occasionally large trees, like the one in the foreground, are undermined and fall from the top of the slope. The bank is so compact that attempts to dig out the fossils usually yield only broken fragments of shell. —Photo by D. Harper

This *Callianassa* burrow, a trace fossil from a shrimplike organism that sheltered beneath the surface but lived on food at the seafloor, is in the Red Bank Formation at Poricy Brook. The shrimp is long gone from this burrow. The trace fossil stands out because the walls of the burrow are slightly harder than the surrounding sand.
—Photo by D. Harper

about a foot thick near the stream level. If fossils are scarce near the bluff at Poricy Brook, move downstream. Even downstream from the bluff, the creek is still wearing away at the Navesink Formation and washing out fossils. Oysters, belemnites, snails, clams, and brachiopods are common. If you are very lucky, you may find a shark tooth or bone fragment. Above and below the shell bed, there are fewer shells, but the sediment is mottled with myriads of fossil burrows. The burrows show on the glauconite-rich sandy clay background as lighter-gray, finer-grained traces with fewer glauconite grains. Some are from animals that spent their entire lives belowground in a subsurface ecosystem, like many of today's marine worms. Others may have been from animals that dug into the bottom for shelter but came out onto the seafloor to forage.

In addition to the shells prized by collectors and the seldom-noticed fossil burrows, there are several kinds of animals that attached onto or burrowed into the shells of other animals. Shells were the only solid places to anchor on the sandy, muddy sea bottom, and most of the shells lying on the bottom became encrusted or burrowed by organisms seeking stability. Many oyster shells are honeycombed with small, round holes up to a few tenths of an inch across. These were hollowed out by a combination of dissolving and grinding by burrowing sponges, the clionids, to create a protected living space. Clionids still exist and clionid borings exactly like those honeycombing many Poricy Brook shells can be found on shells on most Jersey Shore beaches today.

Another common kind of boring on Poricy Brook shells was made by barnacles. Unlike the well-known, tent-shaped barnacles cemented onto rocks and shells on shorelines everywhere, the burrowing barnacles carved tiny living quarters, about the size and shape of an apostrophe printed in very small type, into shells lying on the seafloor. The barnacle borings are not as easily spotted as the much larger holes of the clionid sponges, but after you know what they look like you can usually find some by looking over a few smooth-surfaced shells.

Worm tubes are another common fossil. The tubes are thin, haphazardly meandering, white tubes firmly cemented to shells. They look like dried toothpaste squeezed from a dollhouse-size tube.

Big Brook is in some ways similar to Poricy Brook, but the stream banks are higher and more continuous, and more geologic formations are exposed. In addition to the Navesink and Red Bank Formations, the Wenonah and Mount Laurel Formations are exposed below the Navesink, and Pleistocene sands are exposed above the Red Bank Formation. The Mount Laurel and Wenonah Formations have a slightly older assemblage of fossils, and the Pleistocene sands have, on rare occasions, shed bones and teeth of ice age mammals to the stream. While Big Brook has a wider variety of fossils, there are no picnic tables, museum, and other amenities. The stream is harder to get down to, deeper, faster, and not appropriate for less adventurous collectors.

The third collecting site, well-known since the nineteenth century and still open to the public, is at Shark River County Park. Although the park has many amenities and attractive trails through mixed deciduous and pine forests, the fossil collecting is not for the fainthearted or for small children. For several days after even light rain, the fossil-bearing stream gravel is inaccessible beneath

Belemnitella

Exogyra

Agerostrea

Pycnodonte

shark teeth

Archaeolamna

Fossils from Poricy Brook and Big Brook. The round holes in some of the larger shells are from the boring sponge Cliona. *Scales in millimeters.* —Photos by Carl Mehling

swift, deep water. To get to the fossils, follow a trail paralleling the Garden State Parkway to a wooden bridge over the Shark River. Leave the marked trail just before the bridge and follow unmarked paths upstream along the riverbank across marshes, small tributary streams, and slippery clay. The red staining, iridescent sheens on the water and occasional sulfurous odors are part of the natural process of bog iron formation and are not dangerous. Climb across bouldery rip-rap armoring the stream banks beneath the Garden State Parkway bridge and follow paths above the river to the stream-bank exposures of the Shark River Formation. Long pants are recommended. The undergrowth is dense and thorny.

The fossils here are younger than the shells from Poricy Brook and Big Brook. The Big Brook and Poricy Brook fossils are from the Cretaceous Period of the Mesozoic Era, contemporaneous with the dinosaurs. The fossils at Shark River are from the Eocene and Miocene Epochs of the Cenozoic Era, after the demise of the dinosaurs. There are no intact shells like those at Poricy Brook and Big Brook. The shells have dissolved and left perfect impressions, called molds, in consolidated silty sand. Most collectors, however, go to Shark River for the rare teeth and pieces of bone that can be sieved from the stream gravels, not for the shell molds. Tooth and bone are made of calcium phosphate and are less soluble than the calcium carbonate shells. Unlike the shells, they did not dissolve. You will not find any by looking through the sediment fallen from the banks. Instead, sieve the streambed sand and gravel for fossils left behind when the silt and fine sand washed downstream.

Even if you are interested in the shell molds, do not approach the steep banks. Look only in blocks that have tumbled far toward the river. The steep banks may look stable, but they are not. They are as much a result of groundwater conditions as stream erosion. Groundwater in a sand layer near the base of the exposure is under artesian pressure and constantly discharging from small springs and undermining the cliff. The overlying, more firmly cemented layer eventually falls in a potentially fatal collapse that could be triggered by your weight on the loose, waterlogged sand underneath.

Shrewsbury, Elberon, and Klondike Rocks

The northeastward-trending outcrop belts of New Jersey's Inner Coastal Plain continue eastward across the flooded continental shelf. The same semiconsolidated formations that stand up as the hills of the Inner Coastal Plain crop out offshore as the submarine ledges known as Shrewsbury Rocks off Sea Bright, Elberon Rocks off Elberon, Klondike Rocks still farther south, and a few other low outcrops. Shrewsbury Rocks, about a mile offshore, are the largest of the submerged outcrops and shallow enough to need navigational buoys. Their location can often be judged from the cluster of fishing boats gathered over the rich bottom. As with any bit of stable bottom on the shifting sands offshore from New Jersey, the Shrewsbury Rocks are home to a myriad of attached organisms (seaweeds, sponges, mussels, anemones, bryozoans, and even corals native to these cold waters) and to the free-moving fish, crabs, starfish, sea urchins, and lobsters that use them for food and shelter. Other bits of stable bottom from single shells to the numerous artificial reefs up and down the

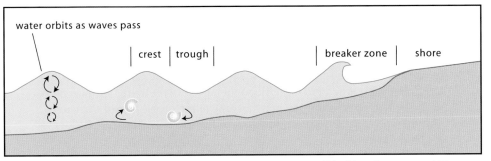

Water does not move uniformly shoreward as a wave passes. If it did, swimmers would be carried to the beach as fast as surfers. Instead, the water moves in circular orbits upward and landward as the crest of the wave approaches, and downward and seaward as the trough approaches. Shells and sand on the bottom are lifted upward and shoreward as the wave crest approaches, especially if pulled by a plume of seaweed extending upward into shallow water. When the trough approaches, shells come to rest on the bottom and are dragged slowly, if at all, seaward. Eventually they are carried to the turbulent breaker zone. From there they may be cast up onto the beach. —Artwork by D. Harper

shore are also colonized, but Shrewsbury Rocks cover a larger area and the ecosystem they support is larger and richer. In the early twentieth century, fishing rights to the rocks were the subject of heated disputes between lobstermen and fishermen using incompatible gear.

Sediment of the offshore ledges is consolidated to the point that waves break off pieces into sea rocks as well as wearing the ledge directly to sand and mud. Some rocks are carried shoreward. The light gray, sandy-surfaced sea rocks, studded with black grains of the mineral glauconite and occasional fossils, are common at Sea Bright and can be picked from the beach as far north as the tip of Sandy Hook. Sea rocks on beaches near Belmar are less common, but some resemble the limy portions of the Vincentown Formation in being composed almost entirely of the firmly cemented calcite remains of bryozoans.

Tinton Falls Iron Works

Tinton Falls is the site of the earliest ironworks in New Jersey, established sometime between 1665 and 1676 to take advantage of the local bog iron. In 1675, Lewis Morris bought a half interest in the venture and had the connections and means to make it successful by securing access to the ore and local wood and arranging a seven-year tax exemption. By 1676 the ironworks was up and running, the only productive ironworks south of New England. With a workforce of sixty or more slaves, the Tinton Falls works was the first notable instance of slavery in New Jersey.

Deal

Deal is close, depending on the weather in the particular year, to a point at which net sand transport to the north is northward toward Sandy Hook and net transport to the south is southward, toward Cape May. Poplar Brook flows directly across Deal Beach and provides a good indicator as to which way the sand is moving at any particular time. Waves from the northeast carry sand into the brook from the north, forcing it southward toward a storm-water culvert crossing the beach near Phillips Avenue. At other times, sand carried by waves from the southeast force the mouth of the brook northward toward a stone breakwater at Roosevelt Avenue. In any year, the brook can shift up to 1,200 feet from the breakwater to the north to the culvert to the south. Through most of the winter, waves from the northeast move the brook toward the culvert. Through most of the summer, waves from the southeast keep brook close to the breakwater.

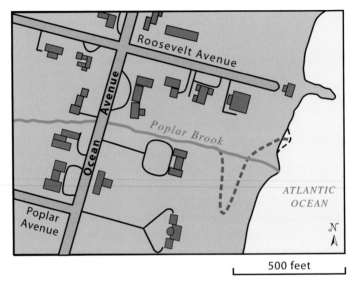

Poplar Brook in Deal changes course near its mouth on a regular basis. Waves from the northeast sometimes carry sand into the brook from the north and force its mouth southward (down). At other times, sand carried by waves from the southeast force the brook north (up). In 2012, the brook flowed straight to the ocean, but in the mid-2000s, the brook made a hairpin turn and flowed north (dashed line).

Because sand on the long-term average moves northward to the north of Deal and southward to the south of Deal, sand movement is usually away from rather than toward Deal. Unless the sand is replaced, the beach will erode. While the beach is not eroding back in a dramatic fashion, an abundance of dark green and black grains of the mineral glauconite on the beach show that much of the sand at Deal is new to the beach environment. Glauconite is soft and does not last long on beaches. In geologic terms, the beach sand at Deal is immature. It matures quickly both northward and southward from Deal because the soft glauconite is destroyed in the high energy of the surf zone. Away from Deal, the sand is increasingly dominated by quartz. The new sand arriving on the beach may be washed in by Poplar Brook, carried onshore by waves, or eroded from the bluffs behind the beach.

Deal Meteorite and Other Asteroid Impacts Affecting New Jersey

Several meteorite landings have been reported in New Jersey, but the only authenticated fall started as a fireball that crossed over New Jersey, broke into pieces, and landed in Deal on August 16, 1829. The *New Jersey Eagle* of Newark reported, "About 1 o'clock on Friday morning last, when the sky was perfectly clear, a meteor of unusual and intense brightness was observed in New York. It shot up from the west and illuminated the city with excessive light. A stream of fiery particles followed in its train, tapering off to a point like a cone. After transversing about 20 degrees of the horizon with prodigious swiftness, it disappeared as suddenly as it had blazed upon the sight." According to the *Morristown Jerseyman*, "About 12 o'clock last night many of our citizens were roused from their slumbers by a report similar to the discharge of a piece of heavy artillery succeeded immediately by a whizzing noise resembling that made by a cannonball passing through the air. Some two or three persons who saw the meteor described it as being a large ball of fire passing rapidly through the air a little south west of this village."

The bulk of the rock, 20.8 grams, went to the Philadelphia Academy of Natural Sciences. Smaller pieces went to the Smithsonian, the Field Museum in Chicago, and museums in Paris, New York, Calcutta, London, Berlin, Rome, and Vienna. None stayed in New Jersey.

While the Deal Meteorite is the only authenticated meteorite to fall in New Jersey in historic times, it is hardly the first meteorite to affect New Jersey. A much larger impact came to be suspected offshore in 1983 when an oceanographic research ship, the *Glomar Challenger*, drilled through a 20-centimeter-thick layer containing tektites and shocked quartz. Tektites are bits of glass formed when molten rock is blown upward from a meteorite impact, cools in the atmosphere, and drops back to Earth. Shocked quartz is known only from nuclear blasts and meteorite impacts and is one of the few pieces of evidence accepted by most workers as a smoking gun, confirming a meteorite impact.

Fossils above and below the meteorite debris dated the impact to the Eocene Epoch, about 35 million years ago. The chief scientist aboard the *Glomar Challenger*, C. Wylie Poag of the U.S. Geological Survey, identified the layer as part of the North American Tektite Field, which had been discovered decades earlier. He reasoned from the shocked quartz, the thickness of the layer, and the abundance of impact debris that the crater might be buried somewhere close by, beneath sediments that had been accumulating through the 35 million years since the impact. A search of seismic profiling records soon led to the discovery of the fairly small Toms Canyon impact crater, about 9 to 12 miles across, near the Toms River submarine canyon about 100 miles off Atlantic City.

At about the same time, core holes drilled into Coastal Plain sediments near Chesapeake Bay found sediments from the Eocene and older to be, instead of horizontally layered as they are in most of the Coastal Plain, broken into blocks and jumbled together without regard to age and at all angles from the horizontal. At first this seemed easily explained as the result of a tsunami from the impact offshore from the Toms River impact, but seismic profiling by Texaco soon showed the disturbed sediment to be part of a second, much larger impact structure beneath Chesapeake Bay.

Allaire State Park

Allaire was well situated for early-nineteenth-century iron manufacturing. There was reliable water power, a good supply of bog iron ore, charcoal fuel from the Pinelands, seashells for flux, and a steep slope for the furnace bank that gave access to the top of the iron furnace. The earliest venture, Williamsburg Forge, was working in the early 1790s, and by the 1820s the village, then known as the Howell Works, was a self-contained community with as many as five hundred residents. The village prospered until larger iron furnaces in the New Jersey Highlands, Pennsylvania, and New York, using richer magnetite ore, fired with coal instead of wood, and fluxed with limestone instead of seashells, doomed the bog iron industry.

The area around Allaire State Park provides a good example of topographic inversion, where former streambeds become hilltops and former hilltops become streambeds. As of about 8 million years ago, a series of streams had become established flowing from northwest to southeast across the area. When the streams eroded their valleys, the sand was carried seaward faster than the pebbles and gravel. The pebbles and gravel remained behind and armored the streambed from further erosion. Instead of cutting down through the gravel, the streams were deflected toward the gravel-free sand of the adjacent stream banks. The streams eventually shifted entirely off their gravelly beds and cut new valleys along the former drainage divides.

The village of Allaire is on a flat terrace 20 to 40 feet above the Manasquan River floodplain, but it is not one of the gravel-capped uplands that started out 8 million years ago as a streambed. It is an abandoned floodplain that developed before the Wisconsinan ice age. The level of today's floodplain was the result of sea level lowering and increased erosion during the ice age. The upland gravels laid down 8 million years ago are exposed about 65 feet higher along Hospital Road at the southern corner of the park. From Squankum Road, follow Hospital Road 1 mile to a parking lot with restrooms. A trail from the lot leads to an abandoned gravel pit where you can see a few feet of the upland gravel overlying gravel-free sand of the Cohansey Formation. Elsewhere, the upland gravel is exposed along I-195 and many other roads where the soil is thin. The gravel at the tops of road cuts may still be in place where it was left by streams mostly about 100 feet higher than today's streambeds. However, much of the gravel is no longer in place. Gravel at road level at the base of road cuts on I-195, for example, has fallen from the tops of the cuts.

The Floodplain Trail, downstream from the village's mill dam, begins at a stairway onto the Manasquan floodplain. The floodplain is not flat like most floodplains, probably due to a combination of mining bog iron from the marshy lowland in the early nineteenth century and erosion by springs. Water soaks into the sand in the flat area at the village and then issues from springs above a clay layer a couple of feet below the surface of the floodplain. When the river is unusually low, you can see the clay along the banks of the Manasquan. Much of the floodplain is soggy and unstable. As is common throughout the

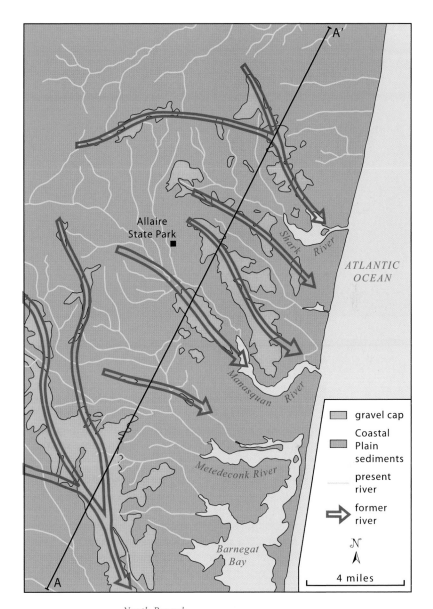

Allaire
State Park

Shark River

*ATLANTIC
OCEAN*

Manasquan River

Metedeconk River

*Barnegat
Bay*

▢	gravel cap
▢	Coastal Plain sediments
—	present river
⇨	former river

$\mathcal{N}$
⋀

4 miles

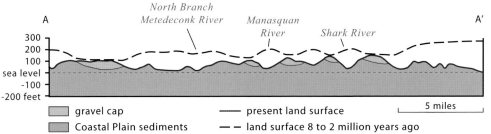

A   A'

*North Branch
Metedeconk River*   *Manasquan
River*   *Shark River*

300
200
100
sea level
-100
-200 feet

5 miles

▢ gravel cap   —— present land surface

▢ Coastal Plain sediments   - - land surface 8 to 2 million years ago

After stream gravel armored the floors of Coastal Plain valleys, streams were deflected toward the gravel-free drainage divides. When they cut downward into the sand, the former streambeds were left standing as the new, gravel-capped upland drainage divides, a process called topographic inversion. —Modified from Stanford, 2005

Gravel overlying dark silty clay along the Manasquan River. Springs issuing from gravel or sand at the top of similarly impermeable silty or clayey beds account for much of the valley widening in the Coastal Plain. —Photo by D. Harper

sandy areas of southern New Jersey, the floodplain here is widening because springs are sapping away at the bottom of the slope, not because streams are cutting away at the walls.

Even though the floodplain is not flat like a typical floodplain, this is a good place to see floodplain processes. A few hundred yards past the stairway, the trail reaches the Manasquan River. The banks are bordered by natural levees a couple of feet above the floodplain. When the river floods, water rises out of the main channel and spreads across the floodplain. Coarse sand settles quickly, close to the stream, and forms the levees. Finer sand and silt settle out farther back on the floodplain where the water is calmer. At a couple of places along the trail, the natural levee is cut by small creeks that rise from springs on the floodplain. During floods, sediment-laden water rushes outward from the river through these channels, spreads onto the floodplain, slows down, and deposits its sand load in splays across the finer sediments covering the rest of the floodplain. Until the summer of 2005, a handful of sediment picked up on the natural levee or from a splay was visibly coarser than sediment picked up a few yards farther back on the floodplain where finer sand and silt settled out. In the summer of 2005, however, the dam upstream burst after prolonged, heavy rainfall, and silty sand was deposited across the entire floodplain. After a few years of more normal sedimentation, there may again be coarser material atop the natural levee and in splays, and finer material farther back.

Past the river, the trail passes close by marshes and a small tributary stream where bright red and orange bog iron is precipitating near springs. The Floodplain Trail ends at the iron furnace. When the furnace was in operation, a timber walkway ran from the furnace bank to fireproof doors at the top of the furnace. The doors could be opened to add ore, flux, and charcoal and could be left partially open, fully open, or closed to help control the blast air pumped through tuyeres at the base of the furnace. Once in blast, the furnace continued operating around the clock, seven days a week, until a shutdown was forced by a mechanical breakdown, freezing of the waterwheel, or a shortage of flux, ore, or charcoal. While the furnace was in blast, charcoal, bog ore, and clamshells for flux were dumped into top of the furnace and blasted with air until the mix was white-hot and melting. Carbon in the charcoal reacted with the oxygen in the iron oxide ore to produce carbon monoxide and molten iron. The iron sank to the bottom of the furnace. The flux reacted with impurities in the ore, mostly quartz sand, to produce slag. The slag floated above the molten iron. Periodically the molten iron and slag were drained off and more charcoal, ore, and flux were added to keep the furnace charged to the top.

The iron furnace at Allaire State Park is unusual in having a circular rather than square cross section. The furnace bank from which ore, charcoal, and flux were carried to the top of the furnace is to the right. —Photo by D. Harper

Cattus Island County Park

Cattus Island is an excellent place to see a wide variety of coastal and beach environments in a small area. A short hike from the nature center takes you across tidal marshes and onto an island with a maritime forest graced with numerous large holly trees. You can see a series of small washover beaches where the beach is moving landward across tidal marshes. The sand is picked up by waves on the beach face and washed over the beach crest and on top of the tidal marshes. Look for marsh plants partially buried behind the beach. A bit of previously overridden marsh is exposed with every wave that carries sand from the front of the beach across the beach ridge and onto the tidal marsh.

A longer hike on trails north of the nature center leads past a small forest of dead cedars at Mosquito Cove. According to some, the dead cedars in Mosquito Cove date from the completion of the Point Pleasant Canal in 1926. Prior to the completion of the canal, the water of the far northern end of Barnegat Bay had been fresh enough that Atlantic white cedars, intolerant of salt, could grow at the water's edge. Ice was commonly thick enough to allow wintertime skating and ice boating. After the completion of the canal, the influx of salty tidal water from the Manasquan River estuary killed the cedar groves and in most years keeps ice from freezing to a safe thickness.

The trail continues to a beach where erosion is obvious and surprisingly rapid given the relatively sheltered bay environment. Trees and large clumps of sod are visibly being undermined and falling into the water. From there trails continue on through woods and open areas to an unusually attractive cedar swamp boardwalk, then into a hardwood swamp, and finally through a second area of maritime forest that contrasts sharply with the maritime forest on the island. Here the forest lacks hollies and is barely distinguishable from inland Pinelands forests even to the point of needing a controlled burn every few years to remain healthy.

Island Beach State Park

Island Beach, almost 10 miles of barrier island, is the longest stretch of nearly natural beach remaining in New Jersey. We have the stock market crash of 1929 to thank for its preservation. The land was bought in 1926 by Henry C. Phipps, a partner in the steel businesses of Andrew Carnegie, with the intention of turning it into a resort for the wealthy. The land was cleared of livestock, fishermen's shacks, and seasonal visitors, but only three of the planned summer mansions had been completed when the stock market collapse brought an end to the work. Eventually the land was bought by the state of New Jersey for parkland. Most of the island is kept in a natural state.

The undisturbed dunes along almost the entire length of the park are the geologic highlight of Island Beach. They are best seen from beach access paths every few hundred feet along the southern natural area. Most of the paths to the beach start within a densely vegetated thicket before passing through the dunes. Though these dunes do not have the beautiful geometric shapes of desert dunes, they have their own wild beauty. Desert dunes are shaped by the interaction of wind and sand. Here plants are equally important. At least two

Dunes at Island Beach show areas stabilized by vegetation, blowouts where wind carried the sand away, and buried fencing and initial reveg-etation by dune grass where the sand came to rest. —Photo by D. Harper

prominent dune ridges can usually be made out, but instead of being continu-ous and graceful, they are ragged: dunes with a bad haircut. Blowout depres-sions resemble great scoops of sand taken out, and odd hillocks are preserved where vegetation somehow survived and kept the sand in place while the sand all around blew away. The deeper blowouts go completely through the wind-blown sand to shells buried decades ago. Debris in a blowout along access path 2 appears to be at least fifty years old.

Sand that the wind is constantly blowing away is deposited elsewhere. Depo-sitional sites are less obvious than the blowouts because plants usually grow upward as fast as the sand is deposited. Look for places where the rail fenc-ing along the access paths goes from waist high to completely buried within a few feet. In late winter and spring, there may be places where blowouts have exposed the yards-long, swooping crossbedding created by sand layers building onto the downwind sides of the dunes.

Walking along the access paths takes one through a series of dune field plant communities resembling an ecologic succession. Unlike the successions of inland fields, where grasses, shrubs, and trees develop in turn, the plant communities of the oceanfront dunes are semipermanent, kept in place by the increasingly inhospitable environment as one goes closer to the beachfront. The plant communities change position only when the dunes build seaward or erode landward. Dune growth begins with colonization of bare sand by beach grasses. Sometimes the grasses take root from plants carried seaward from erod-ing dunes and washed to the high tide line at a downdrift beach. Other times they spread from established dunes or sprout from seed. Increasingly they are planted, often by volunteer groups, where the conditions for dune growth are favorable. Dune grasses trap windblown sand and have evolved to grow upward as the sand accumulates, trapping more sand and building a primary dune.

The primary dune, directly behind the beach, is constantly under salt spray, desert dry except immediately after rainfall, windy, and subject to rapid erosion and deposition. Few plants other than beach grasses can grow here. Back from the primary dune, an increasing number of shrubs and low-growing trees take root in protected hollows. Still farther landward, plants cover the entire dune field and the thicket is pruned into a wedge shape by salt spray: low and mostly on the sheltered side of the dunes near the beach where the salt spray sweeps close above the land surface, and higher landward where dunes and vegetation block the salt spray. The low-growing, seaward part of the wedge includes the thicket just past the parking areas at most of the access paths. As the name implies, the thicket is a virtually impenetrable growth. There is enough fresh-water within the sand to support a wide variety of plants—dozens of species of trees, shrubs, and vines. There are even small freshwater wetlands along some paths. The salt spray keeps the tops of even one-hundred-year-old trees down to a few feet. Essentially the thicket is a forest with a ground level canopy. Before shoreline development, the thicket plant community was widespread up and down the Jersey Shore. The Wildwoods, for example, take their name from the tangle of growth. Before shoreline development, livestock was released into the thickets to fatten on the lush vegetation and drink from the freshwater ponds between the overgrown dunes. Inland from the thicket, the top of the salt-pruned wedge becomes high enough that the canopy rises off the land surface and the land beneath opens up to a resemble a more familiar kind of forest. This maritime forest, though, is still dominated by salt-tolerant species.

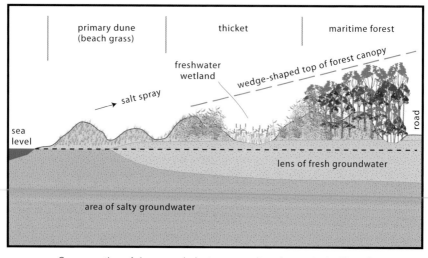

Cross section of dunes and plant communites along a typical beach access path. —Artwork by Mountain Press

At Island Beach, the thicket covers much of the barrier island, and the maritime forest is only sparingly developed. Sandy Hook and Cattus Island have extensive maritime forests, and Barnegat Lighthouse State Park has a small but beautiful pocket of forest. The Fifty-sixth Street beach access at Avalon has one of the clearest examples of the transitions from maritime forest to beachfront in New Jersey.

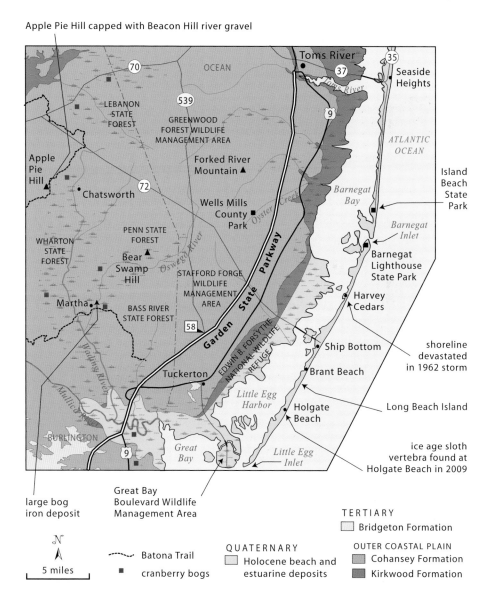

Apple Pie Hill capped with Beacon Hill river gravel

Geology along the Garden State Parkway between Toms River and Little Egg Inlet.
—Compiled from the USGS's Preliminary Integrated Geologic Map Database for the United States, 2006

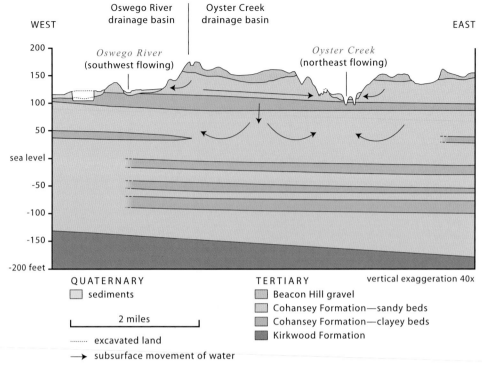

WEST

Oswego River
drainage basin

Oyster Creek
drainage basin

EAST

Oswego River
(southwest flowing)

Oyster Creek
(northeast flowing)

200
150
100
50
sea level
-50
-100
-150
-200 feet

QUATERNARY
☐ sediments

2 miles

······· excavated land

⟶ subsurface movement of water

TERTIARY   vertical exaggeration 40x
☐ Beacon Hill gravel
☐ Cohansey Formation—sandy beds
☐ Cohansey Formation—clayey beds
☐ Kirkwood Formation

*Subsurface water flows above clay layers in the Cohansey Formation
toward the Oyster Creek basin.* —Modified from Stanford, 2011

Wells Mills County Park

Hills at Wells Mills County Park are eroded at their base by springs discharging
where a clay layer intersects the surface. Slope retreat has created wide, rounded
amphitheater valleys back from Oyster Creek, and people venturing off the
trails may find soggy ground where the springs discharge. The springwater
comes from the Oswego River drainage basin. Unlike in the bedrock areas of
northern New Jersey, in the Coastal Plain water commonly flows underground
from one drainage basin to another. In one striking example, water seeping
downward in the Oswego River drainage basin reaches a clayey layer and flows
eastward across the clay into the Oyster Creek basin. The sandy clay is not thick
enough or impermeable enough to be a true confining layer but causes some
underground water to follow the shorter, steeper path to the ocean by way
of Oyster Creek. As a result of water loss to Oyster Creek and other streams,
annual outflow at the Oswego River is equivalent to only 14 inches of rainfall.
Outflow at Oyster Creek is equivalent to 48 inches of rainfall.

Apple Pie Hill and Erosion in the Coastal Plain

The hike from the Carranza Memorial to the Apple Pie Hill fire tower is
among the favorite Pinelands hikes and one of the few to have a 360-degree
view. Carranza Memorial honors a Mexican aviator who, shortly after Charles

Lindbergh's historic flight, crashed here flying back to Mexico to complete a historic goodwill flight. The 8-mile out-and-back hike, which follows a portion of New Jersey's 50-mile Batona Trail, passes through pine forests, skirts cedar swamps, and crosses a small hill before reaching Apple Pie Hill. The view from a fire tower at the top of the hill crosses the width of New Jersey from the Atlantic City casinos to the Philadelphia skyline.

Apple Pie Hill, the Forked River Mountains of Ocean County, Bear Swamp Hill in Penn State Forest, Beacon Hill in Monmouth County, and a few other small hills and ridges in the Pinelands are capped with remnants of the Beacon Hill river gravel, deposited between 15 and 10 million years ago when the Coastal Plain was newly emerged from beneath the ocean and little eroded. The gravel is part of the Cohansey Formation. To imagine how much sand has been carried away in the past 10 million years, stand atop the fire tower on the hill and imagine a plain slightly above the streambed gravel capping Apple Pie Hill stretching westward past the Delaware River and eastward past Atlantic City. The surface area of Apple Pie Hill is small enough that very little rainwater recharges the groundwater feeding springs at its base. The springs are only slowly sapping away the remaining upland, if at all.

Beacon Hill gravel at Apple Pie Hill. —Photo by D. Harper

An area of dwarf pines can be accessed from Penn State Forest's Bear Swamp Hill parking area. Sand roads (Stave Road and Lost Lane Road) north of the hill pass through isolated stretches of the pine plains where you can be alone in an almost surreal, disorienting setting once described as "desolate stretches of white sand barrens for the most part devoid of trees higher than one's knees." Although you may be alone, you may not have quiet. This is a practice area for military aircraft.

Meteorite Impact Evidence at Bass River State Forest

Yet another instance of a meteorite affecting New Jersey, in this case a much larger impact affecting the entire Earth, is at the Cretaceous-Paleocene boundary, a time horizon marking one of the five greatest mass extinctions in Earth history. Dinosaurs were the most famous group to die off, but this event also saw the end of the many plants, invertebrates, and species of ocean plankton. By the 1990s, the extinctions had been widely and confidently, if not universally, attributed to an immense meteorite impact. A 110-mile-diameter crater in the Yucatán Peninsula near Chicxulub, Mexico, was the likely point of impact. The timing of the extinctions is well dated at many places around the world, and a thin layer of meteorite debris is found at numerous places with many species below and fewer species above. At Chicxulub, however, the layers of rock older than the impact were exploded into blocks, mixed, turned upside down, and otherwise thoroughly disrupted—too severely disturbed to determine the time of impact. It is also difficult to correlate thin layers of meteorite ejecta from far away, which coincide with the extinctions, definitively to the Chicxulub impact. In order to demonstrate that the Chicxulub impact was simultaneous with the extinctions, deposits were needed close enough to show that the impact materials became thicker and coarser toward the impact, and were thus related, but also far enough away that seismic shock, debris fallout, mudflows, tsunamis, and other catastrophic effects had not disturbed fossils. The deposits also had to be in water deep enough that storms had not erased the impact layer and quiet enough that submarine currents had not carried it away.

glauconitic
clay with
early Cenozoic
fossils

ejecta from
Chicxulub
impact

glauconite
clay with
late Mesozoic
fossils

A well-drilling core from Bass River State Forest included a 2.5-inch-thick layer of ejecta from the Chicxulub meteorite impact at the end of Cretaceous time in Mexico's Yucután Peninsula. Bass River is about 1,700 miles from Chicxulub. The debris reached Bass River about 10 minutes after the impact, then settled through 300 feet of water to the seafloor.
—Photo by Richard K. Olsson

Investigation of the impact was a minor consideration in the drilling of a well to almost 2,000 feet in Bass River State Forest in 1997. The drilling was part of a worldwide effort to understand the history of climate change, sea level change, atmospheric composition, and other factors important to the investigation of human impacts on the Earth and its climate. The Bass River core is one of several collected onshore and offshore in New Jersey but stood out because at 1,260 feet below the surface there was an interval beginning, from the bottom up, with glauconitic clay with typical Cretaceous fossils, then a 2.5-inch-thick layer of debris from the meteorite impact, then, still further upward, a glauconitic clay with far fewer fossils and none of the species that became extinct at the end of Cretaceous time. After similar findings had been replicated at several other sites, the link between the Chicxulub impact and the extinctions became almost indisputable.

Sloth Fossil at Holgate Beach

The beach is not an intuitively obvious place to find fossils, certainly not an 8-inch-by-10-inch vertebra of an extinct giant ground sloth, *Megalonyx*, from the ice age. One such vertebra, though, was picked up by beachcombers in 2009 at Holgate Beach. A cell phone photo of the bone was sent to the New Jersey State Museum, where David Parris confirmed that it was a fossil, possibly 20,000 years old.

Atlantic City—A Drumstick Island

Atlantic City and Ocean City sit on drumstick barrier islands, fatter in the updrift direction (the direction from which sand is coming) like the meaty end of a turkey drumstick and thinner on the bone end downdrift (the direction in which sand is going). Net transport of sand in the Atlantic City region is to the south. Atlantic City is now on an artificially stabilized island. Absecon Inlet to the north and Great Egg Harbor Inlet to the south are held in place by jetties and dredging. The beach is held in place by seawalls and groins. The island on which Ocean City sits is in a somewhat more natural state.

Drumstick islands are typical of coastlines where inlets are relatively stable and enough sand is carried out with ebb tides to form an ebb-tide delta despite wave action. Some sand accumulates at the meaty end simply because waves are blocked by the delta. In addition, through wave refraction (the bending of waves around obstacles), the predominant southwestward-moving wave crests along this section of the shore are turned northwestward and carry sand northward, in the opposite direction of the predominant longshore drift of sand. The north ends of the islands built outward because sand was carried toward the inlet from both sides. The south ends of the islands, deprived of the southward-moving sand, became sediment starved and eroded to a narrow point.

Tidal Marshes near Atlantic City

The last 3 miles of the Atlantic City Expressway cross over tidal marshes that have built up over the last 6,000 or so years to where they now fill much of the back-barrier lagoon between the mainland and the barrier island on which Atlantic City is built. The sediment below the marsh grass is predominantly

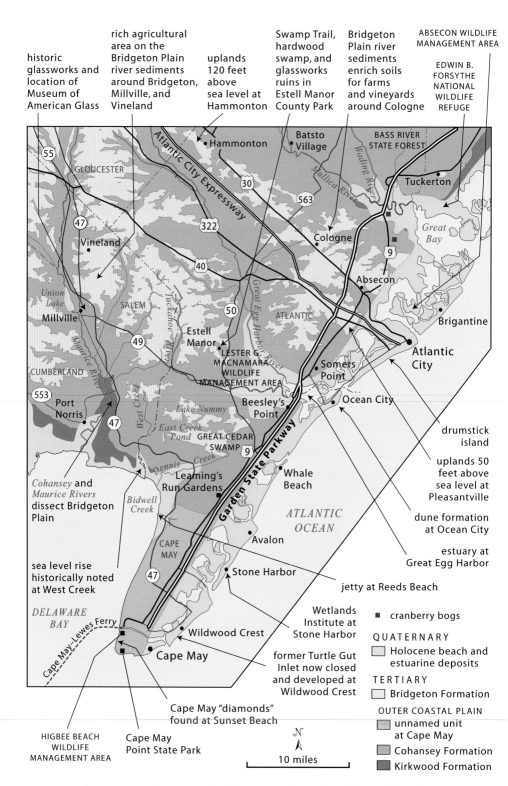

historic glassworks and location of Museum of American Glass

rich agricultural area on the Bridgeton Plain river sediments around Bridgeton, Millville, and Vineland

uplands 120 feet above sea level at Hammonton

Swamp Trail, hardwood swamp, and glassworks ruins in Estell Manor County Park

Bridgeton Plain river sediments enrich soils for farms and vineyards around Cologne

ABSECON WILDLIFE MANAGEMENT AREA

EDWIN B. FORSYTHE NATIONAL WILDLIFE REFUGE

55
GLOUCESTER
Hammonton
Batsto Village
BASS RIVER STATE FOREST
Tuckerton
47
30
563
Atlantic City Expressway
Mullica River
Wading River
322
Vineland
40
Cologne
Great Bay
9
Absecon
Union Lake
SALEM
50
ATLANTIC
Brigantine
Millville
Estell Manor
LESTER G. MACNAMARA WILDLIFE MANAGEMENT AREA
Somers Point
Atlantic City
CUMBERLAND
49
Great Egg Harbor River
553
Beesley's Point
Ocean City
Port Norris
47
Lake Nummy
East Creek Pond
GREAT CEDAR SWAMP
9
drumstick island
Cohansey and Maurice Rivers dissect Bridgeton Plain
Leaming's Run Gardens
Whale Beach
uplands 50 feet above sea level at Pleasantville
Bidwell Creek
ATLANTIC OCEAN
dune formation at Ocean City
sea level rise historically noted at West Creek
CAPE MAY
Avalon
estuary at Great Egg Harbor
DELAWARE BAY
47
Stone Harbor
jetty at Reeds Beach
Cape May-Lewes Ferry
Wildwood Crest
Cape May
Wetlands Institute at Stone Harbor
cranberry bogs
QUATERNARY
former Turtle Gut Inlet now closed and developed at Wildwood Crest
Holocene beach and estuarine deposits
TERTIARY
Bridgeton Formation
OUTER COASTAL PLAIN
unnamed unit at Cape May
HIGBEE BEACH WILDLIFE MANAGEMENT AREA
Cape May Point State Park
Cape May "diamonds" found at Sunset Beach
N
10 miles
Cohansey Formation
Kirkwood Formation

Geology along the Garden State Parkway between Great Bay and Cape May.
—Compiled from the USGS's Preliminary Integrated Geologic Map Database for the United States, 2006

sand, silt, and clay, not peat, and must have come either from rivers emptying to the tidal marshes or from offshore. Although it is normal to think of sediment originating on land and being washed offshore, the rivers along this section of New Jersey carry little sediment, and the likely source is offshore.

Two roads lead far into the marshlands of the Great Egg Harbor estuary: the auto nature trail through the Lester G. MacNamara Wildlife Management Area (formerly the Tuckahoe WMA) and Great Bay Boulevard (also known as Seven Bridges Road for seven increasingly rickety bridges it crosses outward onto the marsh). Great Bay Boulevard has the added attraction of passing by a precolonial shell midden near the inland edge of the marshes. The midden is low and inconspicuous, surrounded by marsh, and inaccessible from the road. It at first seems odd that the midden is slightly offshore, not on land where the Indians would presumably have feasted and piled the shells. It was, however,

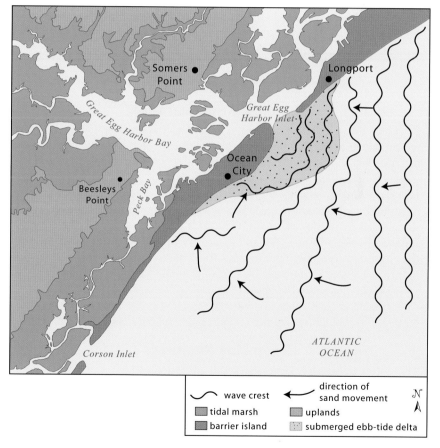

Wave refraction across ebb-tide deltas can contribute to the formation of drumstick islands by causing reversal of the direction of sand movement along the beach. This leads to buildup of the wide, meaty end of the drumstick (at Ocean City) and sediment starvation and erosion at the bone end (at Longport). The effect is exaggerated here for clarity. —Artwork by D. Harper

on land when the shells were piled up. With sea level rising at about 2.7 millimeters per year, even allowing for recent increases in sea level rise, the water is about 3 feet higher than it was when the Indian population was decimated by disease in the 1600s. The offshore location of this midden may have saved it from destruction. Middens were common along the coast in the 1800s and were mined for lime for soil improvement and the flux needed to smelt the bog iron ores of the Pinelands.

Ocean City Dunes

Dunes did not exist at Ocean City in 1990. Now there are, in places, four dune ridges between the beach and shorefront buildings. The oldest dunes, just landward of oceanfront buildings, were built by bulldozing sand into a ridge, putting up sand-trapping fences, and planting grasses. The remaining three dune ridges are not related to any deliberate dune building or dune protection. They formed because beach nourishment provided an ample supply of sand and because the beach was a nesting site for an endangered bird, the piping plover. The plovers nest during the tourist season, and the sea wrack, the debris washed up at high tide, cannot be raked up, as it is on most New Jersey beaches, because of the nearby bird roosts. Beach grasses in the wrack took root, and dune growth began when the grasses trapped windblown sand.

Leaming's Run Gardens

Leaming's Run Gardens, off exit 13 of the Parkway, is the largest annual garden in the United States and has been cited as one of the top twenty gardens in the East. It is also fun, with resident and migratory hummingbirds, migratory monarch butterflies, tobacco and cotton plants, and farm animals including rare and wonderful breeds of chickens. It is included here because it houses a magnificent Atlantic white cedar that somehow escaped the boatbuilders and shingle makers for over three hundred years. The tree is close to the Thomas Leaming house, built in 1706, and must have been loved more for its beauty than its monetary value. With its thick trunk and surprisingly small canopy of branches, the tree is more reminiscent of a small California sequoia than the younger, thinner, more branched-out cedars of today's Pinelands. Even in its solitary state, it gives some idea what the cedar swamps, such as Great Cedar Swamp near Woodbine, were like when 2,000-year-old trees were dominant.

Cape May Peninsula

The entire Cape May Peninsula south of Dennis Creek and Great Cedar Swamp has, since the incision of the Pensauken River in the Pliocene Epoch, been something of an irregular part of New Jersey: sometimes land, sometimes partly or mostly underwater, and at least once crossed midway down the peninsula by the Delaware River. Even now much of the peninsula is low-lying and swampy. After one particularly severe storm in the 1800s, it was reportedly possible to row from the Atlantic across the Great Cedar Swamp to Delaware Bay. The beach sands and river deposits of the Cohansey Formation and the river deposits of the Bridgeton Formation were probably deposited across Cape May but were eroded by the Pensauken River. What remains is an erosional surface at the top of Miocene offshore deposits and, above that, river, beach, and off-shore deposits alternately deposited when sea level rose and eroded when sea level fell.

Beaches older than those we enjoy today have been inferred both landward and seaward of today's shore. Seaward, linear sand ridges up to 70 miles offshore have been interpreted as beach ridges from the lowered sea levels of the ice age. Landward, the sharp inland edge of the back-barrier tidal marshes remains from a shoreline dating from the last interglacial period, about 125,000 years ago. This was before the sea level drop of the Wisconsinan glaciation. In some places the pre-Wisconsinan shoreline, a few feet higher than today's sea level was bordered by wave-cut banks up to 50 feet high. These are now obscured by slumping and slope wash during warmer times, soil flow during the permafrost of the ice age, and development.

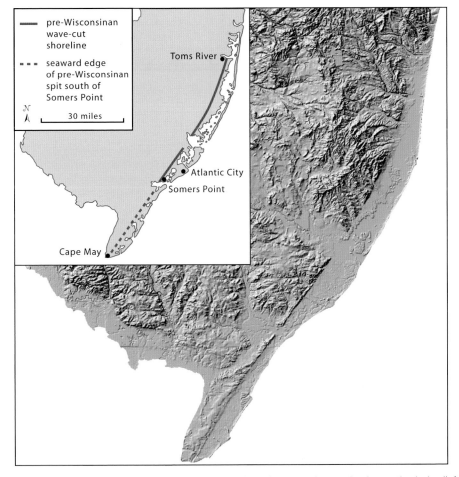

The wave-cut shoreline from before the Wisconsinan ice age shows clearly on shaded relief maps but is seldom noticed on the ground. The elevation rises from sea level to as much as 50 feet within a couple of blocks inland from the base of the ancient shoreline, but the slope is developed along much of its length and easily overlooked. —Landscape image from Ted Pallis, N.J. Geological Survey

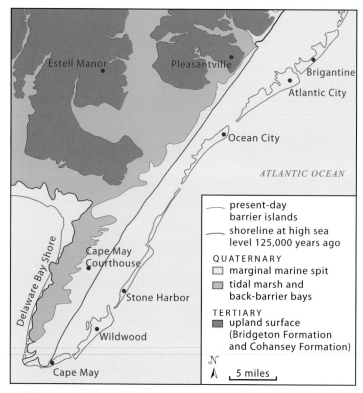

The spit at Cape May formed 125,000 years ago during the intergla-cial period when sea level was higher. —Modified from Newell and others, 2000

To the south of Somers Point, the land had been cut downward by the Delaware River before the pre-Wisconsinan shoreline formed along the inner edge of the marshes, and the ocean fronted on an estuary rather than the mainland. Instead of beaches being cut into the land, the waves built a spit, similar to Sandy Hook at the northern tip of the Jersey Shore, but southward rather than northward. The spit built at least 30 miles to where it is cut off at the eroding tip of the Cape May Peninsula. US 9 follows the crest of the spit, and at many places there is a visible slope from US 9 eastward toward what was open water and westward toward what was tidal marsh.

Shoreline Changes at Wildwood Crest

Residents of the Jersey Shore and taxpayers asked to pay for shoreline protection measures, cleanups after disastrous storms, and beach replenishments, have become accustomed to thinking of the shoreline as constantly eroding. Many sections would erode under natural conditions, but other sections would build seaward. At Wildwood Crest, the shoreline has moved slightly seaward between 1920 and 2002. Turtle Gut Inlet closed in 1922 due to a combination of human and natural causes. Between 1920 and 2002 the barrier island has grown about three blocks seaward.

1920 shoreline

Former Turtle Gut Inlet

Satellite image of Wildwood Crest in 2002. Turtle Gut has closed and the shoreline has been built several blocks seaward and southward since 1920. —Photo from N.J. Office of Geographic Information Systems

Cape May Salt Water Intrusion

Salt water moving into aquifers has been a problem in a number of places along the Jersey Shore and along Raritan Bay, but nowhere has the problem been as severe as in southern Cape May County. Prior to about 1890, water level in each of five southern Cape May aquifers was above sea level, and water flowed from the aquifers toward streams, wetlands, Delaware Bay, and the Atlantic Ocean. Soon after the first deep wells were sunk, however, water levels began to drop, flow reversed from upward to downward, and salinity began to increase in wells near the bay and ocean. Between 1940 and the early 1960s, at least 120 wells had to be abandoned because of saltiness. The experience of the City of Cape May may be extreme, but other places are not far behind. The city installed its first two wells, wells 1 and 2 within 3,400 feet of the ocean in 1940 and 1945. By 1950, well 1 had to be abandoned because of increased saltiness. Well 3 was installed farther inland. Salinity in wells 2 and 3 increased until well 2 had to be abandoned. Wells 4 and 5 were installed still farther inland in 1965. Well 3 continued to be used, but only when peak summertime demand exceeded the capacities of wells 4 and 5. When well 3 was used, the water had to be blended with fresher water. With no place for wells farther inland and salinity continuing to increase, the city began aquifer storage and recovery at well 4. Excess water is purchased from a water company farther inland during the winter, pumped down well 4, and then pumped back out to meet summertime demand.

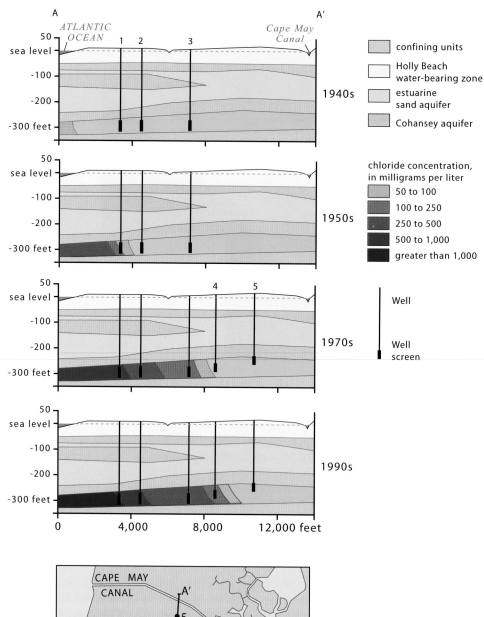

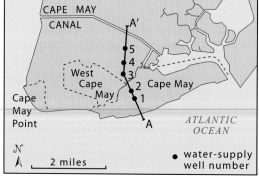

Pumping of water from the Cohansey aquifer caused salty water to move inland and into Cape May's water supply wells. —Modified from Lacombe and Carleton, 2002

To slow the growth in demand, Cape May raised water rates to double that of inland communities, required low-flow toilets and showerheads in tourist facilities, and began monitoring water use by farms, golf courses, and landscapers. Still, greater needs were projected. Cape May chose to go with a desalination plant, which uses reverse osmosis to remove some salt from the water. In an approach usually associated with desert areas, two new wells, 6 and 7, were drilled into a deep aquifer known to be somewhat salty. The water is sent to the desalination plant. The further desalinated water is then blended with fresher water to obtain a drinkable mix. The Cape May plant was one of the first municipal desalination plants in the United States when it came on line in 1998. It has by all accounts succeeded in reducing the stress on southern Cape May's aquifers but has by no account succeeded in addressing the long-term water needs of the area.

Sunset Beach and Cape May "Diamonds"

The clear quartz pebbles known as Cape May diamonds have been collected, according to legend, since at least 1790 when a handful were brought to a Philadelphia gem dealer. Clear quartz pebbles can be picked up along the entire Jersey Shore, but clear, fracture-free pebbles may be most abundant at Cape May because that is where the sediment is most mature. Some pebbles arriving at Cape May have been washed the entire length of the shore, being rolled in gravel by the waves, resuspended and redeposited thousands or millions of times, carried offshore, returned shoreward, dropped to the gravelly washes at the bottoms of tidal inlets, carried back onto the beaches for more pounding in the surf, and otherwise maltreated until only the hardest, most fracture-resistant pebbles survived. Some of these qualify as Cape May diamonds. Most of the Cape May beach pebbles are not so perfect. Many probably took a shorter route, carried by the rivers that cut across the Coastal Plain after the Miocene drop in sea level.

Clear quartz pebbles known as Cape May diamonds.
—Photo by John Dooley, N.J. Geological Survey

Anyone who has walked on Island Beach, 10 miles of sand with scarcely a pebble, will question that any pebbles traveled the entire length of the Jersey Shore, but remember that the beaches are constantly changing and geologic processes work over long time spans. Before the Wisconsinan glaciation, the beaches north of Cape May were not on a barrier island. They were directly against the mainland and littered with millions of pebbles. Whether the stones matured during a long journey down the coast or are less mature after a journey down the rivers that crossed the Coastal Plain in the geologic past, Sunset Beach is a favored place for collecting the gems or visiting shops selling the polished "diamonds." Tidal currents are funneled between the shoreline and a sunken World War I–era concrete ship. The current carries away the sand and leaves the diamonds behind.

Eroding Delaware Bay Beaches

Walking north from Sunset Beach across Bond Creek brings you to Higbee Beach, a good place for relaxing, birding, and watching the comings and goings of the Cape May–Lewes Ferry. It is also one of many eroding shorelines along the Delaware Bay shore. At Higbee Beach, the erosion is obvious because of the scarp at the base of the dunes. Along most of the Delaware Bay shore, however, the beaches are only a few tens of feet wide and directly in front of tidal marshes. There is no erosional scarp to signal beach erosion, but the erosion can usually be inferred from marsh peat cropping out on the bay side. Property owners along the beaches from as long ago as the mid-1800s needed no

Reeds Beach on the Delaware Bay. By accumulating sand, the jetty at the center protects Bidwell Creek and houses along Reeds Beach (south of the jetty). It also prevents sand from nourishing beaches across the mouth of the creek. —Aerial photo from New Jersey Geographic Information Warehouse

geologic features to know that their land was disappearing, in some places at 12 feet per year. At some other places, landmarks provide the clearest evidence of beach erosion. A concrete artillery bunker built 900 feet from the beach in 1942 is now in the surf zone at Cape May Point State Park.

The beaches in front of tidal marshes are moving landward by washover. Many Delaware Bay beaches are only a few yards wide and a couple of feet above high tide. Heavy weather easily overtops these beaches, washing sand from the shore face onto the marsh behind. Only a small volume of sand may be moved, but there is only a small volume of sand on the beach. When the sand is washed from the front of the beach back onto the marsh behind, marsh covered over only a few years earlier is exposed as a bench of silt and peat along the beach.

Offshore from many bay beaches, you can walk hundreds of feet into Delaware Bay before reaching deep water. This is the platform left by wave action as it planes off the marsh sediment and sand down to the wave base, the depth below which waves can no longer move sediment across the bottom. The wave base is not fixed but is shallower in calm weather and deeper during storms. In summertime, you may step into soft mud before you reach deep water. The mud is not marsh sediment uncovered by erosion. It is simply mud that settled below the summertime wave base. Come back in winter when the wave base is deeper, and the mud will be gone.

Delaware Estuary

The Delaware estuary contrasts sharply with the Hudson estuary in its geologic surroundings and water circulation. The Hudson estuary is rock-bound on both sides and 40 to 60 feet deep between New Jersey and Manhattan Island. The Delaware estuary is wide, bordered by sand, and in many places less than 20 feet deep. Because it is narrow and deep, tidal flow in the Hudson estuary is stratified. Under flood tide, relatively heavy salt water flows upstream along the river bottom as a salt wedge. Under ebb tide, relatively light freshwater flows downstream, across the top of the saltier, heavier water. In contrast, water mixes in the shallow Delaware estuary. Instead of a being a well-developed salt wedge estuary, Delaware Bay is only moderately stratified, and less stratified when the water is mixed under the influence of heavy weather or the turbulence associated with unusually high tides. Also unlike the Hudson estuary, surface water flow in the Delaware estuary is substantially influenced by the Coriolis effect, which is related to the spinning of the Earth. The Coriolis effect causes moving objects to be deflected to the right in the northern hemisphere and to the left in the southern hemisphere. Tidewaters entering Delaware Bay are deflected to the right and along the Cape May shoreline. Ebb flow from the bay is also deflected to the right, but along the Delaware shore.

GLOSSARY

alluvial fan. A relatively flat to gently dipping, fan-shaped wedge of unconsolidated sediments deposited by a stream, especially in semiarid regions, where it flows out of a narrow valley onto a wider, flatter area.

amphibolite. A dark-colored metamorphic rock consisting mainly of the minerals amphibole and plagioclase.

anticline. In layered rocks, a fold that is upward arching, with the oldest rocks exposed in the center.

aquifer. A body of saturated rock or sediment through which water can move readily.

back-arc basin. An ocean basin on the opposite side of a volcanic island arc from the oceanic trench of a subduction zone.

back-barrier lagoon. Shallow, tidal, brackish water lying between a barrier island and the mainland.

barrier island. A long, narrow, low-elevation, sandy coastal ridge lying parallel to the shore but separated from it by a lagoon, marshes, or back bays.

basalt. A black or very dark gray volcanic rock that consists mainly of microscopic crystals of the minerals plagioclase feldspar, pyroxene, and perhaps olivine.

beach nourishment. The process of artificially adding sand to a beach.

bedding. Layering in sedimentary rocks.

bedrock. Solid rock that is exposed in places or that underlies unconsolidated sediments and soil.

biotite. Dark mica, a platy mineral. It is a minor but common mineral in igneous and metamorphic rocks.

bituminous coal. Soft coal with a large content of volatiles, often banded with layers of plant material.

bog. A freshwater wetland in a cold region. Many (but not all) in New Jersey were formed over 10,000 years ago when the glaciers retreated.

bog iron. An iron oxide that precipitates from springwater, forming deposits in wet areas.

boulder. A rounded stone larger than 10 inches in diameter.

boulder field. A flat or gently sloping area covered with large angular blocks of rock derived from bedrock by glacial or periglacial freeze-and-thaw wedging.

brackish water. Water that is slightly salty (less than seawater), such as the waters of Chesapeake and Delaware Bays, where freshwater from rivers mixes with salt water brought in by tidal currents.

breakwater. An offshore man-made structure that absorbs the energy of waves and allows for quiet water (and sometimes unwanted deposition) nearshore.

breccia. A sedimentary rock composed of angular fragments in a fine-grained matrix, the fragments having not moved far from their source area.

brittle deformation. When rocks are broken, or fractured, by stresses within the Earth.

brownstone. A dark, reddish brown quartz sandstone that is quarried for building stone.

calcareous. Rock consisting of more than 50 percent calcium carbonate.

calcite. Calcium carbonate, the most common nonsilicate mineral. Limestone and marble are made of calcite.

calcium carbonate. A crystalline compound found in limestone and the shells of some marine animals.

carbonate bank. An accumulation of calcium and magnesium carbonate in a shallow ocean. Similar to a modern reef but lacking skeletal remains of organisms such as corals.

carbonate rock. A sedimentary rock composed of carbonate minerals, such as calcite and dolomite.

cement. Solid material that precipitates from solution in the pore spaces of underwater sediments and binds together the grains into solid rock.

chalcocite. A copper sulfide mineral, a major source of copper.

channel. The deeper part of a stream or river, often used for navigation.

chattermarks. A series of small cracks made by rocks imbedded in glacial ice as they chip the bedrock surface.

clast. A grain or fragment of a rock produced by disintegration of a larger rock mass. Clastic rock is sedimentary rock composed of broken fragments derived from preexisting rocks.

clay. A sedimentary material composed of weathered minerals with grain sizes less than $\frac{1}{256}$ millimeter in diameter.

cleavage. A planar fabric in an unmetamorphosed, or weakly metamorphosed, fine-grained rock.

coal. A sedimentary rock formed from the compaction of incompletely decayed plant material. Occurs in layers or seams.

coarse-grained. A relative term used to describe the size of constituents in a rock. Said of igneous rocks with minerals larger than 0.2 inch in diameter. Said of sedimentary rocks with particles larger than 0.08 inch in diameter.

coastal plain. A low, gently sloping region on the margin of an ocean.

cobble. A rounded particle 2.5 to 10 inches in diameter.

conglomerate. A coarse-grained sedimentary rock composed of pebbles, cobbles, or boulders set in a fine-grained matrix of silt or sand.

continent. A large landmass that is, or was, comparable in size to a modern continent. Laurentia, a Precambrian continent, evolved into the larger North American continent.

continental glacier. An ice sheet of regional or continental size, common during ice ages.

continental margin arc. A line of volcanoes on a continent above a subduction zone where ocean crust is subducting below a continent. The Andes of South America are a continental margin arc.

continental shelf. The gently dipping part of the continental landmass between the shoreline and the more steeply dipping continental slope.

continental slope. The most steeply sloped part of the continental margin, between the shelf and the rise.

correlation. Determining historical time equivalency of physically separated rock units.

country rock. Any rock that was older than and intruded by a molten igneous body.

creep. Slow downslope movement of surface soil due to freeze and thaw of moist soil.

crossbed/crossbedding. A sedimentary bed, usually in sand or silt, that is at an angle to the main bedding.

crust. The upper surface of the lithosphere. Continental crust consists mainly of granite, gneiss, and schist; oceanic crust consists of basalt.

delta. A nearly flat accumulation of clay, sand, and gravel deposited in a lake or ocean at the mouth of a river.

diabase. An igneous rock with the composition of basalt but which cooled far enough beneath the surface to have visible crystals.

differential erosion. Weathering that occurs at different rates due primarily to the chemical composition of the rock. Limestone, for example, weathers much more quickly than sandstone.

dike. A tabular structure of igneous rock that formed when molten magma filled a fracture in a solid rock. A dike is not parallel to the layering in the country rock.

dip. The sloping angle of a planar surface in rocks, such as a sedimentary bed or fault surface.

dissection (of the land). The weathering and erosion of a level or continuous surface into stream valleys and gullies.

dolomite. A calcium magnesium carbonate mineral formed by alteration of calcium carbonate (limestone) by magnesium-rich solutions.

downdrift. The direction in which sand is carried along a beach by longshore drift.

drainage basin. The land area drained by a stream and all of its tributaries.

drainage divide. A line of high elevations that outlines a drainage basin and demarcates the runoff flow into that basin from the flow into neighboring basins.

drumlins. A streamlined deposit of glacial till elongated in the direction of ice movement.

dune. A mound or ridge of windblown sand.

ebb tide. The tide as it falls or lowers to low tide.

erosion. Movement or transport of weathered material. Agents include water, ice, wind, and gravity.

erratic. A block of rock transported by glacial ice and deposited at some distance from the bedrock outcrop it came from.

escarpment/scarp. A steep face that terminates relatively high lands along an edge. On Delmarva the escarpments mark wave-cut banks that were bluffs of ancient, high-standing seas.

esker. A long narrow, commonly sinuous ridge deposited by a stream flowing in a tunnel beneath an ice sheet.

estuary. Lower courses of rivers that have been backflooded into bays by sea levels that rose after the ending of the last ice age. Chesapeake Bay is the largest estuary in the United States.

fall line. A line connecting locations on rivers where navigators encountered the first major rapids—the boundary of hard bedrock and unconsolidated Coastal Plain deposits.

fault. A fracture or zone of fractures in the Earth's crust along which blocks of rock on either side have shifted. A **normal fault** forms under extensional forces, and one side drops relative to the other side. A **reverse fault** forms under compressional forces, and one side is pushed up and over the other side. In a **strike-slip fault**, rock on one side moves sideways relative to rock on the other side.

feldspar. The most abundant rock-forming mineral group, making up 60 percent of the Earth's crust and including calcium, sodium, or potassium with aluminum silicate. Includes plagioclase feldspars (albite and anorthite) and alkali feldspars (orthoclase and microcline).

fine-grained. A relative term used to describe the size of constituents in a rock. Said of igneous rocks with minerals too small to see with the unaided eye. Said of sedimentary rocks with silt-size or smaller particles.

flood basalt. A vast accumulation of horizontal basalt flows that formed when large volumes of lava flooded across the landscape.

floodplain. The portion of a river valley adjacent to the river that is built of sediments deposited when the river overflows its banks during flooding.

flux. A compound that helps fuse or separate metals; in an iron furnace, limestone (calcium carbonate) combines with impurities in ore to allow elemental iron to separate.

fold. A bend in a rock layer. Though hard and brittle today, the rock was once buried, under great pressure and at high temperatures, which made it plastic or bendable under tectonic forces of compression.

formation. A body of sedimentary, igneous, or metamorphic rock that can be recognized over a large area. It is the basic stratigraphic unit in geologic mapping. A formation may be part of a larger group and may be broken into members.

fossils. Traces or impressions of plants or animals preserved in rock. Any remains of once-living matter or its imprint preserved in rock.

gabbro. A dark igneous rock consisting mainly of the minerals plagioclase and pyroxene in crystals large enough to see with a simple magnifier. Gabbro has the same composition as basalt but contains much larger mineral grains.

glacial outwash. Sediment deposited by large quantities of meltwater emerging from the terminus of a glacier.

glacial rebound. The rise, or uplift, of the land on the plastic mantle after glacial melting. A kind of buoyancy to achieve equilibrium, similar to how a boat rises in water when unloaded.

glacier. A large and long-lasting mass of ice on land, originating from the compacting of snow.

glauconite. A greenish clay mineral.

global warming. Climatic changes during Earth history that have occurred in cycles of various lengths—from tens of thousands to hundreds of years—during which average global temperature warms or cools by a few degrees or tenths of degrees Celsius. Today's trend is global warming, perhaps a natural cycle accelerated by human-generated greenhouse gases.

gneiss. A coarse-grained metamorphic rock with a streaky foliation due to parallel alignment of minerals, usually in bands of light- and dark-colored minerals.

gorge. A steep-sided bedrock valley with a narrow bottom containing a stream or river.

gradient. Similar to slope, the degree of inclination, or the rate of ascent or descent, as in stream gradient, measured in number of vertical feet of drop per mile of travel.

granite. An igneous rock composed mostly of the minerals orthoclase feldspar and quartz in grains large enough to see without using a magnifier. Most granites also contain mica or amphibole. **Granite gneiss** is metamorphosed granite.

gravel. Rounded rock particles larger than 0.5 inch in diameter.

graywacke. A dark-colored sandstone with angular quartz and feldspar grains in a matrix of clay.

greensand. Bluish green sand deposit originating in a shallow-shelf, marine environment and containing the mineral glauconite, often formed as pellets.

groin. A structure or wall of boulders built out into the water (most notably, the ocean) at right angles to the shoreline to catch drifting sand and control beach erosion.

groundwater. Subsurface water occupying the saturated zone, contained in fractures and pores of rock and soil.

half graben. In normal block faulting, a downdropped block of crust that has tilted and slid downward on only one side along a vertical to nearly vertical fault.

headland. Any projection of the land into the sea, such as Cape Henlopen, Delaware.

headward erosion. The elongation of a stream valley by erosion into the uplands.

hematite. An iron oxide; the principal ore of iron.

hummocky. Said of a landscape with lots of small hills and depressions.

Iapetus Ocean. The ocean that existed in the general position of the Atlantic Ocean before the assembly of the continental masses that made up the Pangean supercontinent in Paleozoic time.

ice ages (Pleistocene). A span of geologic time, the last 3 to 1 million years, during which periods of extensive continental glaciation alternated with warmer interglacial periods of glacial retreat.

igneous rock. Rock that solidified from the cooling of molten magma.

impermeable. Having a texture that does not permit water to move through. Clay is often considered a relatively impermeable sediment.

Inner Coastal Plain. The northwestern band of the Coastal Plain characterized by sandy and clayey formations of Cretaceous to Miocene age.

interbedding. Alternately layered as interbedded sandstone and shale.

interglacial period. A period of global warming between ice ages when glaciers retreat and sea level rises. Some scientists believe that we might now be in an interglacial period.

intrusive igneous rocks. Rocks that cool from magma beneath the surface of the Earth. The body of rock is called an **intrusion**.

ironstone. A sedimentary rock cemented together with iron oxides.

island arc. An offshore volcanic arc, or linear chain of volcanoes.

jetty. A structure or rock wall built above water level to protect a harbor entrance or a barrier island inlet from sediment deposition and storm waves.

joint. A planar fracture or crack in a rock along which there has been no movement (no faulting).

karst. A rolling, pitted topography characterized by caverns, sinkholes, springs, and disappearing streams, caused by solution weathering of limestone bedrock.

kettles. A bowl-shaped depression or hole in glacial sediment formed by the melting of a buried block of ice.

klippe. An erosional remnant of a sheet of rock thrust into place during mountain building.

knob and kettle topography. An undulating, irregular landscape of mounds and depressions of glacial sediment.

lagoon. A semi-enclosed, quiet body of water between a barrier island and the mainland.

land subsidence. Lowering of the elevation of the land surface due to excessive groundwater withdrawal or to long-term accumulation of sediments.

Laurentia. The continental nucleus that eventually became North America.

lava. Molten rock erupted on the surface of the Earth.

limestone. A sedimentary rock composed of calcium carbonate.

lithification. Compaction and cementation of sediment into sedimentary rock.

longshore drift. Drift of sand in the ocean breaker zone generated by the angular approach toward shore of wind-generated waves.

magma. Molten rock within the earth.

magnetite. A strongly magnetic iron mineral mined for iron ore.

mantle. The part of the Earth between the interior core and the outer crust.

marble. Metamorphosed limestone.

marine. Pertaining to the sea.

marl. A calcareous clay.

marsh. A type of wetland that is frequently or continuously underwater; usually the water is shallow and the vegetation is grasses and reeds. Marshes may be freshwater, saltwater, or brackish.

meanders. Sinuous bends or loops in the course of a stream.

metamorphic rock. Rock derived from preexisting rock that has changed mineralogically, texturally, or both in response to changes in temperature and/or pressure, usually deep within the Earth.

metamorphism. Recrystallization of an existing rock. Metamorphism typically occurs at high temperatures and often high pressures.

metasedimentary rock. The initial classification given in the field to a metamorphosed sedimentary rock.

metavolcanic. A metamorphosed volcanic rock.

mica. A family of silicate minerals, including biotite and muscovite, that crystallize into thin flakes. Micas are common in many kinds of igneous and metamorphic rock.

moraine. A landform made of glacial till. It typically is deposited at the edge of the ice where material in the ice is released as the ice melts.

mountain building event. An event in which rocks are folded, thrust faulted, metamorphosed, and/or uplifted. Intrusive and extrusive igneous activity often accompanies it.

mouth. The outflow at the lowest end of a stream or river where it discharges into a larger body of water, such as a larger river, a bay, or the ocean.

mudstone. A sedimentary rock composed of mud.

normal fault. A fault in which rocks on one side move down relative to rocks on the other side in response to extensional forces.

olivine. An iron and magnesium silicate mineral that typically forms glassy green crystals. A common mineral in gabbro, basalt, and peridotite.

oolites. Small round accretionary bodies (about 1 millimeter in diameter) formed of concentric layers around a nucleus.

orogeny. A major episode of convergent mountain building processes, including folding, faulting, metamorphism, volcanism, and igneous intrusion.

orthoclase. A potassium-rich alkali feldspar and a common rock-forming mineral. It forms at higher temperatures than microcline.

outcrop. A section of rock that is exposed on the land surface.

Outer Coastal Plain. The part of the Coastal Plain veneered by sandy Tertiary deposits of the Pinelands.

outwash. Sand and gravel deposited by meltwater from a receding glacier. A large amount of outwash deposited over a large area is called an **outwash plain.**

overwash. The flooding over of a barrier island by ocean storm waves, often accelerating the landward migration of the sandy barrier island.

oxidation. In chemistry, a reaction in which the loss of electrons occurs, as when an elemental metal has combined with atmospheric oxygen to form an oxide; many metal ores, such as hematite, are oxides.

Pangea. A supercontinent that assembled through plate convergences about 300 million years ago. It broke into the modern continents through divergences beginning about 200 million years ago.

passive continental margin. A situation, such as the east coast of North America, in which the edge of a continent is not also the edge of a tectonic plate.

peat. An unconsolidated deposit of semicoalified plant remains in a bog.

pebble. A rounded rock particle 0.5 to 2.5 inches in diameter.

pegmatite. An igneous rock, generally granitic, composed of extremely large crystals.

peneplain. A landscape eroded to a level surface.

permafrost. Ground that remains permanently frozen for many years.

Pinelands. A region in southern New Jersey with very sandy nutrient-poor soil that supports a unique ecosystem dominated by pitch pines.

plagioclase. A feldspar mineral rich in sodium and calcium. One of the most common rock-forming minerals in igneous and metamorphic rocks.

plate tectonics. A theory that the Earth's surface is comprised of large crustal plates that move slowly and change in size, with intense geological activity at plate boundaries.

pothole. A cylindrical depression in rock eroded by the swirling, abrasive action of sand and gravel within a rapidly flowing stream.

precipitation (mineral). The precipitation of minerals from solution is the change of a compound from a dissolved state into solid form.

province. An area or region with a common geologic history, underlying structure, or composition.

pyrite. An iron sulfide with a cube-shaped crystal.

pyroxene. An iron/magnesium-bearing silicate mineral, abundant in basaltic rock.

quartz. A mineral form of silica. Quartz is one of the most abundant and widely distributed minerals in rocks. It comes in a wide variety of forms, including clear crystals, sand grains, and chert.

quartzite. A metamorphic rock composed of mainly quartz and formed by the metamorphism of sandstone.

radioactive. Containing an unstable element that breaks down to stable daughter elements.

radiometric dating. The calculation of age based on the rate of time it takes for radioactive elements to decay.

red bed. Sandstone, siltstone, or shale that is predominantly red due to hematite, an iron oxide.

rift. A long, narrow rupture in the earth's crust. A **rift basin** or **rift valley** is the trough formed by the rift.

ripple marks. Wavelike ridges formed on sediment surfaces produced by wind or water waves or currents.

roche moutonnée. A small knob of bedrock shaped by glacial ice and elongated in the direction of ice movement.

Rodinia. A supercontinent that formed 1 billion years ago.

runoff. Rainwater or meltwater running off the land surface and into streams, as opposed to that which soaks into pores of soil and rock.

salinity. A measure of the percentage of dissolved salts in a body of water. In Chesapeake Bay, for example, salinity varies with the amount of discharge of freshwater rivers into the bay.

salt marsh. A wetland in a cove or bay area that is protected from the surf. Made saline by the tides, the marsh supports herbaceous plants without woody stems. Also called a **tidal marsh**.

sand. Weathered mineral grains, most commonly quartz, between $\frac{1}{16}$ millimeter and 2 millimeters in diameter.

sandbar. A ridge of sand built up to or near the water surface by river currents or coastal wave action.

sandstone. A sedimentary rock made primarily of sand.

schist. A metamorphic rock that is strongly foliated due to an abundance of platy minerals.

sedimentary rock. A rock formed from the compaction and cementation of loose sediment.

sedimentation/siltation. The filling of a navigable river channel or harbor with large quantities of waterborne sediment, especially from muds running off from cleared or cultivated land. Many colonial shipping lanes and harbors were made too shallow by heavy erosion and deposition.

serpentine. A group of minerals derived from alteration of magnesium-rich silicate minerals and producing poor soils. **Serpentinite** is a rock made of serpentine.

shale. A deposit of clay, silt, or mud solidified into more or less solid rock.

shearing. The action and deformation caused by two bodies of rock sliding past each other.

silica. The compound **silicon dioxide**. The most common silica-containing mineral is quartz.

silicate. A large group of minerals whose main building block is one silicon atom surrounded by four oxygen atoms.

sill. An igneous intrusion that parallels the planar structure or bedding of the country rock.

silt. Weathered particles larger than clay but smaller than sand (between $\frac{1}{256}$ and $\frac{1}{16}$ millimeter in diameter).

siltstone. A sedimentary rock made primarily of silt.

sinkhole. A funnel-shaped depression in the land surface, generally in a limestone area, resulting from collapse over a solution cavern.

slag. Glassy material separated during the reduction of a metal from its ore, as in the early iron furnaces.

slate. Slightly metamorphosed shale or mudstone that breaks easily along parallel surfaces.

spillway. The overflow channel from a body of water, such as a glacial lake.

spit. A long, narrow, fingerlike ridge of sand extending into the water from the shore.

spring. A place where groundwater flows out of rock onto the land surface.

strata. Layers of sedimentary rock. A single layer is a stratum. Layered rock is called **stratified**.

striations. Linear scratches on rocks left by a rock embedded in moving glacial ice.

strip mining. Removal of vegetation and overburden of soil and rock to reach a vein of ore or coal.

stromatolite. A mound-shaped sedimentary structure formed by the trapping and binding of sediment by the growth and activity of blue-green algae.

subduction zone. A long, narrow zone where an oceanic plate descends into the mantle below a continental plate at a collision boundary.

supercontinent. A clustering of all of the Earth's continental masses into one major landmass; this has occurred at least three times in geologic history.

suspended sediment. Sediment in a stream that remains lifted or transported due to the turbulence and energy of the water. When the current slows, suspended sediment falls to the bottom.

swamp. A wetland in which the dominant vegetation is woody plants. The bottom layer, usually saturated during the growing season, is typically peat.

syncline. In layered rocks, a downfolded trough with the youngest rocks exposed in the center.

tailings. Residue left from a mining operation.

talus. An accumulation of rock fragments derived from and resting at the base of a cliff.

tectonics. A branch of geology dealing with the structure and forces within the outer parts of the Earth, including continental plate movements.

terrace. An erosional remnant of a former river valley, standing above the present river.

thrust fault. A low-angle reverse fault.

thrust sheet. A body of rock above a thrust fault.

tidal inlet. A narrow channel in a barrier island through which tidal currents flow.

tidal marsh. A saltwater wetland in a cove or bay protected from ocean surf. Vegetation is herbaceous plants without woody stems.

tidal range. The difference between high tide and low tide at a given point.

tide. The periodic rise and fall of ocean level resulting from the gravitational pull of the Moon as it revolves around the Earth.

till. Unsorted and unstratified sediment deposited directly from glacial ice. Can contain rock fragments of all sizes.

traprock. A dark, fine-grained rock, such as basalt, that is used for crushed rock.

trench, oceanic. A narrow, elongate depression that develops where the ocean floor begins its descent into a subduction zone at a convergent plate boundary.

tributary. A relatively small stream flowing into a larger one, adding water to it.

unconformity. A break or gap in the geologic record where one rock unit is overlain by another that is not next in the stratigraphic succession.

unconsolidated. Referring to sediment grains that are loose, separate, or uncemented to one another.

updrift. The direction opposite that of the predominant direction sand is carried along a beach.

uplift. Rise in elevation of a land area due to tectonic convergence or to isostatic rebound.

varves. Alternating layers of fine-grained sediment deposited annually in a glacial water body. The lighter, silt-size particles represent the summer layer, and the darker, clay-size particles represent the winter layer.

vein. A deposit of minerals that fills a fracture in rock.

volcanic arc. A chain of island volcanoes that formed above an ocean-floor subduction zone.

water gap. A pass in a mountain ridge through which a stream or river flows.

weathering. The physical disintegration and chemical decomposition of rock at the Earth's surface.

wetland. An area in which most soil is saturated with water long enough during the growing season that there is no longer sufficient oxygen for land-based plants. Water may come from rain, runoff, groundwater, floods, or coastal waters. Types include marsh, swamp, and bog.

wind gap. A pass in a mountain ridge through which a stream or river flowed during a previous geologic time.

REFERENCES

Bennington, J. B., and C. Merguerian. 2007. Geology of New York and New Jersey. In *Geology of the New York Tri-State Area*. Hempstead, NY: Hofstra University and Thomson Brooks/Cole Corporation.

Benson, R. N. 1979. *Hydrocarbon Resource Potential of the Baltimore Canyon Trough*. Delaware Geological Survey Report of Investigations no. 31.

Berkey, C. P. 1933. Engineering geology of the City of New York: Sixteenth International Geological Congress, United States, Guidebook 9, New York City and vicinity, p. 77–122.

Bouma, A. H. 1962. *Sedimentology of Some Flysch Deposits: A Graphic Approach to Facies Interpretation*. Amsterdam: Elsevier.

Cleaveland, P. 1816. Elementary treatise on geology and mineralogy, includes geologic map of North America, scale 1:7,500,000, Boston.

Cook, G. H. 1868. *Geology of New Jersey*. N.J. Geological Survey.

Cook, G. H. 1857. *Geology of the County of Cape May*. N.J. Geological Survey.

Davis, W. M. 1889. The Rivers and Valleys of Pennsylvania. *National Geographic Magazine* 1: 183–253.

Dott, R. H., and J. W. Attig. 2004. *Roadside Geology of Wisconsin*. Missoula, MT: Mountain Press.

Doyle, R. G. 1982. *History of Oil and Gas Exploration in the Mid-Atlantic Region and Delaware's Involvement in the Federal OCS Leasing Program*. Newark, DE: Delaware Geological Survey.

Drake, A. A., Jr., and P. T. Lyttle. 1985. *Geologic Map of the Blairstown Quadrangle, Warren County, New Jersey*. U.S. Geological Survey, Geologic Quadrangle Map GQ-1585, scale 1:24,000.

Drake, A. A., Jr., R. A. Volkert Jr., D. H. Monteverde, G. C. Herman, H. F. Houghton, R. A. Parker, and R. F. Dalton. 1996. *Bedrock Geologic Map of Northern New Jersey*. U.S. Geological Survey Miscellaneous Investigations Series Map I-2540-A, scale 1:100,000.

Duncan, C. S., and J. A. Goff. 2001. Relict iceberg keel marks on the New Jersey outer shelf, southern Hudson apron. *Geology* 29(5): 411–14.

Eby, G. N. 2004. Petrology, Geochronology, Mineralogy, and Geochemistry of the Beemerville Alkaline Complex, Northern New Jersey. In J. H. Puffer and R. A. Volkert (eds.), *Neoproterozoic, Paleozoic, and Mesozoic Intrusive Rocks of*

Northern New Jersey and Southeastern New York. Twenty-First Annual Meeting Geological Association of New Jersey, Mahwah, NJ, 52–68.

Epstein, J. B. 2001. Structural geology of the Delaware Water Gap National Recreation Area. In *2001: A Delaware River Odyssey, 66th Field Conference of Pennsylvania Geologists,* 14–21.

Farrrell, S, and others. 2008. *New Jersey Beach Profile Network: 20-Year Report on Shoreline Changes in New Jersey, Raritan Bay to Delaware Bay.* Galloway, NJ: Richard Stockton College Coastal Research Center.

Fusillo, T. V., J. C. Schornick Jr., H. E. Koester, and D. A. Harriman. 1980. *Investigations of Acidity and Other Water-Quality Characteristics of Upper Oyster Creek, Ocean County, New Jersey.* U.S. Geological Survey, Water Resources Investigations 80-10.

Harmon, K. P. 1968. Late Pleistocene forest succession in northern New Jersey. Rutgers University, unpublished PhD dissertation.

Husch, J. M. 1990. Palisades sill: Origin of the olivine zone by separate magmatic injection rather than gravity settling. *Geology* 18(8): 699–702.

Kalczynski, M., A. E. Gates, M. L. Gorring, and M. V. Lupulescu. 2007. Hydrothermal alteration, mass transfer and magnetite mineralization in dextral shear zones, western Hudson Highlands, NY. New York Geological Survey T3-1.

Kious, W. J., and R. I. Tilling. 1996. *This Dynamic Earth: The Story of Plate Tectonics.* U. S. Geological Survey.

Kitchell, W. 1855. *First Annual Report of the Geological Survey of the State of New Jersey for the year 1854.* New Brunswick, NJ.

Kominz, M. A., J. V. Browning, K. G. Miller, P. J. Sugarman, S. Mizintseva, and C. R. Scotese. 2008. Late Cretaceous to Miocene sea-level estimates from the New Jersey and Delaware coastal plain coreholes: An error analysis. *Basin Research* 20(2): 211–26.

Koteff, C. 1974. The morphologic sequence concept and deglaciation of southern New England. In *Glacial Geomorphology,* ed. D. R. Coates. Binghampton, NY: Publications in Geomorphology, State University of New York.

Lacombe, P. J., and G. B. Carleton. 2002. *Hydrogeologic Framework, Availability of Water Supplies, and Saltwater Intrusion, Cape May, New Jersey.* U.S. Geological Survey Water Resources Investigations Report 01-4246.

Lupo, T. 1997. Basin inversion in the Newark Basin using data from the borehole televiewer. *McNair Scholars Journal* 1(1): Article 7.

McHone, J. G. 2002. *Volatile Emissions from Central Atlantic Magmatic Province Basalts: Mass Assumptions and Environmental Consequences.* American Geophysical Union Monograph.

McLelland, J., J. S. Daly, and J. M. McLelland. 1996. The Grenville orogenic cycle (ca. 1350-1000 Ma): An Adirondack perspective. *Tectonophysics* 265(1–2): 1–28.

Merguerian, C., and J. E. Sanders. 1995. NE-, not SE-, directed paleoflow of the Palisades magma north of Staten Island: New evidence from xenoliths and contact relationships. In G. N Hanson (chair), *Geology of Long Island and Metropolitan New York*, 22 April State University of New York at Stony Brook, NY, Long Island Geologists Program with Abstracts, 64–77.

Miller, K. G. 1997. Coastal plain drilling and the New Jersey sea-level transect. In K. G. Miller and S. W. Snyder (eds.). Proceedings of the Ocean Drilling Program, Scientific Results, volume 150X.

Minard, J. P. 1974. *Slump Blocks in the Atlantic Highlands of New Jersey*. U. S. Geological Survey Professional Paper 898.

Monteverde, D. H. 2004. Stratigraphy and correlation of the Paleozoic sedimentary units of New Jersey. In A. E. Gates (chair), *National Association of Geology Teachers—Eastern Section Field Trip Guide*, 44–102.

Newberry, J. S. 1895. *The Flora of the Amboy Clays*. U.S. Geological Survey Monograph 26.

Newell, W. L., D. S. Powars, J. P. Owens, S. D. Stanford, and B. D. Stone. 2000. *Surficial Geologic Map of Central and Southern New Jersey*. U.S. Geological Survey Miscellaneous Investigations Series Map I-2540-D, scale 1:100,000.

Nicholson, S. W., C. L. Dicken, J. D. Horton, M. P. Foose, J. A. L. Mueller, and R. Hon. 2006. *Preliminary Integrated Geologic Map Databases for the United States: Connecticut, Maine, Massachusetts, New Hampshire, New Jersey, Rhode Island and Vermont*. U.S. Geological Survey Open-File Report 2006-1272, updated December 2007.

Olsen, P. E., D. V. Kent, B. Cornet, W. K. Witte, and R. W. Schlische. 1996. High-resolution stratigraphy of the Newark rift basin (early Mesozoic, eastern North America). *Geological Society of America Bulletin* 108(1): 40–77.

Olsen, P. E., D. V. Kent, and J. H. Whiteside. 2004. *The Newark Basin, the Central Atlantic Magmatic Province, and the Triassic-Jurassic Boundary, Field Trip Guide*. Eighth Annual DOSECC Workshop on Continental Scientific Drilling, May 22–25, Rutgers University, New Brunswick, New Jersey.

Olsson, R. K. 1991. Cretaceous to Eocene sea level fluctuations on the New Jersey margin. *Sedimentary Geology* 70(2–4): 195–208.

Olsson, R. K., K. G. Miller, J. V. Browning, D. Habin, and P. J. Sugarman. 1997. Ejecta layer at the Cretaceous-Tertiary boundary, Bass River, New Jersey (Ocean Drilling Program Log 174AX). *Geology* 25(8): 759–62.

Owens, J. P., P. J. Sugarman, N. F. Sohl, R. A. Parker, H. F. Houghton, R. A. Volkert, A. A. Drake, and R. C. Orndorff. 1998. *Bedrock Geologic Map of Central and Southern New Jersey*. U.S. Geological Survey Miscellaneous Investigations Series Map I-2540-B, scale 1:100,000.

Peck, W. H., R. A. Volkert, A. T. Mansur, and B. A. Doverspike. 2009. Stable isotope and petrologic evidence for the origin of regional marble-hosted magnetite deposits and the zinc deposits at Franklin and Sterling Hill, New Jersey Highlands, United States. *Economic Geology* 104(7): 1037–54.

Press, F., and R. Siever, 1994. *Understanding the Earth.* New York: W. H. Freeman and Co.

Rey, P., O. Vanderhaeghe, and C. Teyssier. 2001. Gravitational collapse of the continental crust: Definition, regimes, and modes. *Tectonophysics* 342(3–4): 435–49.

Rhodehamel, E. C. 1970. *A Hydrologic Analysis of the New Jersey Pine Barrens Region.* U.S. Geological Survey Open-File Report 70-274.

Rogers, H. 1840. *Description of the Geology of the State of New Jersey.* N.J. Geological Survey.

Salisbury, R. D. 1902. *The Glacial Geology of New Jersey.* N.J. Geological Survey Final Report 5.

Sanders, J. E., and C. Merguerian. 1997. *On the Rocks Field Trips: Geology of the Palisades and Newark Basin of New Jersey.* September 14, 92nd Street Y, New York, NY.

Schlische, R. W. 2003. Progress in understanding the structural geology, basin evolution, and tectonic history of the eastern North American rift system. In P. M. LeTourneau and P. E. Olsen (eds.), *The Great Rift Valleys of Pangea in Eastern North America. Volume One: Tectonics, Structure, and Volcanism.* New York: Columbia University Press.

Sims, P. K. 1958. *Geology of the Dover Magnetite District, Morris County, New Jersey.* U.S. Geological Survey Professional Paper 287.

Smith, J. L. 1891. Map accompanying Appendix H, "Proposed System of Water Supply from Southern New Jersey", a plan of Joseph Wharton to supply Philadelphia with water. Available online from the Philadelphia Water Department Historical Collection.

Stanford, S. D. 2011. *Geology of the Brookville Quadrangle, Ocean County, New Jersey.* N. J. Geological Survey Open-File Map 81, scale 1:24,000.

Stanford, S. D. 2010. *Surficial Geology of the Hackettstown Quadrangle, Morris, Warren, and Hunterdon Counties, New Jersey.* New Jersey Geological Survey, Open-File Map OFM-79, scale 1:24,000.

Stanford, S. D. 2009. Onshore record of Hudson River drainage to the continental shelf from the late Miocene through the late Wisconsinan deglaciation, USA. *Boreas* 39(1): 1–17.

Stanford, S. D. 2007. Glacial Lake Passaic. *Unearthing New Jersey* 3(2): 1–4.

Stanford, S. D. 2005. The geologic history of New Jersey's landscapes. *Unearthing New Jersey* 1(2): 1–8.

Stanford, S. D. 1994. *Surficial Geology of the Hackensack Quadrangle, Bergen and Passaic Counties, New Jersey.* Department of Environmental Protection and Energy, Division of Science and Research, N.J. Geological Survey, Open-File Map OFM-14, scale 1:24,000.

Stanford, S. D., and D. H. Harper. 1991. Glacial lakes of the lower Passaic, Hackensack, and lower Hudson valleys, New Jersey and New York. *Northeastern Geology* 13(4): 271–86.

Stone, B. D., S. D. Stanford, and R. W. Witte. 2002. *Surficial Geologic Map of Northern New Jersey.* U.S. Geological Survey Miscellaneous Investigations Series Map I-2540-C, scale 1:100,000.

Strahler, A. N. 1951. *Physical Geography.* New York: John Wiley.

U.S. Geological Survey. 2007. The mineral industry of New Jersey. In *2007 Minerals Yearbook.*

U.S. Geological Survey. 2006. Preliminary Integrated Geologic Map Database for the United States. Online data.

U.S. Geological Survey. New York City Regional Geology website.

Van Diver, B. B. 1990. *Roadside Geology of Pennsylvania.* Mountain Press, Missoula, MT.

Volkert, R. A., J. N. Aleinikoff, and C. M. Fanning. 2010. Tectonic, magmatic, and metamorphic history of the New Jersey Highlands: New insights from SHRIMP U-Pb geochronology. In R. P. Tollo and others (eds.), *From Rodinia to Pangea: The Lithotectonic Record of the Appalachians.* Geological Society of America Memoir 206: 307–46.

Woodward, H. P. 1944. *Copper Mines and Mining in New Jersey.* New Jersey Geological Survey Bulletin 57, Department of Conservation and Development, State of New Jersey.

Zapecza, O. S., L. M. Voronin, and M. Martin. 1987. *Ground-Water-Withdrawal and Water-Level Data used to Simulate Regional Flow in the Major Coastal Plain Aquifers of New Jersey.* U.S. Geological Survey Water-Resources Investigations Report 87-4038.

INDEX

Page numerals in boldface are photos.

About the Author

David P. Harper was with the New Jersey Geological Survey for twenty years and the New Jersey Site Remediation Program for eight years before retiring in 2002 to work as a site remediation consultant. During his long career as an educator, he taught geology at Rider University, Mercer County Community College, and New Jersey City University and served as President of the Geological Association of New Jersey.